FRANK J. O'HARA, C.S.C., Ph.D.

UNIVERSITY OF NOTRE DAME, NOTRE DAME,
INDIANA; HOLY CROSS CENTRAL SCHOOL
OF NURSING, SOUTH BEND, INDIANA

PSYCHOLOGY AND THE NURSE

FIFTH EDITION

W. B. SAUNDERS COMPANY

PHILADELPHIA   1960   LONDON

PREFACE TO THE FIFTH EDITION

In this, the fifth edition, the general plan of the previous editions has been retained to present principles of General Psychology clearly and concisely to the freshmen students in schools of nursing, and, as far as possible, to omit abstract and abstruse arguments that serve to confuse the beginner. The author has endeavored to provide principles, materials, methods and facts of psychology which will be of value and of service to the nurse: (1) to develop the concept of the intrinsic value of personality by emphasizing the psychodynamic importance of the nurse-patient relationships; (2) to obtain an insight into the powers of the human mind and an understanding of the way in which the mind reacts; (3) to help the student nurse to know how learning takes place; and to guide her in the acquisition of techniques and learning; (4) to strengthen effectively her active participation in the emotional, social and moral adjustments of the patient.

Each chapter of the text except the first four may be adapted for a panel discussion. The instructor, if she chooses, may select a chairman and five panelists from her students to prepare and present the subject matter of separate chapters. The "Questions for Review" and the "Topics for Class Discussion" at the end of each chapter are sufficient to encourage other members of the class to participate in each panel.

The author has presented the Freudian concepts of the unconscious mind in a new chapter, *Activities of the Mind*. As an isolated dynamic system, Freudism is out of date. The Freudian theory, however, has exerted such a strong influence on the terminology and the literature of psychology and psychiatry that it seems imperative that a student nurse should know at least the basic Freudian divisions of the mind. The controversial application of the theory is considered in Psychiatry and not in General Psychology. A new chapter, *Frustration and Adjustments,* has replaced the former chapter on *Conflicts and Adjustments.* The chapter on *Mental Disorders* has been reorganized to meet the trend of the changing classification and treatment of the neurotic patients.

Content and bibliography have been brought up to date. Abstract ideas have been clarified by the application of practical examples to nursing situations, and also by the inclusion of new diagrammatic sketches. Although the sequence, as printed, places the dynamic appetitive material before the cognitive factors, it becomes possible to adapt the text to the requirements of a given course.

I should like to acknowledge my indebtedness to those who, during the past twenty-five years, have helped me prepare the five editions of this book. My greatest debt is to the student nurses with whom I have worked, and to those other student nurses throughout the States who have studied Psychology from this text. The point of view and much of the information given here come from my association with them. This text is largely *their* book.

I deem it a special privilege to pay public acknowledgment to Father Raymond A. Pieper, C.S.C., Professor of English, University of Portland, Portland, Oregon, not only for the many hours of work preparing each manuscript during these years but especially for his patience and encouragement.

A word of thanks is due to Sister Mary Gertrude, Sister of Charity, of Austin, Texas, now at St. Paul's Hospital, St. Louis, Missouri, who encouraged me and almost demanded that I write the first edition for "her sutdents"; to Sister Mary Robert, R.S.M., of Scranton, Pennsylvania, and to Sister John Francis, C.S.C., Holy Cross Central School of Nursing, South Bend, Indiana, for their interest and constant support.

Finally, I am especially grateful to the W. B. Saunders Company for many suggestions and excellent cooperation in every way during the preparation of each edition.

FRANK J. O'HARA, C.S.C., Ph.D.

CONTENTS

Psychology is a study of human beings from the point of view of their mental states, made manifest in internal and external activity. The mind is the directive force by which man's whole being is animated, by which he lives, feels, knows, wills and behaves. Psychology deals primarily with the mental powers that we possess and their effect upon our personalities. We shall consider personality to be a combination of qualities—mental and physical—which distinguishes one individual from all other individuals. Many factors influence personality development: intelligence, home life, emotions, friends, attitudes, religion, occupation, environment, dispositions, ideas, physical appearance, and many others.

Psychology is interesting because it deals with our everyday life. It points out the manner by which we may get along with ourselves, with others and with our work. It furnishes the reasons people of differing interests and emotional responses think and behave as they do: why some are flighty and unsettled because of some unsolved frustration or vexing life problem, while others are reserved and thoughtful; why some spend their time dreaming about things that might happen, but never do; why some at times react violently to trivial things, and at other times are calmer under the same circumstances. Thus, psychology, far from being a theoretical study dreaded by the nurse, is a practical study of the powers and limitations of mental activities and their physiologic reactions. By understanding the principles of psychology, the nurse can render efficient service to the *whole personality* of the patient, helping him physically, emotionally and spiritually, thereby developing a smooth nurse-patient relationship. The term "psychology" is derived from two Greek words, *psyche* (mind) and *logos* (science), and means the science of the mind, or of the soul. It has been used in different senses by many authors, and it is impossible to obtain an agreement as to the exact definition of the word. Some define the word as a study of the mind; others, as the study of the soul, the study of personality, or the study of behavior. In this book the definition of Moore is adopted, that "Psychology is the science of human beings developed by analysis of their mental life by experiments, by observations, by everything that will enable us to obtain insight into the minds of men—how they know, how they think, how they reason, how they feel, how they react in the difficulties of life."[1]

NEED FOR THE STUDY OF PSYCHOLOGY

The girl who enters training to become a nurse needs to study psychology for the following reasons: *(1) to understand the patient and herself; (2) to advance rapidly in her studies; (3) to help her in her professional career.*

To Understand the Patient and Herself

The nurse must be able to adjust herself to various situations because she meets different kinds of patients. She is expected to care

[1] Moore, Thomas V., *The Driving Forces of Human Nature* (New York: Grune & Stratton, 1948), p. 6.

for the rich and the poor, the moody and the cheerful, the sick and the convalescent, the pleasant, grateful patient and the harsh, disagreeable ingrate. To do this requires adequate knowledge of human nature, and consummate tact. Like a successful doctor or priest, the nurse must not only know *what to do* in each case, but also *how to do it*. Each patient is different, and no set formula of action can be followed. The nurse who "uses her head" as well as the proper medical remedy will be the successful nurse on the floor. This requires some knowledge of the mental activity of those under her care. The nurse who can *use the art of pleasing* and who knows how to deal with the disposition, emotions, moods and peculiarities of each patient will save herself many hours of disagreeable work and will at the same time contribute to the early recovery of the patient.

The following types of patients will be recognized as common problem cases: the officious person who wishes to determine the method of treatment; the medical man who knows too much; the sick nurse who wants to use her own remedies; the patient who refuses to be restricted; the delirious, melancholic, hysterical or neurotic patient; the drug addict; the impetuous person who wants immediate attention; and many others. Every hospital is a laboratory for the student of psychology.

A nurse should develop an even temperament and a well-balanced personality. She should endeavor to be pleasant at all times so that she may make herself acceptable to every patient. These same principles of action suggested to the nurse when she is administering to the sick are applicable to her daily life, both in her association with people other than patients, and in the development of a pleasing personality.

Be Cheerful and Greet the Patient with a Smile

When a nurse regards a patient as a friend, a smile comes naturally. A smile creates a pleasant atmosphere and forms a bond of friendship when two people meet. As feelings and emotions play a big part in everyone's life, it is the duty of the nurse to provide an atmosphere of ease and happiness in the sick room. She can do this by considering the moods, sentiments and attitudes of her patient, and by keeping the room free of any object that might tend to irritate the sick. The patient expects some form of confidence in the nurse, and a pleasant demeanor will inspire trustfulness and a sense of security. The nurse should be able to bring courage to those who are afraid, solace to those who are sad and cheerless, and trust in God to those who are dangerously ill.

Learn to Like the Patient

It is easy to take care of a person one likes and admires. However, there are *many good qualities in every patient,* and the nurse must be on the watch to detect them and bring them out. She should direct her mind to like the one to whom she is administering. The patient desires to become the object of personal interest; he resents, however, all display of sentiment and pity. The nurse has, therefore, to find a middle way; she must take a personal interest in the patient so that he will not feel that he is merely the object of a perfunctory attitude, and at the same time she must beware of displaying too much interest in his personal affairs. If she tries to like the patient for whom she is caring, she will find her work pleasant and win the good will of that sick person.

There is no other way to gain influence over a patient than by understanding; if the nurse does not know the mental attitude of a patient she has in her charge, she can never give him satisfactory nursing care. Understanding means sharing the patient's point of view. The nurse should consider the age, condition, feeling, and personality of the person with whom she is dealing. *Every patient is a world unto himself.* In his own mind he is all-important. He is the one who is sick and whom the nurse must try to understand. All conversation should be directed to his affairs, his comfort, his point of view. He should be made to feel that his every whim, every desire, and every thought is important.

A person who is sick is faced with unusual circumstances. He is out of his regular routine and work; hence, his usual habits of action are repressed. It is very difficult for a patient to go through a siege of sickness. He leaves his family, friends and familiar activities of life and comes to the hospital where he knows no one, where the routine is strange and different. His well-formed habits of thinking, if not actually sharpened by his illness, are the same as in his regular life outside the hospital. Sickness, however, upsets his emotional balance. Apprehension and fear are increased. The patient tends to worry about the expenses of his illness, about his family and about his job. He loses most of his independence and must rely on the nurse for his needs. This tends to make him self-conscious. He needs the understanding and patience of the nurse to build up self-confidence. She must help him to re-learn to do things for himself when he regains his strength, and remind him continually that soon he will recover his health. As each patient lives in his own world— and this world is what he feels, what he imagines, thinks, perceives and experiences—the nurse must remember that even the smallest thing she does for the patient may hasten his recovery.

It is necessary to make the patient feel important, as he will then be somewhat relaxed and will cooperate more readily with the doctors and with the treatment he receives. In reality, the patient is the most important person in the hospital. Without the patient there would be no hospital and no need for doctors or nurses.

Do Not Treat Every Patient the Same

All persons cannot be treated in the same way since all natures are not made of the same mold. Each patient is different intellectually and emotionally, and what is correct treatment for one may be entirely wrong for another, even though they may have the same illness, the same background, the same name. A nurse has to consider every patient as a new challenge to her ingenuity and ability. The patient is fearful of treatments and procedures. The very fact that he is in the hospital and out of his natural environment is enough to make a person feel different. He is apprehensive and the wrong approach can make him obstinate. The nurse should carefully choose the right words and actions for each individual patient, particularly if he is known to be hesitant and fearful. Thus, it is impossible to put down a rule of action that will be satisfactory for every patient.

Cheerfulness should always be present, and the nurse must learn what will please each individual. Whenever the patient expresses a desire that can be satisfied, the nurse should endeavor to fulfill the wish. Tact, which comes from experience, is required in meeting or refusing the requests of patients. The nurse should treat each patient according to his intelligence and according to his desires and feelings.

Learn to Listen

The successful nurse is the one who listens to the needs, desires, hopes and disappointments of her patients. Often a patient becomes despondent because of worry about his illness, the cost of treatment and the prospect of recovery. Many of the worries of the patient can be alleviated by a nurse who is willing to listen to his problems. By treating the patient with kindness and courtesy the nurse is building up his self-confidence, as he knows that she is interested in him, not as another patient but as an individual. Early in her training a nurse should learn the secret of listening. Listening does not necessarily mean silence, but includes the *ability to keep the conversation on the topics that interest the patient,* and to avoid topics that may be not only uninteresting but even offensive to him. Thus, it is advisable for the nurse to find out as much as possible about her patient before actually meeting him. This will help her to adjust more readily. By looking on the patient's chart, she will find such information as age, residence, illness, needs and whether he is married or single. She is then prepared to converse intelligently with the patient, to make him feel at ease and to create confidence in herself, as well as in his doctor and in the hospital. The nurse also should keep in mind that the patient thinks that his life and his personal affairs—his business, wife, children, home, friends—are the most important interests in his world. The patient, not the nurse, should do most of the talking.

Give Indirect Praise

Everyone likes to be given merited consideration. When the patient deserves credit for some special qualities, such as patience, ability to suffer quietly, kindness, consideration for friends or any other good traits, the nurse should speak of these. She may tell his friends of his virtues and thereby give indirect praise. There is a tendency in human nature to magnify defects and to overlook good qualities. Life is hard enough under any circumstances, and it is particularly hard during periods of sickness. Too many persons forget to praise those who deserve commendation for good qualities they have cultivated.

Make It Easy for the Patient to Say Yes

Instead of ordering the patient to do certain things, the nurse might win his good will by appealing to his sense of values, urging the reason of health, improvement, doctor's orders, or of some reward. She may also encourage the patient to do things for himself if he is physically able to do so. Even the slightest bit of help that he may give builds faith in his own ability. The patient might be allowed to do minor things first, then the more difficult tasks, until he is finally independent of the nurse's help. Another means of getting the patient's cooperation is to compliment him on his satisfactory progress or on some pleasing quality of his personality; this will help to strengthen his confidence, and encourage him to look forward to a speedy recovery.

To Advance in Her Studies

A graduate nurse is respected in a community as an educated woman. A truly cultured woman is presumed to have knowledge adequate to make her a leader in society. This *leadership* implies more than a thorough knowledge of preventive medicine and the care of the sick; it implies (1) a refined personality having control of her emotional life, (2) an understanding of her abilities and tendencies, and (3) an efficiency in logical reasoning. Such a person adjusts herself easily to difficult and changing environments. The nurse in training is required to know the fundamentals of many subjects, such as anatomy, chemistry, materia medica, obstetrics, pediatrics and professional adjustments, and this requires a great deal of preparation. The nurse's time for study is limited because of the many hours that she must spend on the floor. Her long hours of work and its nature militate against perfect study conditions, yet she is expected to be efficient in her studies, as well as in her routine on duty.

This demands that the prospective *nurse learn in the freshman year the art of study, the method of obtaining a good memory, the means for the development of a creative imagination, and the manner of increasing the analytical powers* in detecting the errors of false reasoning. The course in psychology endeavors to provide these aids, so that she may acquire the fundamentals of her other courses of study more easily and rapidly. Mastery of the facts and the laws of psychology helps the nurse also to understand herself more fully. It clarifies her mind, strengthens her will, and helps toward the healthy development of her character.

To Help the Nurse in Her Professional Career

A graduate nurse who knows human nature and appreciates the powers of the mind, the traits of character, and the weaknesses and the peculiarities of mentally defective cases has more chance of being successful than the nurse who lacks this knowledge. She expects to find differences in character, and she knows something of the remedies and the ways of dealing with individual cases. Then, too, she is alert to discover weaknesses in herself and to make the correct adjustments by which she will avoid unpleasant situations arising from indiscriminate judgment. Happiness is the goal of every life; and the knowledge of oneself and of others obtained through the study of psychology should be helpful in attaining it.

METHOD OF STUDYING PSYCHOLOGY

There are two methods generally used in studying psychology, namely, *introspection* and *experimentation*. In our study we shall endeavor to use both methods without emphasizing either. We shall study the nervous mechanism the mind uses to obtain its impressions from the outside world, and the activities of the mind that have a special reference to the nurse, whether this knowledge be obtained by the objective or the introspective method.

INTROSPECTION

Since psychology deals with the mental processes of our conscious life, such as thoughts, feelings, moods, memories, hopes, regrets, fears, likes and dislikes, the nurse may obtain first-hand information by introspection—that is, by observing the manner in which her own mental processes function. *Introspection means the turning of the mind inward; it is placing one's attention on the activity of one's own mind in order to study experiences that take place in this inner world.* This method of investigation is self-observation. This is what people are inviting us to do when they ask, "Why so sad this morning?" or "What's on your mind?" or when they offer a "penny for your thoughts."

All internal acts refer to some object, whether external or internal. An image, a thought, and all processes of the mind deal with some object. When a nurse sees, she sees something; when she thinks, she thinks of something; when she hears, she hears something; when she is afraid, she is afraid of something. Thus, internal experiences always have a subjective-objective feature and do not exist without reference to some object.

According to the introspective method, the nurse uses her own mind as the textbook of its activity. She carefully examines her mental processes in order to learn what takes place, and how it takes place. She can compare and contrast her sensations and thoughts according to the objects that cause the reactions as she directs her attention to her own acts and internal experiences. For example, when a nurse who has been transferred to a different floor finds it difficult to adjust to the new type of work, she can analyze through introspection the circumstances, the feelings, the other nurses, her methods of applying herself while on duty, and arrive at an explanation of her present mood. At the same time she can lay out plans to overcome similar reactions in the future. The normal self is the best book on psychology. By introspection, the person knows that he exists and that he possesses certain powers of the mind, such as *perception, imagination, memory, feelings, emotions, inclinations, intellect and will.*

Introspection, however, has its limitations and is not sufficient for complete understanding of psychology without the application of the objective method. It applies to personal reactions without reference to mental operations of others. Introspection is limited for the following reasons: (*a*) The states of mind tend to change and become modified when the subject observes his mental processes. When an angry person begins to analyze his emotion, the feeling of resentment fades, and reason takes the place of emotion. (*b*) It is not applicable to children or defective or insane persons. (*c*) Mental states change so rapidly that introspection does not furnish complete information. (*d*) The results obtained by introspection cannot be verified by others, since no two persons react the same way.

EXPERIMENTATION: THE OBJECTIVE METHOD

The experimental method is the use of special means of observing the capabilities of *other persons' minds and their activity* in order to obtain knowledge of mental processes that influence their actions. In this method we use *experiments, observations, tests, questionnaires, case studies, surveys and genetic methods.* We study people's conduct in various situations: to understand how they act, to analyze mental capacity, to obtain quantitative norms of comparison for different groups, to learn how mental activities influence action, to understand human nature, to know the best methods of efficiency, to derive general and particular laws of learning, to discover what powers of the mind should be held in check under definite circumstances and what mental activity is most suited for other circumstances.

The *experiments* in psychologic phenomena must be conducted by a trained observer who knows what to observe, and who is equipped with instruments and methods to aid him in observing more exactly. The experiments must be controlled, so that the same experiment may be repeated by others. Prejudices, bias or personal opinions must be kept out of the investigation. This demands exactness and impartial judgment of results. The data must be standardized by many experiments that agree with the observations of others who carry on the same kind of experimentation. This requires that the observations be studied in relation to other known facts as published in scientific psychologic articles, reports and books on the same subject.

In psychologic research the experimenter deals with human nature, and is confronted with countless factors that render his experimentations difficult. Man is a complex being and is subject to physical, physiologic and mental conditions. *Changes in interest, fatigue, emotional reactions and sickness are likely to vitiate the results of experimentation.* These variations must be considered when we apply the objective method. Nevertheless, observation and experimentation have been developed to a point where tests and scientific data may be applied advantageously in numerous nursing situations.

Observation in psychology consists of the study of mental life as expressed in the acts and conduct of others. From the bodily acts the observer infers the accompanying mental states. This method is similar to that of a doctor observing the symptoms and the reactions of a patient being diagnosed for a physical ailment. For example, restlessness and hand tremors might denote fear or emotional upset. We say "might" because those symptoms could be produced by other causes. *The limitation of observation as a method is its subjectivity.* In order to counteract this defect, the observer tries to isolate a definite factor while other factors either are constant or varied systematically. This procedure is possible in laboratory experiments, but in field work the same situation viewed by several people may be observed in various ways. This disagreement is very evident in the testimony of many witnesses to an accident on the highway, as well as in the answers of a group of students in regard to the position of various objects in the classroom.

A test is any instrument or situation by means of which a subject's reaction may be measured in relation to the reactions of other individuals. We know that some persons have a superior memory, and that some can solve problems more rapidly than others. In the same class, some students are superior in mental qualities to others. Tests are given to measure quantitative differences among individuals. Intelligence tests indicate the extent of one's capabilities of acquiring new knowledge in comparison to those of someone else; memory tests measure one's ability to retain that which is learned. Apt materials are available to measure intelligence, achievement, interests, and aptitudes. All tests, however, should be used in conjunction with other information, and should never be considered infallible.

The *questionnaire* consists of a list of questions on a specific problem. A questionnaire should be as short as possible, and provisions should be made to enable a person to give short answers. The responses should be treated with caution as all answers are subjective and may be biased, as could be, for example, those of a supervisor when asked whether conditions have improved on her floor during the past six months.

A *case study* in psychology is a method borrowed from medicine, law and social service. It applies here to problems of abnormality, brightness, dullness, adjustment, adolescence, problem children, special talents and defects, mental and physical growth. For example, why should a student nurse of normal intelligence fail in her studies? In a case study, one reviews past school records, observes home conditions of the student, her companions, her study habits, her emotional resonance, and her personality traits. It might be found, for instance, that the conditions at home or some personal worries are the cause. Once the cause is known and corrected, it is possible for the girl to be successful in her career.

The *survey method* attempts to discover the prevailing conditions with regard to a particular fact or situation, or it may seek to draw comparisons between the history of nations, regions, states, counties, cities, districts in relation to the mental development and psychologic changes among the people. This method uses questionnaires, tests, check lists, rating scales, score cards and interviews.

The *genetic method* is applied principally to long-time investigations whose purpose is primarily the study of change, growth and development. It is generally concerned with normal life processes, whereas the case study tends to be limited to the study of atypical individuals or situations. One may study an individual at various times over a period of years, or he may study a group to discover some common likenesses. The genetic method may be likened to an extended case study. Special subdivisions of this method include child psychology and the psychology of adolescence. These have greatly increased our knowledge of psychologic principles.

SUMMARY

1. Psychology is a study of human beings from the point of view of their mental states manifested by internal and external activity.

2. Mental states influence various types of behavior; the study of psychology enables the nurse to understand why people think and act as they do.

3. Psychology is a practical subject. It gives the nurse an insight into her own thoughts and conduct in relation to those of other people.

4. The general aims of the course in Psychology and the Nurse are: (1) To obtain an insight into the powers of the human mind and to direct this knowledge toward the improvement of the individual nurse; (2) to help the student nurse to know how learning takes place and the best methods for the acquisition of knowledge; (3) to enable the nurse to understand different qualities of personality in herself and in others in order to render competent service to the patients.

5. The nurse needs to study psychology in order to understand

the patient; to advance rapidly in her studies; to help her in her professional career.

6. The following suggestions to gain influence over a patient are also applicable to the nurse in her other daily associations: to be pleasant at all times; to take a personal interest in other people; to give indirect praise; to appeal to an individual's sense of values rather than to command him to act.

7. In dealing with psychologic subject matter, we have compared the experimental method of study with the introspective.

8. The experimental method uses observation, experiments, tests, questionnaires, case studies, surveys and genetic histories.

QUESTIONS FOR REVIEW

Essay Type

1. Define and explain these terms: psychology, personality, genetic method, objective method, subjective method.
2. What six suggestions were given on how to understand the patient?
3. List three reasons a nurse should study psychology. Discuss each reason.
4. How can you indirectly praise your roommate?
5. Specify three experiences in which it was more prudent to listen than to talk.
6. How can a nurse adjust to the patient?
7. What do you mean by introspection? Why is this method unsatisfactory with a group?
8. How can the study of psychology aid the student nurse? The professional nurse?
9. Why is psychology a practical study for the nurse?
10. Name eight powers of the mind.
11. List five reasons the experimental method is used in studying psychology.
12. What human variations render experimentation in psychology difficult?
13. What circumstances cause worry for a patient who enters a hospital?
14. How can you make it "easy for the patient to say yes"?

Matching and Completion Type*

* The correct answers—usually present on the same page as the matching type of questions—are omitted because they may easily be found in the preceding chapter of the text.

Fill in the correct words:

1. Four ways suggested for a nurse to understand the patient and herself are:

   a .... c ....

   b .... d ....

2. The study of human beings from the point of view of their mental and

   external activities is called ....

3. The following types of patients are recognized as common problem cases:

   a .... c ....

   b .... d ....

4. Any instrument or situation by means of which a subject's reaction may be measured in relation to the reaction of other individuals is

5. The three qualities of a nurse implied in leadership are:

   a .... c ....

   b ....

6. A prospective nurse should know from psychology at least four principles of learning in order to advance in her studies.

   a .... c ....

   b .... d ....

7. Three fundamental reasons why introspection has its limitations and is not sufficient for complete understanding of psychology are:

   a .... c ....

   b ....

8. The three special needs of psychology for the nurse are:

   a .... c ....

   b ....

9. A method used in psychology in which the activities of one's own mind

   ....

   are studied is ....

10. A certain experimental method consisting of submitting to a selection of people a list of questions on a specific problem is . . . .
. . . .

11. Four reasons each patient cannot be treated the same are:

    a . . . .   c . . . .

    b . . . .   d . . . .

12. An objective method applied principally to long-time investigations, whose purpose is primarily that of studying change, growth and mental development, is . . . .

13. Four reasons we study people by the objective method are:

    a . . . .   c . . . .

    b . . . .   d . . . .

Topics for Class Discussion

1. There is no other way to gain influence over a patient than by means of understanding.
2. Every patient is a world unto himself.
3. The limitation of observation as a method in psychology is its subjectivity.
4. The personality qualities that make you "you."
5. The six suggestions listed in the text on how to understand the patient.
6. What patients have given you the most difficulty? List the qualities of disposition, moods, emotions and peculiarities of each. What specific tact did you use in dealing with each of these patients?
7. The topics of conversation that a nurse should emphasize.
8. The successful nurse is the one who listens to the needs, hopes and disappointments of her patient.
9. Comment on the statement: "A pleasant atmosphere is created by a smile."
10. "The man I hope to marry" from the point of view of the following personality traits: (1) physical, (2) mental, (3) social, (4) religious and idealistic, (5) emotional.

Sources and References

Brennan, Robert E., *General Psychology*, rev. ed. (New York: Macmillan, 1952), Chap. II.

Harmon, Francis L., *Principles of Psychology*, rev. ed. (Milwaukee: Bruce, 1951), Chap. I.

Moore, Thomas V., *The Driving Forces of Human Nature* (New York: Grune & Stratton, 1948), Chap. I.

Morgan, John J. B., *How to Keep a Sound Mind* (New York: Macmillan, 1946), Chap. II.

Render, Helena W., *Nurse-Patient Relationships in Psychiatry* (New York: McGraw-Hill, 1947), Chap. III.

Sheehy, Sr. Maurice, and Harmon, Francis L., *Psychology for Nurses* (Milwaukee: Bruce, 1958).

2 • THE ART OF STUDY

GENERAL CONSIDERATIONS

The art of study is placed early in the study of psychology, as a student nurse has necessarily only a limited time for study. In this time she is required to absorb, retain and use the essentials of many courses. The manner of achieving economic use of one's time in study, however, is not by more study or more concentration, but by developing efficient methods of study. We will endeavor, then, to learn immediately certain of these methods.

All students have some ability to study, but few have developed it to a high degree of efficiency. This difference in study habits may have resulted from many causes, namely (1) training or lack of training in apt methods of acquiring knowledge, (2) varying use of distributed time spacing for study, (3) ability or lack of ability to adapt suitable methods of organizing, associating and planning the various types of subject matter the student may be studying, and

(4) ability to create and construct activities similar to ideas learned during the time of study.

In order to help the student nurse organize her studies and learn efficiently the knowledge necessary for her profession, we propose to consider at this time the orderly manner of efficient study, and suggest aids for study whereby the student may acquire and use knowledge readily and accurately.

ATTITUDE

Study should be a pleasure, not a drudgery. The student should realize that *willingness to learn* is the most important factor in learning. She should get down to study in a businesslike manner, and with zeal and vigor give her attention to her studies. Such an attitude makes one receptive to new ideas, critical of the important points, convinced of the fact that success is certain, and that after a reasonable amount of study any student nurse with average intelligence can achieve success in any type of work. Many subjects seem hard at times because of our own ignorance and because of the fact that we have no clear idea of the matter. It is the purpose of study to obtain this knowledge. Once we understand the subject, the mind receives the feeling of satisfaction and pleasure. It is necessary, though, to apply oneself, and this requires effort. Yet it is only by hard and steady work that success follows any form of activity. Some students make the mistake of trying too hard, especially at examination time. Tension, produced by over-trying, definitely slows down the mental process, prevents learning, and begets nervousness and mental confusion.

Endeavor to like and desire to know the subject you are studying. *Interest stimulates the learning process* and the capacity to remember. The greater the interest you have in a subject, the easier it will be for you to intensify and increase your ability to study. When interest in any subject is high, long periods of study seem short. To stimulate and keep up your interest, you must realize that each subject you are required to learn is valuable for you personally; each subject has been carefully chosen to form you into an efficient, skilled, and educated graduate.

STUDY AND PHYSICAL EXERCISE

Physical exercise is one of the best preparations for study, provided it is not overdone. From it, the mind takes on renewed vigor, circulation increases and the nervous mechanism works with greater facility. Fresh air and recreation are two aids to profitable study. Prolonged serious study causes physical tension in the nerves and muscles; physical exercise at regular intervals works off pent-up feelings of tension generated in or out of class. As the cycle of work and relaxation is necessary for highest efficiency, the freshman nurse should study but one hour at a time. Then should follow a break of five or ten minutes for recreation before the next study period. Since their study time is very much limited because of floor duty, juniors and seniors may study a longer time; yet, in each case, they should have plenty of time for relaxation. Recreation facilities for tennis, dancing, volley ball, softball, table tennis, swimming, skating and other games should be available. The school should also provide plenty of opportunities for social gatherings in the form of dances, picnics and social meetings. A nurse who exercises and takes reasonable recreation can accomplish more in a shorter time than one who neglects physical exercise.

DISTRACTIONS

It is impossible for the ordinary person to study when there are many distractions, either external or internal. Loud or unusual noise keeps the mind from concentrating. For instance, the nurse cannot study if others in the room are talking, or laughing, or if the radio is blasting. Amusement is good in its place, but not during study time. The "daydreamer," with fanciful thoughts about personal problems, current events, and social engagements, wastes her time if she does not bring her attention to the subject to be learned.

A student should determine what subject she is going to study before she sits down at her desk. So often a student wastes the first part of study by aimlessly looking around, carelessly leafing through her book, or gazing into her mirror while she renews her make-up. One may counteract these distractions by initiating study activities as soon as one starts to study.

SYSTEMATIC PROCEDURES AND AIDS FOR STUDY

Systematic Procedures of Study

We will consider five important procedures designed to increase retention of knowledge, namely: (1) *whole, partial, and progressive-part methods;* (2) *distribution of repetition;* (3) *overlearning;* (4) *self-recitation;* and (5) *frequent review.*

Whole, Partial and Progressive-part Methods

There are three general methods used to establish an impression firmly in the mind, namely, the whole method, the partial method, and the progressive-part method.

The *whole method* is that type of studying in which the entire assignment is read through from the beginning to the end until it is mastered. *This method is advantageous if the material is meaningful, not too long nor too difficult.* The whole method saves time in learning and also improves retention, particularly for delayed recall, provided the student has the ability to understand the content of the assignment and correlates the subject matter with previous knowledge. The use of the whole method is very practical in the study of History of Nursing, Sociology, short units in Psychology and Psychiatry. However, if the whole method is used with material that does not lend itself to this type of study, the student tends to lose interest and become fatigued, because through this method the results of learning are not manifest at once, but only after a long period of time and work.

The *partial method* of studying consists of breaking up the subject matter into sections, each of which is learned separately. Long and difficult types of material must ordinarily be subdivided for efficient mastery, and either the partial or the progressive-part methods must be used.

The *progressive-part method* unites the other two methods by relating parts learned to previous parts and to the whole assignment. This method is used advantageously when the units are long and difficult. The whole assignment is read over to find the general organization and the main points and to establish associations from the beginning to the end of the lesson. Each section is then studied in detail. Finally, the sectional parts are united by outlining the complete assignment from memory. Those topics and ideas that one cannot recall while making the outline should be restudied. A nurse should use this progressive-parts methods in studying Anatomy, Chemistry, Pharmacology, and most of her subjects.

Distribution of Repetition

The period of study of any one subject should not be too long. The study period should be divided into *short sessions* for different subjects, for the mind remains alert and attentive when we change at intervals from one to another type of subject matter. The average student nurse should be able to remain at study for one hour before taking relief. Then, after an hour of study, a five or ten minute break is highly recommended. During the intervening period of rest, she should take part in activity entirely different from study, such as walking or playing a game. *The cycle of study and rest is necessary for efficiency.* Sleep immediately after study is the best diversion and helps most effectively in retaining the material learned during the period of study.

Material is retained longer if the study of a subject is *distributed over several sessions* rather than over a long, continuous period. Some beneficial coordination leading to better assimilation and organization of material to be remembered occurs in the memory during intervening periods of repetition (Reminiscence, p. 123). The amount of knowledge, for example, retained in the mind by distributing the study of anatomy for one hour a day over a period of four days is greater than the retention of knowledge through the study of the same subject for four hours in one day. It is even better to distribute the study to one hour on the first day, and one hour on the second, the fourth and the eighth days. If the ability to recall is tested a day or two later, one continuous period of study is as effective as the divided repetition; however, if it is tested after a long period of time—especially at examination time—the effect of the concentrated study wears away and the distributed repetition is more than twice as effective.

Overlearning

After a student has mastered an assignment for study, she should repeat the essential and difficult points of the lesson time and time again. *Reinforced repetition* of this nature once the material is mastered is called *overlearning*. Thus, overlearning does not mean learning more than is necessary. It means repeating what has been learned several times for the sake of greater retention.

Self-recitation

Self-recitation, rather than re-reading, is the preferred way to study to remember. Ordinarily, the more study time spent in self-recitation, the better the retention. A student should first read the lesson, then endeavor to recall the essential parts that she has read. She should try to recall silently and at the same time write down as much as she can remember without prompting or benefit of the book. Another reading will serve to determine errors, and will be valuable for re-impressing the weak and strong points of the material studied.

In each case the student should study the material with a view toward the manner in which it is to be used. Generally, the student nurse prepares her daily assignments first to know the subject matter, and later to be prepared to answer a written examination. Thus, the self-recitation should be mental first and then rewritten several times. If, however, the student is to lead some discussion in class or give a speech, she should practice the subject matter aloud, emphasizing the important words and ideas, and using appropriate visual aids and demonstrations to exemplify her thoughts.

Frequent Review

A student should review an assignment immediately before the class period, review class lessons as soon as possible after class, review periodically, and review all the material before examinations and at the end of the course. Since the mind can remember related ideas with greater ease and certainty, it is an excellent idea to organize ideas around the central theme after completing a unit, a chapter or even a course of study. This type of review unifies and coordinates the ideas into a logical sequence and increases their retention.

AIDS FOR STUDY

General Consideration

A pencil in hand is a great aid. Write in your books. Read rapidly without lip movements the entire lesson to be studied. By reading the complete lesson you will obtain a general understanding of the thought structure of the entire section. *Underline the points of interest* and what you consider to be important. Jot down references or thoughts that the subject matter may suggest. Look up in the dictionary any word the meaning of which you do not know. Thus, know what the subject means before you try to learn its intricate subdivisions. Re-read each paragraph, endeavoring to *pick out the topic sentence and then underline it.* That sentence expresses the essential idea, and all other sentences of the paragraph supplement and develop that idea. Finally, *outline the essential and important points of the lesson.* After you have studied the outline, try to recall the salient topics you have learned. Many points will come back to the mind immediately, but you must look up what you have forgotten. Continue to study the material until you can easily recall the whole outline. Recall the same material after a few hours, and again within a few days.

Make Knowledge Practical

Learning is of little value unless the nurse can use and relate the material to the other things she learns. Too often knowledge is left stagnant and is not used or made practical. This form of learning readily leaves the mind. Always apply the new knowledge to yourself and, if possible, to two or three examples. Obtain a clear practical application by finding the answers to the ordinary words: *what, why, how, when, where. What* is the subject about? *Why* does it function? *How* can I use this knowledge? *When* did it happen? *Where* will it be used? At examination time the nurse should never leave a question unanswered; she should jot down something in answer to these five important words. These aids stimulate interest and help the memory to form a perfect impression.

Sketch, whenever possible, to obtain a visual image of the subject, especially in the study of Anatomy. Always print the labels of the sketch with the first letter of the structure (Law of Similarity, p. 125). When you have the opportunity, study the same subject matter in reference books. No two minds present the same material in exactly the same way, and many new trains of thought will be suggested if you refer to other authors.

One of the great aids to remembering and understanding a subject is to *discuss it with your roommates and friends.* It is surprising how much you do not know when you try to explain the subject to one who will ask questions. Your friends are ideal subjects if they ask unexpected questions that force you to think and seek correct answers. Be on guard, though, that you do not become a "bore" by speaking always of those things that interest you, and by failing to listen to what interests others.

Time to Study

The mind is more receptive at certain periods of the day. Some authors suggest that we can do the maximum amount of studying from nine o'clock in the morning until eleven, and from three until four in the afternoon. This depends a great deal on the student and the type of work studied. It seems best to study the hardest subjects when the mind is freshest. Some students find it easier to study the same subjects at the same time each day. The nurse on night duty finds it difficult to designate any period when her mind is fresh for study. If the student studies the same subject each day of the week at the same time and in the same place, she knows exactly what she is going to do, and she is ready to get down to business without wasting her time. For a science subject it seems that the best time for review and study is immediately after a lecture or as soon as possible after class.

Each evening a nurse must study two or three different subjects during her study periods if she hopes to keep up in her classwork. Since her study time is limited, the nurse must divide each period into short sessions so that she may prepare for her classes for the next day. This distribution of her study time is due to her heavy schedule during the first year, and to the fact that she is busy on the floor most of the day during her junior and senior years. This manner of studying a number of subjects within a short period militates against the theory of *retroactive inhibition,* which states that the effects of a period of study of one subject are to some extent wiped out when, just after the period of study, one introduces a second period of mental activity in place of a quiet time of relaxation (p. 127). This gradual decrease of retention is more pronounced if the next subject studied is similar in content to the first material studied. Now, if we apply this principle of "retroactive inhibition" to the divided study hour, it would seem better to rotate the study of science subjects with those of general knowledge. For example, rotate the study of Anatomy for the first half hour with the study of Nursing Arts for the remaining period; rotate the study of Chemistry with the study of History of Nursing, or with that of Psychology or Pharmacology. Since a period of relaxation increases retention by giving the mind sufficient time to coordinate and to organize the new material with former knowledge (reminiscence), the ideal method would be to study what one must learn by heart just before she goes to sleep.

After studying a subject in the evening, she should review the subject matter the next day before she attends class, and review the whole subject every few weeks. The memory is strengthened each time the material is studied, and closer bonds of association are established by repeating a subject in the mind.

Study means applying oneself to learn. A nurse should keep a cheerful attitude, and concentrate on what she is doing. In this way she strengthens her memory and erects a storehouse of practical material. The subject that seemed so hard at first will gradually clarify itself, and the mind will claim it as its own. The greatest happiness should be the hours of study.

OUTLINE ON How TO STUDY

Attitude and Physical Condition

(*a*) Endeavor to like and desire to know the subject you are studying.

(*b*) Get down to business.
1. Keep yourself in the best physical condition by exercise and hygiene.
2. Determine what you are going to study before you sit down at your desk.
3. Avoid external and internal distractions.
4. Get a sheet of paper ready and a pencil in hand.

Method of Obtaining the Subject Matter

(*a*) Read the subject as a unit first. Jot down and underline in your book the points of interest and what you consider to be important.

(*b*) Re-read each paragraph, endeavoring to understand the topic sentence and the substance of the paragraph. Underline the topic sentence.

(*c*) Whenever possible, sketch and label to get a visual image of the subject matter.

(*d*) Outline the topics of importance.

(*e*) Define each term used, and form each definition in your own words.

(*f*) Look up in the dictionary any word the meaning of which you do not understand.

Use of the Subject Matter Studied

(*a*) Ask yourself these questions concerning the subject: what, how, why, where, when?

(*b*) Apply the subject to yourself, if possible.

(*c*) Make up two or three examples or situations where the subject will apply.

(*d*) Endeavor to recall the subject and look up again the points you do not remember.

(*e*) Read the same material in other books.

(*f*) Discuss your ideas with your friends.

Time to Study

(*a*) Review the assignment immediately after class or as soon as possible. Prepare the next day's work at once, if time permits.

(*b*) Study the hardest subject when you are freshest.

(*c*) It is better to study a subject for thirty minutes each day than for hours on only one day.

(*d*) Alternate the study of a science subject with that of a cultural subject.

(*e*) Do not study too long. Take recreation after each hour of study.

(*f*) Study the outlines of your next day's classes just before you go to sleep.

(*g*) Review the subject the next day after you have studied to find out how much you have forgotten. Look over this matter again. Always review immediately before a class.

(*h*) Review the unit's work every third day. Review the whole subject every few weeks.

SUMMARY

1. The way to achieve economic use of one's time in study is to develop efficient methods of acquiring knowledge.

2. The suggested approaches to study are: the whole, partial, and progressive-part methods, distribution of repetition, overlearning, self-recitation, and frequent reviews.

3. The effectiveness of study depends upon the attitude of the mind, interest, methods of applying the mind, manner of using knowledge, and the manner of retaining the subject learned.

4. Interest stimulates the learning process and intensifies one's ability to study.

5. Reasonable exercise is necessary for high efficiency in the learning process.

6. The whole method is advantageous if the assignment to be studied is meaningful and not too long.

7. The progressive-part method unites the whole and the partial methods into a unit method of study.

8. Knowledge is retained longer if the study of a subject is distributed over several sessions.

9. More self-recitation and less re-reading is the preferred way to study to remember.

10. Frequent review unifies and coordinates one's ideas into logical sequences.

11. One should apply the theories learned during study to practical situations in caring for the sick.

12. One should study the same subject each day of the week at the same time and in the same place.

Questions for Review

Essay Type

1. Why is interest so necessary for efficient learning?
2. List the advantageous effects of physical exercise.
3. What recreational facilities are available in your school of nursing?
4. What are the five important ways of increasing retention of knowledge?

5. Describe the progressive-parts method.
6. Explain what is meant by: (1) whole method, (2) partial method, (3) progressive-part method. What conclusions have been reached with regard to the use of each method?
7. Make a chart of the time and subjects studied last week. Have you employed the ideal distribution of your time?
8. Comment: "Material is retained longer if the study of a subject is distributed over several sessions."
9. What is the meaning of "overlearning"?
10. Why is self-recitation so important in studying?
11. Pick out the topic sentence from any three paragraphs of your text.
12. When is the "whole method" better than the "partial method"?
13. How can you make your study practical?
14. How often should a student review the subject matter she has been studying?
15. When is the best time for you to study? Give reasons.
16. What is meant by the suggestion of rotating your study in accordance with the theory of retroactive inhibition?

Matching and Completion Type

Fill in the correct words:

1. The four causes which partially explain why study habits of each student may vary are:

    a . . . . c . . . .

    b . . . . d . . . .

2. Physical exercise has the following effects on the mind:

    a . . . . c . . . .

    b . . . . d . . . .

3. Five important ways designated to increase retention of knowledge are:

    a . . . . d . . . .

    b . . . . e . . . .

    c . . . .

4. The name of the theory that implies that the study of science subjects should be rotated with the study of culture studies is . . . .

    . . . .

5. The sentence that expresses the essential idea of a paragraph is ......

....

6. Reinforced repetition of the essential points of an assignment is termed

....

7. After a freshman student has studied an hour, the length of recreation time between study periods should be ....

8. The whole method is less effective when the material is too long and

....

9. The three methods of study used to acquire knowledge are:

   a .... b .... c ....

10. The five common words that are applied to make knowledge practical are:

    a .... d ....
    b .... e ....
    c ....

11. The larger percentage of study time should be spent, not in re-reading, but in endeavoring to recall the essentials of the lesson. This manner

    of studying is termed ....

12. Frequent review, which unifies and coordinates ideas in a logical manner, should be spaced in the following time intervals:

    a .... c ....
    b .... d ....

13. Five of the multiple distractions during study period are:

    a .... d ....
    b .... e ....
    c ....

14. The study of science subjects should be rotated with the study of

....

Topics for Class Discussion

1. Interest stimulates the learning process.
2. The "whole and the progressive-part methods" should be used in studying Anatomy.
3. It is better to study a subject for thirty minutes each day than for hours on only one day.
4. The cycle of study and rest is necessary for efficiency.
5. An outline is necessary for efficient study.
6. The larger amount of study time spent in self-recitation, the better the retention.
7. Artificial aids that have no relationship to material to be studied should not be used.
8. One should study the same subject at the same time each day.
9. The five essential words to keep in mind in order to make one's studies practical are: what, why, how, when, where.
10. Physical exercise and efficient study are closely associated.

Sources and References

DiMichael, Salvatore G., *Improving Personality and Study Skills in College* (Milwaukee: Bruce, 1951), Chaps. X, XII.

Fox, Charles, *Educational Psychology*, 4th ed. (London: Routledge & Kegan Paul, 1950), Chap. VIII.

Garrett, Henry E., *Great Experiments in Psychology*, 3rd ed. (New York: Appleton-Century-Crofts, 1951), Chap. VI.

McGeoch, John A., and Irion, Arthur L., *The Psychology of Human Learning* (New York: Longmans, Green, 1952), Chap. V.

Munn, Norman L., *Psychology,* 2nd ed. (Boston: Houghton Mifflin, 1956), Chap. IX.

Murphy, Gardner, *An Introduction to Psychology* (New York: Harpers, 1951), Chap. XV.

Mursell, James L., *Psychology for Modern Education* (New York: Norton, 1952), Chap. VII.

3 • THE MIND AND THE REACTING MECHANISM

The mind, which is the source of mental activity, is the directive force controlling human action. Within me is the mind with which I feel, think, will and act. Impressions from external objects are received by the nerves and carried to the center of activity, the brain. Then I, the Ego, interpret these impressions. Stimuli of the external objects are transferred mechanically through the nervous system to the brain, and the reaction takes place. But there is something more than mere mechanical activity; the mind correlates the stimuli and then *directs* the acts. That which acts is the mind, the Ego, the person herself—a psychosomatic human being.

The nervous system is the mechanism on which the action of the mind depends. As the receptive mechanism of a radio depends on perfect action of the tubes and wires, so does the perfect functioning

of the mind depend on the effective functioning of the nervous
system.

A nurse must understand at least the elementary structures of the
receptors and center of nervous reactions in order to understand
general psychology.

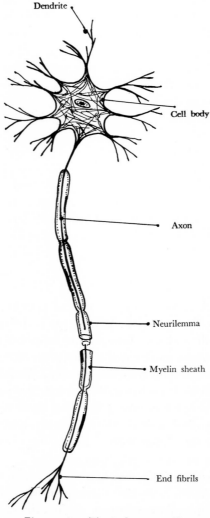

Figure 1.   Typical nerve cell.

Thus we shall treat briefly: (1) *a typical nerve cell,* (2) *the brain,* (3) *the spinal cord,* (4) *the receptors.*

A TYPICAL NERVE CELL

A cell is a nucleated mass of protoplasm and is the unit structure of the body. It is a living unit, activated by the nucleus, the essential structure of a cell. The human body is made up of these units. The cells are diversified in their structure, shape and functions. Similar cells are grouped together to perform special functions; these groupings are called *tissue.* The nervous tissues are composed of cells that respond to stimuli and carry a reaction to different parts of the body. The typical nerve cell is made up of the cell body and its protoplasmic extensions (Fig. 1).

The body of the nerve cell contains the nucleus and regulates the activity of the cell. The multiple brushlike protoplasm, called *dendrites,* transports the impulse *to* the cell body; and the *axon,* a single protoplasmic extension, carries the impulse *away from* the nerve cell body. The axon terminates in small branched nerve endings. Sometimes the axon is protected by the inner myelin sheath and the outer neurilemma, especially in the white substance of the central nervous system.

Synapse

A synapse is the region where the end-fibrils of the axon of one nerve interlink with the dendrites of another nerve fiber (Fig. 2). It functions (1) as a *relay station* when the fiber is not long enough to reach from the center of the cord or brain to the organ which the axon supplies; (2) as a *center of potential connections* to carry the impulse to nerve fibers where many synapses occur, as in the brain and the gray matter of the cord.

THE BRAIN

The brain, located in the skull, is the center of nervous action. It has five regions: telencephalon, diencephalon, mesencephalon, metencephalon and myelencephalon. The first three regions are

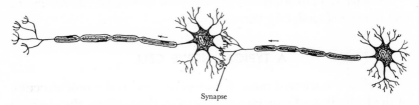

Synapse

Figure 2.   Synapse: Axon of one nerve touches dendrites of another. ʹ

usually spoken of under one name, the *cerebrum* or *cortex*. The last
two regions are generally called *cerebellum* and *medulla oblongata*
(Fig. 3).

The *cerebrum* is the largest part of the brain. Its surface has many
convolutions caused by furrows and a few deep indentations. A shal-
low furrow is termed a *sulcus;* a deep indentation is a *fissure;* a convolution or *gyrus* is an elevation between depressions. The sagittal
fissure partially separates the right and left hemispheres of the cerebrum. The Sylvian fissures are the horizontal depressions on the
lateral sides of the cerebrum; the fissures of Rolando are the per-
pendicular indentations on each side of the cerebrum (Fig. 3).

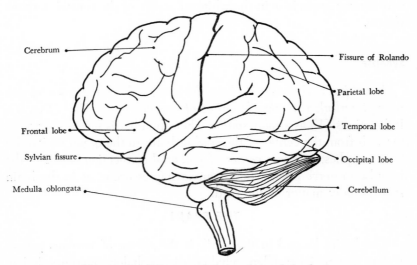

Figure 3.   Diagram of the regions of the brain.

The four lobes of the cerebrum have the same names as the bones that cover them, namely: frontal, parietal, temporal and occipital (Fig. 3).

The cerebrum is the center of all the *higher mental powers of man*—intelligence, memory, imagination; also of the sensory centers of sight, hearing, smell, touch, pain, heat and cold; and of various motor activities that regulate movements of legs, arms, face, tongue and many other parts of the body (Fig. 4).

The *cerebellum* (Fig. 3) contains the centers of balance or *equilibrium;* that is, this region of the brain plays a most important part in the coordination of the actions, nervous and muscular, by which the movements of the body are carried out. When the cerebellum is removed from an animal, there is no change from the normal in regard to the special senses such as hearing and sight, but

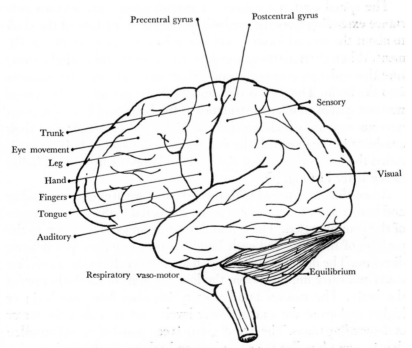

Figure 4. Centers of localization in the brain.

there is a great difference apparent in regard to the movements of the body. Movements are now clumsy and lack coordination and orderliness.

The *medulla oblongata* controls *physiologic reflexes,* such as *respiration, circulation,* and *vasomotor* reactions. All impulses passing up and down between the higher parts of the brain and spinal cord must make their way through the medulla oblongata. All sensory nerves, other than the nerves of sight and smell, must also pass through the medulla oblongata. Thus this area is an important pathway for impulses to travel from distant regions to the higher centers of the brain; it is also a vital respiratory and circulatory center. Then, too, the medulla is important in regulating emotions and many ordinary reflexes.

SPINAL CORD AND REFLEXES

The spinal cord is a column of grayish-white, soft nervous substance extending from the medulla oblongata at the base of the skull to about the second lumbar vertebra, where it tapers off into a filament. When the nervous system develops, it consists of a tubular structure that enlarges anteriorly, and this cranial swelling differentiates into the brain. The *cord* is the caudal tubular portion of the central nervous system, similar in structure to the brain and having its own nervous centers, which consist essentially of nerve cells and their dendrites in synapse with the end-fibers of the axons. This region is called the *gray substance* of the cord, and appears in a form similar to the letter H (Fig. 5).

Axons that are covered with their sheaths are arranged in bundles and have a *whitish* appearance when compared to the *gray* substance of the central region. These bundles are arranged in relation to the position of the cord, and each bundle carries impulses in a definite direction. The *dorsal* bundles, which are sensory, form the *ascending tracts* and carry impulses from the lower regions of the body *toward* the brain. The *ventral* bundles carry impulses from the brain or higher regions of the cord to lower levels, and are called the *motor* or *descending* tracts. The *lateral* group is composed of *mixed* bundles; that is, some bundles are ascending and others are descending.

Between the vertebrae there emerge paired nerves, one dorsal, the other ventral, which transport impulses to and from the cord. The stimulus is received by the small fibrils that have their ramification in the skin. These end-fibrils are called the *receptors*. Then the impulse travels by the dorsal or sensory nerve to the *spinal ganglion*, which is a swollen area consisting essentially of nerve cells and their dendrites. This dorsal ganglion is a relay station where the nerve forms a synapse with another nerve cell that, in turn, carries the impulse to the *gray* matter of the dorsal region of the cord. In the gray matter the sensory nerve fibers form *synapses* with other nerves, some of which transport the impulse immediately out of the cord to a muscle fiber by means of the *motor* nerve that emerges from the gray matter of the ventral region of the cord. These two nerves, namely, the *dorsal sensory* and the *ventral motor* nerves, which are paired on either side of the cord, are called the *spinal nerves* (Fig. 5). The impulse that was transported to the synapse in the gray matter of the cord comes in contact with nerve cells of other nerves and can be transferred up the cord to different levels, even up to the brain, by means of the *ascending tracts;* or the sensation may be carried to the lower region of the cord by the *descending tracts;* or again the impulse may be transferred from one side of the cord to the other by *association fibers*. In this way the impulse is transported up and down the cord and the whole body may act as one unit in regard to any given **stimulation.**

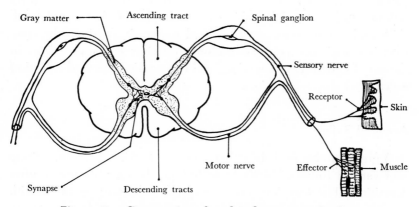

Figure 5. Cross section of cord and structure of reflex.

Simple Reflex

Some reactions are carried out by the action of the spinal cord with slight reference to the brain. Later the higher powers of the mind may be made aware of the reaction. For instance, if a child touches a piece of hot iron, he will jerk his hand away immediately. If one crosses the leg and the patella, or kneecap, is stimulated by a slight blow, the whole leg gives a jerk. These reactions are *performed by the synapses of the cord*. In the simplest reaction, such as pulling the hand away when stimulated by heat, the impulse is received by the receptor nerves and transported by the sensory nerve to the spinal ganglion and on to the synapse in the gray matter with the nerve cells of the motor area; the sensation is then immediately sent from the cell body to the effector or the nerve endings in the muscles by means of the motor nerve. Thus the following structures are affected by a simple reflex: *skin, receptor, sensory nerve, synapse in the cord with the motor nerve, motor axon, effector* and finally the *muscles* (Fig. 6).

Some authors differentiate three levels of reflexes according to whether the nervous center is localized in the cord or in certain parts of the brain. The nervous center of *first level* reflexes is in the spinal cord; that of the *second level* is in either the cerebellum or the medulla oblongata; and finally, the nervous center of the *third level* reflexes is in the cerebrum. The simple reflexes, such as the patellar reflex and the twitching of a foot muscle, are first level reflexes; walking and breathing are examples of the second level; skills and rote memory are third level responses. At times the stimulus is consciously perceived before the reflex is completed, as in the act of coughing or sneezing, and the reaction is called a *cortical reflex*.

Acquired Reflex

A great number of daily actions, such as dressing, reading, writing and various forms of skills in technique, become automatic after repetition. The learning process requires voluntary attention with planned conscious effort. Gradually the responses become reflexive and are performed with ease, proficiency and simplicity. While learning to drive an automobile, one has to make separate volitional efforts with each type of movement in adjusting the clutch, shifting gears and watching the road. In time, conscious effort diminishes and, although many complex operations of muscle reactions are involved, coordinated movement of hands, feet and eyes takes place automatically. These actions require association of nervous mechanism with centers in the cord and also in the motor area of the cortex. They are termed *acquired reflexes* because of the similarity of mechanical modes of action to unconscious vital movements.

Conditioned Reflex

The term "conditioned reflex" was first used by a Russian physiologist, Ivan Petrovich Pavlov, who experimented with the "psychic secretion" of the salivary glands of dogs. He noticed that the sight or smell of food stimulated the flow of saliva in the dog's mouth.

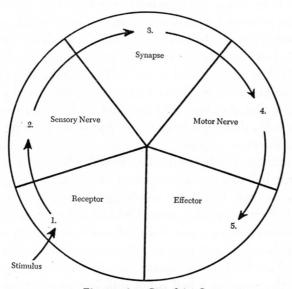

Figure 6. Simple reflex.

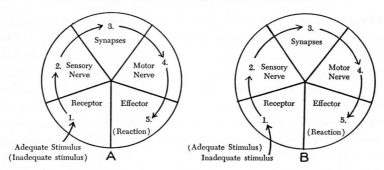

Figure 7. Diagrammatic representation of a conditioned reflex (Primary Laws of Association). *A*, An adequate stimulus and an inadequate stimulus are learned at the same time. The adequate stimulus causes the reaction. *B*, Later the inadequate stimulus is sufficient to cause a reaction that formerly required an adequate stimulus.

He rang a bell every time his dog began to eat, and learned that eventually he could make the dog's mouth water simply by ringing the bell. He found that the same salivary response could become conditioned to almost any inappropriate or inadequate stimuli, such as lights, whistles, touch and even mild electric shocks, provided each stimulus was presented a number of times simultaneously with the food. He proved that if a bell were rung a few seconds before the dog was given its food, and the same act repeated a number of times, the saliva would flow at the sound of the bell before the dog even saw the food. Furthermore, he found that this reaction could be established so well that the dog could discriminate between the sounds of different bells. Although in the early part of its training the dog would show the same response to the ringing of any bell, it could be so trained that the conditioned reflex would follow only upon the ringing of the bell that had accompanied the food. In an experiment he was able to show that a dog would give a certain response to a note of 800 vibrations while a note of 812 vibrations was ineffective.

A conditioned reflex is a reaction produced by an inadequate stimulus learned in association with an adequate one. The odor and the sight of food would be the adequate stimuli in Pavlov's experiment. Ordinarily, the sound of a bell is not sufficient to cause the flow of saliva in the mouth. In this case, however, the adequate and the inadequate stimuli were learned at the same time, and then afterward, the inadequate stimulus—the sound of the bell—was sufficient to bring about the stimulation of the salivary glands (Fig. 7). A conditioned response of this nature will not persist indefinitely. The subject must be reconditioned from time to time with the adequate stimulus. For example, if the "conditioned" dog hears the ringing of a bell a few times and the food is not forthcoming, the flow of saliva gradually becomes weaker.

Some authorities do not consider these responses to be true reflexive actions for the following reasons: the time required for the beginning of the response is nearly the same as for voluntary activities; the "conditioned response," though similar to ordinary reflexes, has characteristics of anticipatory responses, such as "licking the chops" and readiness to go after the food, rather than characteristics of a reflex; the response is less stable than the natural reflex and gradually disappears unless it is reconditioned.

On the other hand, many psychologists believe that conditioning is an example of the most primitive kind of learning in man. Some authors contend that association of ideas and images, such as those of similarity, contrast, and relationship in time and space, are learned by conditioned reflexive action. Animals and children are easily conditioned, but with adults there is more difficulty. Certainly, it is clear that conditioning plays only a minor role in adult learning in normal life, and there is still some doubt about its influence on the learning of the child in normal environment, where the voluntary attention of the child plays the predominant part, and where repetition of responses is made to a stimulus changed by continually distracting situations caused by other children and surrounding objects.

REACTION HYPOTHESIS AND THE STIMULUS-RESPONSE BONDS

The Behavioristic School of Psychology endeavors to explain human actions according to stimulus and response. The reaction hypothesis assumes that all forms of behavior are reactions to specific stimuli. The word *stimulus* means any force that may cause a reaction. This force may be either external or internal. *Situation* is a term commonly used instead of stimulus because it contains the idea of many forces acting at the same time. A *response* is the reaction that follows a stimulus. It may include motor, glandular, emotional and mental reactions. For example, a number of nurses may be gathered in the chart room talking about a peculiar patient; the activity changes to either silence or immediate activity of writing and work when the head nurse enters the room. In this case the head nurse is regarded as the stimulus, and the change of activity is the response.

The S-R Bond

The nervous system tends to react in the same way when similar situations occur. A pathway is set up in the nervous tissues when a reaction takes place, and the nerves tend to carry all future stimuli of the same kind along this pathway. This is very pronounced at the synapse where the dendrites of one nerve and the axon of another meet. *This tendency of an impulse toward taking the same pathway at the synapse is termed the S-R bond.* Thus, when a given stimulus has passed over the same way a number of times, there is a tendency for the stimulus to follow that same path each time. There is a bond of union, not actual but preferred. This bond is formed in the central cord, and the stimulation is likely to follow the same preferred course. Thus, we have a bond formed in the synapse of the nervous tissue; and *when the same stimulus is present, the same form of reaction is likely to occur.* This theory of the stimulus-response bond explains motor skills, mechanical habits and reflexes.

The reaction hypothesis does *not* explain *all* behavior. Furthermore, it assumes too much. It is satisfied to explain human acts from a mechanical point of view; it does not endeavor to explain the *underlying basis, the mind,* which assimilates the stimuli and causes the organism to act as a unit. The mind is the selector of the reactions and causes the stimuli to be directed toward a definite purpose. This is not considered by the reaction hypothesis.

This theory, though useful in explaining motor skills and simple reflexes, *fails to explain the higher powers of the mind,* such as the action of the intellect and the will. Although in any particular situation, a nurse may have a tendency to react in the same manner she did in previous situations of the same kind, it does not follow that she cannot act otherwise. She may choose to react in a different way if she so desires. The will is free to choose many courses, and if the intellect becomes enlightened by knowledge and an appreciation of motives since the previous situation occurred, the nurse may exercise her powers of reason and choose to resist the tendency to act in the same way. The mind is the ultimate source of activity, and behavior is not always the result of mechanical stimulus-response reactions. Thus, the S-R bond, which explains some reactions of the mind, does not account for the higher powers of mental activity, such as the ability to reason and to choose one course of action rather than another.

RECEPTORS

It is better to use an objective classification of receptors rather than the old subjective list of the five senses. The scholastic writers included under the sensation of touch many reactions that can be better understood by considering the adequate stimulus of receptors, rather than the sensation produced through them. In this way, we have an objective instead of a subjective basis for classification, which includes certain known receptors for which no corresponding sensation is recognized.

A receptor is an end-organ of a nerve which receives a specific type of stimulation. There are three great groups of receptors: *exteroceptors, interoceptors* and *proprioceptors.* Exteroceptors include all sense organs that receive stimuli from outside the body, namely, touch, heat, cold, pain, taste, smell, sight and hearing. Interoceptors, closely associated with the digestive tract, respond to bodily stimuli from within the organism, such as hunger, thirst, appetite and fatigue. Proprioceptors, though located in the deep regions of the body, control the muscular reactions of the individual, for instance, those of balance, writing and the sense of weight.

We will group and study the sense organs in the following manner: (1) *cutaneous sense organs,* (2) *chemical senses,* (3) *sight and hearing,* and (4) *internal sensory mechanism.*

CUTANEOUS SENSE ORGANS

There are many sense organs located in the skin, such as organs of *touch* or *pressure, temperature* and *pain.* These nerves are distinct and specific; that is, each nerve ending is responsive to a definite kind of stimulation and to that kind only. For instance, the nerve ending of heat will carry the stimulus of heat and only heat; it will not be stimulated by a cold object. All the other senses are specialized in the same manner and respond only to particular kinds of stimuli.

Receptors of Touch

The term *touch* has to do with the receptors that transfer stimuli of solids, liquids and gases that are in direct contact with the body. *Pressure* refers to stimulation that is sustained beyond transient contact.

The whole surface of the body is supplied with the sense of touch, though some areas are more sensitive than others. A number of *free nerve endings* supply each area of the skin. These nerves branch and rebranch to form a network of overlapping nerve fibers in the corium and in the malpighian layer of the skin. The tactile receptors are not evenly distributed throughout the skin. They are located in abundance where the surface is most likely to come in contact with external objects. The sense of touch, for example, is more acute on the inside of the hand and fingertips than on the forehead or cheek. Then, too, there seems to be a reciprocal relation between the presence of hair on the skin and specific tactile organs. The hair acts as a lever to the tactile spiral nerve endings at its base.

Some tactile nerves, known as *modified nerve endings,* are encapsulated in fluid-filled bulbs to increase the effective tactile surface of the skin. These bulbs are very sensitive to any stimulus of touch and

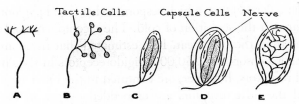

Figure 8. Nerve endings of touch. *A,* Free nerve ending; *B,* tactile corpuscle; *C,* Krause end-bulb; *D,* Vater-Pacini corpuscle; *E,* Meissner's corpuscle.

pressure. A stimulus which may be some distance from the location of the bulb, for instance, is sufficient to increase the pressure of the fluid within the bulb to stimulate the enclosed nerve.

The following touch corpuscles are of special importance (Fig. 8): (1) Krause end-bulb in the mucous membrane of the lips and the tongue; (2) Vater-Pacini corpuscle in the subcutaneous layer of the skin; (3) Meissner's corpuscle in the papilla of the skin, especially of the fingertips; (4) tactile corpuscle in the fingers and other parts of skin.

Touch is the great confirmatory sense. Man is not satisfied with the mere sight of an object; he has the desire to touch and feel it. Watch the reaction of the nurses when you appear with a new hat. The other girls will not only give their impression of its appearance, they will want to handle and try on the hat for themselves. The baby must touch everything it can reach before it is satisfied.

Receptors of Temperature

Heat is a form of energy. Heat has primary existence in Nature but cold does not. When an object has less heat than our bodies, we call it "cold"; when it has more heat, we call it "hot." The relative amounts of heat of two objects of the same weight and material are in the same ratio as their temperature. An object with higher temperature ordinarily has more heat than one with a lower temperature, and feels hotter.

Thermoceptors transfer the stimulus of *temperature.* They are of two kinds: *caloreceptors,* which respond to heat, and *frigidoreceptors,* which transmit the sensation of cold. The receptors of cold are more numerous than those of heat. It is estimated that there are at least 30,000 caloreceptors and 250,000 frigidoreceptors in the entire skin. The cold receptors, however, are confined to the *outer* region of the skin, and the heat receptors are embedded *deeper* in the corium. This is the reason a patient will react immediately to cold water, but more slowly to a hot stimulus. Then, too, the sensation of heat remains longer than the sensation of cold after the stimuli have been withdrawn.

The sensation of temperature is conditioned by the immediately previous condition of the body. A warm room seems hot and heavy to one who has just entered from the cold air on a winter day, but it feels somewhat cool to another who has been dancing or exercising. If one hand is immersed for a few minutes in ice water at the same time the other is thrust into hot water, then both are withdrawn and plunged together in tepid water, the former hand will feel warm and the latter cold, although both are being subjected to the same thermal stimulus (Experiment 3, p. 70).

The relative response to heat and cold depends on the number of receptors involved. The total effect experienced when a few drops of cold water are poured on the hand is quite different from that when a basin of cold water is poured all over the body.

The thermal receptors can become *negatively adapted* to the thermal stimulus; i.e., with the steady application of a stimulus, there is a gradual decline in the sensory effect. A patient may become seriously burned unknowingly if the nurse continues to add hotter applications. The nurse should use a thermometer to determine the temperature of the water rather than judge the heat of the water by the red or blue coloration of the skin of the child who is put into the bath. The nerve endings of heat and cold are distributed in various patterns in the skin. It is possible to map out a given area in definite patches where these receptors are located (Experiment 1, p. 70). Each patch will carry its specific stimulation, and is as distinct for its adequate stimulus as the eye is distinct specifically for light, and the ear for sound.

Receptors of Pain

The sense of *pain* has a peculiarly important role in the life of the individual. It gives a warning signal when he should be cautious and adjust his activity for his own good. Because of this, there is great merit in the claim that pain is a friend of man and not his enemy, since it checks and insists that the individual discontinue a certain course of action which could be injurious, and even disastrous. The inconveniences of pain are compensated for by the service it renders. Like a warning signal on the highway, pain is an index of hidden danger. If the first contact with a sharp edge did not hurt us, how could we avoid cuts and injuries? If the first sensation of burning did not warn us, how could we pull back from being more seriously burned? Painful symptoms give us warning of organ disturbances; where the symptoms are painless, disease may continue unchecked and cause widespread damage.

Pain receptors are specialized free nerve endings in the skin and tissue. They are distributed irregularly. On the inside of the cheek there are only a few, while in the eyeball and underneath the fingernails they are very dense. It is not always easy to localize pain at an exact point of origin. It *diffuses* along a wide area. Thus, a small bit of steel in the cornea causes the whole eye to smart; a sore arm is felt even in the neck and shoulder regions.

The nerve endings of pain may be injured in many ways: they may be pierced by a needle; cut by some sharp instrument; burned by excessive heat; harmed by chemical agents; shocked by an electric stimulus. Such injuries of the free nerve endings arouse the experience of pain. There is a variety of pains—aches, burns, itching and stinging. Each has its peculiar introspective stimulation. "Hot" is the result of stimulation of "pain" and "warm spots." Some of these pains are caused by mechanical pressure, heat and cold, chemical accumulations in the tissues and skin.

Experience gives evidence that *pain becomes more intense from constant stimulation*. If the dentist continues to drill, the patient in the chair does not become negatively adapted to the sense of pain. The pain becomes greater. Every nurse has noticed that a patient forgets minor ailments when a "shooting" pain is experienced; when the intense pain is alleviated, the small aches become pronounced again. Again, if two extreme pains are present at the same time, one hurts more than the other when the patient places his attention on that particular spot, although the other does not pass entirely from consciousness. Even in such a case as this, one never becomes entirely adapted to pain.

Cutaneous Sense Organs and the Nurse

A *thoughtful* nurse, who realizes that the skin receptors are generally hypersensitive during illness, takes precautions that the patient does not become chilled during morning care; that the water is warm; that her cold hands or cold articles do not touch the patient. She is willing to supply extra covers when a patient requests them, even if the room is well heated. She adjusts any wrinkles in the sheet or uncomfortable position of the pillows; her hands are smooth, so that the patient cannot complain that "an alcohol rub feels like a moist massage with sandpaper"; she is watchful to alleviate irritation that results from tight bandages or continued confinement in bed; she is gentle while moving a patient from one position to another; she is alert to adjust or remove hot applications before they can possibly irritate the skin; and finally, she can detect irregular pulse, excessive moisture or dryness of the skin, and signs on the face of intense pain.

SPECIAL CHEMICAL SENSES

Chemical stimulation of *taste* and *smell* is brought about by contact with solutions of various substances. Taste and smell are chemical senses because they distinguish between things that are chemically different. By chemically different we mean they are composed of different substances—for example, salt and sugar. These senses can be stimulated by solids, liquids, or gases, provided the solid or gas is first converted to a liquid. This conversion occurs readily in the mouth with many substances. Ordinarily, only gases are allowed to enter the nose, but it is likely that they must be dissolved in a liquid before they can be smelled. This probably explains in part why the olfactory epithelium is continually moist from mucus.

Receptors of Smell

The sense of smell is located in the back part of the nasal passage along the septum that divides the nostrils. There is present a special olfactory epithelium that contains the endings of the olfactory nerve. The vapors which pass over this area are the only adequate stimulation for these specialized smell receptors. Frequently, one who detects a substance sniffs to force the vapor into the upper regions of the nose where the receptors are present.

The attempt to classify different odors has not been very successful. The existence of several specific kinds of olfactory receptors, adequate only for particular odors, is quite likely. In 1916 Henning proposed six different categories of odors: foul, flowery, fruity, burnt, spicy and resinous. There are many possible intergrades among these six primary odors.

Olfactory Sense and the Nurse

The nurse should understand the importance of having the room of the sick free from all offensive odors. Some disagreeable odors from medicine, anesthetics, body odors, pungent breath of the patients, perspiration or bandages may at times be present temporarily in any hospital room. The nurse must use every means to keep the room well ventilated and free from smells that may be nauseating to the patient by removing waste and using deodorants, and by perfect cleanliness.

The nurse herself needs to take care that she does not carry any repugnant odor to the sickroom. The smell of cigarettes on the breath of a nurse is often offensive to a patient. Then, too, the odor of phenol, ether or traces of disinfectants on the clothing should be avoided by keeping the uniform clean and wholesome.

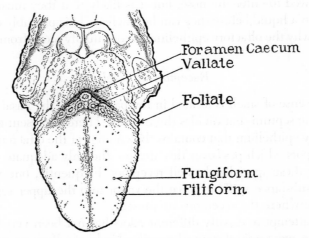

Foramen Caecum
Vallate

Foliate

Fungiform
Filiform

Figure 9.   Diagram of tongue showing relation of papillae.

Receptors of Taste

The organs of the sense of taste are composed of a cluster of cells called "taste buds," arranged along small elevations of the tongue, the papillae. The surface of the tongue resembles a Brussels carpet with four kinds of small projections, the papillae, giving it a velvety appearance (Fig. 9).

(*a*) *Filiform papillae* are tiny threadlike conical elevations. They have no taste buds.

(*b*) *Fungiform papillae* are elevations from the surface of the mucous membrane that suggest the shape of a mushroom; hence, the name. They can be readily recognized by their deep reddish appearance and they are studded with taste buds along their edges. Over the surface of the human tongue, there may be as many as three or four hundred of these papillae.

(*c*) *Foliate papillae*, which are located near the base of the tongue, are tiny ridges bearing taste buds.

(*d*) *Vallate papillae* resemble projecting knobs surrounded by grooves, like the moat around a castle; they serve to retain dissolved food substances. They are arranged in the shape of an inverted V at the back of the tongue.

The sense of taste is located in the *taste buds*. Each *bud* (Fig. 10) is flask-shaped and consists of an outer wall made up of elongated cells placed side by side like the staves of a barrel, with an opening toward the surface of the papilla. The inside of the bud is filled with the true *gustatory* cells, packed side by side into the cavity of the bud. Each of these cells is long and very thin, with a large nucleus and long, stiff cilia which project through the open mouth of the bud.

There appear to be at least four kinds of receptors, when the nature of the stimuli to which they react is considered. Receptors for *sour* predominate along the edge of the tongue; those for *salty* are both at its tip and at the edge; for *sweet,* at the tip; and for *bitter,* at the base. This arrangement seems to have furnished the basis for the expression "sweet to the taste, but bitter to the belly."

Taste is a complex condition closely *associated with the senses of smell, heat, cold and sight.* Although we speak of tasty or tasteless dishes, most of the flavor and the richness come from olfactory stimulation, and not from the sensations of the taste buds. If the nose of a blindfolded person is closed mechanically, he cannot tell whether he is drinking onion juice or orange juice. When the sense of smell is dulled by colds or excessive smoking, the patient's world of taste shrinks appreciably. Under such conditions, he experiences difficulty in distinguishing various kinds of food and beverages. Food loses its zest and flavor. When we speak of a slimy, smooth, or gritty taste, we are referring to tactile stimulation. For these reasons, it is necessary to control or take into account the non-gustatory stimulation in searching for the existence of various types of tastes.

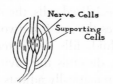

Figure 10. Taste bud.

Food that smells good tastes good. A good juicy steak is appetizing to anyone since its odor penetrates the olfactory cells and stimulates the flow of saliva and the gastric juices. Nurses should endeavor to serve food hot and attractive to whet the appetite of the patient. The reason food in the hospital is often tasteless and insipid is that some conditions of illness block the nasal passageways in such a way as to prevent odor from supplementing taste, and the mucus on the coated tongue keeps the dissolved parts of the food from penetrating the taste buds. This condition can be partially remedied by rinsing the mouth of the patient. So often, too, the nurse can improve the attractiveness of institutional cooking and avoid monotony by making the trays attractive. The food on the tray should have "eye appeal," and should be served in such a form and fashion as will bring pleasure to eating.

SIGHT AND HEARING

The Sense of Sight

The sense of sight is our most important source of knowledge. We depend on sight during all of our working hours and its loss is probably the most serious of all possible afflictions.

The Structure of the Eye (Fig. 11)

Three layers of various tissues form the eyeball, namely, *sclera*, *choroid* and *retina*. The *sclera*, the "white of the eye," is a complete outer protective layer; anteriorly, where it becomes thin and transparent, it is known as the *cornea*. The *choroid* contains many blood vessels which nourish the eye. The *retina* is a nervous sensitive tissue made up essentially of specialized cells, the *rods* and *cones* (Fig. 12).

The fibrous *lens* divides the eye into two chambers. The *aqueous humor,* a thin serous fluid, fills the anterior cavity; the *vitreous humor,* a jelly-like body, distends the cavity back of the lens. The muscular *ciliary body* automatically adjusts the spherical lens to distant or near objects.

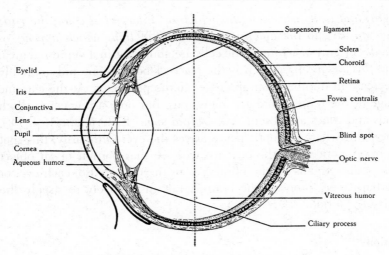

Figure II. Structure of the eye.

The colored muscular *iris* is part of the choroid layer around the front of the lens. Its shutter-like action regulates the amount of light entering the eye. The *pupil* is the rounded area at the opening of the iris. It dilates in dim light when the iris contracts, and becomes smaller in bright light as the iris expands.

The *retina* is a delicate, white membrane that forms the inner nervous mechanism of the eye. As there are ten different layers in the retina, we would expect the cell receptors to be very close to the source of light, next to the vitreous humor; but instead, the essential cells, the *rods* and *cones,* which are the true receptors of light, are next to the choroid layer. *The* **cones** *are sensitive to the kind of*

Rod   Cone

Figure 12. Rod and cone of the retina.

light, that is, its wave lengths, which we interpret as color; the **rods** are sensitive to the amount or intensity of light which appears as shades of gray or white. Cone cells are abundant in a depressed area, the *fovea centralis,* which is the place of best vision, and gradually decrease in number from the fovea to the perimeter. At the extreme edge of the retina there are many rods, but only a few cones. Both rods and cones are absent at the *blind spot* (Experiment 4, p. 71), the point where the optic nerve leaves the eye. Ordinarily, this spot is never noticed, as the one eye will see that portion of an object whose image falls on the blind spot of the other. Also, each eye, or perhaps more properly the brain, tends instinctively to supply the missing portion.

Vision

Light is a form of energy. It leaves a source and travels out in all directions as waves analogous to the motion of the waves in the sea. In this analogy, the distance between crests is the *wavelength,* and height of a crest above sea level is the *amplitude.* The number of crests passing a point in one second is the *frequency.*

Different wavelengths of light are measured by numbers when we speak in technically accurate terms; but when we speak approximately we may use words such as red, green, blue and many others. When waves of possible wavelengths are moving together, the light is called white. A complete absence of light is called blackness.

A body may emit light, absorb it, reflect it from its surface or transmit it through itself. Other objects, however, react differently to different light, absorbing, transmitting or reflecting some but not other wavelengths. Light waves move through space in straight paths, and their amplitude is always very small compared to perceptible distance. For this reason a bundle of waves going from one point to another can be considered as a very thin rod or ray. This can be pictured as a straight line on paper.

Sight is a reaction of the visual center of the brain caused by light stimulating the specific rods or cones of the eye. Light entering the eye reaches first the conjunctiva and cornea, then passes through the aqueous humor between the iris, through the crystalline lens and through the vitreous humor to fall on the sensitive retina, which is the receiving screen of the eye. The image on the retina, however, is inverted. The objects do not appear to us to be upside down because our actual visual sensations take place in the brain and not in the eye, and because we learn from experience to interpret each object as it is, in its correct relation with the surrounding area.

Visual Sensations

Visual sensations are divided into two varieties: (*a*) chromatic (color) series, and (*b*) achromatic (colorless) series.

Chromatic Series

The chromatic series consists of those qualities of visual sensations to which we give the name of colors. When a glass prism transmits a light wave (Fig. 13), the ray bends as it enters the glass and again as it leaves it. This is called *the refraction of light*. The angle of bend is different for light of different wavelengths, smaller for red than for violet. When a bundle containing waves of all wavelengths,

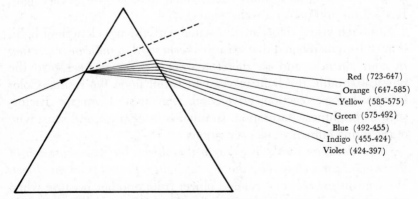

Red (723-647)
Orange (647-585)
Yellow (585-575)
Green (575-492)
Blue (492-455)
Indigo (455-424)
Violet (424-397)

Figure 13.   Representation of the deflection of white light passing through a spectrum.

which we call a ray of white light, passes through a prism the different waves are bent differently, and there emerges on the other side of the prism a fan of rays arranged according to the length of the light waves. The fan is called a spectrum, and we say the white light has been resolved into its components. The visual wavelengths extend from 725 millimicrons to approximately 400 millimicrons.

If sunlight is passed through a prism, its rays are split into multiple colors of the spectrum—as many as 180, according to some observers —and each color has definite wavelengths. A specific name is given to those colors, which stand sufficiently far apart to represent quite distinctive sensations, namely, *red, orange, yellow, green, blue, indigo and violet.* These seven colors are the qualitative color series of the spectrum. Red has the longest wavelengths and violet, the shortest. The limiting wavelengths measured in millimicrons (millionths of a millimeter) are the following:

Red	723-647	Blue	492-455
Orange	647-585	Indigo	455-424
Yellow	585-575	Violet	424-397
Green	575-492		

Beyond the end of the visible spectrum at the red end are still longer wavelengths, which our eyes are incapable of perceiving. These are spoken of as infrared light. Beyond the violet end are shorter wavelengths, also invisible, which are called ultraviolet light. Beyond the ultraviolet are the x-rays.

Although visual colors are associated with the wavelength of light, it must be remembered that *color is a term used to indicate a reaction in consciousness* and is, therefore, not strictly applicable to the physical stimuli, the light waves which fall upon the retina. Color is a psychologic reaction; wavelength is a physical concept. Factors such as brightness, saturation, simultaneous contrast and sensitivity of the retina influence color sensations.

Color does not reside as color in the object, but is a sensation of the visual center caused by the rays of light reflected from an object. We can distinguish one colored object from another because when white light falls on an object, light of specific wavelengths is absorbed by various substances of the object; light of other wavelengths is reflected to the eye. These *reflected* light waves cause the retina to react in such a way that the stimulus is taken to the visual center of the brain and the sensation of color is experienced. For example, we can distinguish one colored object from another—such as a red sweater from a blue one—because the material of each sweater absorbs different wavelengths from the surrounding white light and reflects the remaining wavelengths of the spectrum to the eye. The substance of the red sweater *absorbs* all the wavelengths of white light except the range of wavelengths between 723-647 millimicrons, which are *reflected* from the cloth back to the eye, stimulating the cone receptors. This stimulus is carried to the visual center of the brain and I perceived the object as a red sweater. The material of the blue sweater absorbs the wavelengths except those between 492-455 millimicrons, which are reflected to the retina. The cone cells of the retina receive the stimuli caused by the reflected wave lengths, and the optic nerve carries the impulse to the visual center of the brain. The resulting red color of one sweater and the blue of another are reactive processes of the visual center. Thus, the wavelengths reflected to the eye cause the sensation of color, but color itself is a psychologic phenomenon. Colors of red, green and blue are not sent from New York to stimulate color television receptors in Los Angeles. The wavelengths of a specific number are transmitted by the sending station, and the viewer interprets these wavelengths in terms of color. Certain light waves are called color because we see them as colored, and not because color is a property of light waves.

PRIMARY COLORS

The primary colors are *red, green* and *blue-violet.* These three colors are the broad bands of light of the spectrum. They are known as *additive primaries,* because they can be added together in various combinations to give us the sensation of white, and also the sensation of any other color of the spectrum. For example, the reflection of all the primaries gives the sensation of white; the absorption of all the primaries gives a sensation of black; a mixture of greenish light and red light forms yellow; a union of red and blue light produces purple; a combination of blue and green results in aquamarine. In color mixtures, such as red and green, the eye does not see the colors separately and then mix them to form a yellow sensation; rather, the two colors arrive simultaneously on the same area of the retina.

Many other combinations of color, such as red, yellow and blue, are sometimes called primary colors in art classes and in industry, because the purpose of mixing pigments is to obtain various hues and not the sensation of white. The white and black pigments are added to obtain the desired color effect. In psychology, however, we are dealing with sensations, which include white and black, as well as all the other colors; the three colors, red, green and blue-violet, are called primaries because these three will yield white, and all other colors of the spectrum if the experimenter adjusts them adequately.

Brightness or *intensity* depends on the amount of light that falls on the retina in a given time. *Saturation* is the amount of admixture with white light; that is, the color is pale if mixed with white, or it is deep and full if unmixed with white. Yellow and red are the brightest, and blue is the darkest color in the daytime, but all are dimmer in twilight. Green and blue are comparatively bright at twilight.

YOUNG-HELMHOLTZ THEORY OF VISION

There are many theories of vision. None of them has been entirely satisfactory. One of these theories, that of Young-Helmholtz, which is almost universally accepted, contains most of the ideas that have been advanced. It may be explained briefly.

The theory rests upon the assumption that there are three fundamental color sensations, red, green and blue-violet. Corresponding to these colors are three types of cones, each with its own peculiar photochemical substance; one responds to red light, another to green, and the third to violet. When these three cone types are adequately stimulated, a sensation of white light results, and their simultaneous stimulation of varying degrees gives rise to the sensations of all the other colors; the absence of stimulation gives black.

COLOR BLINDNESS

Some people cannot distinguish certain colors. This phenomenon is called color blindness. There are three forms of color blindness: *red-green, yellow-blue* and *wholly color blind.* The usual form is the red-green, found in about 8 per cent of males, but rarely in women. Such people cannot distinguish red from the green light, except that the red appears brighter than the green. Yellow-blue and total color blindness are rare. The disorder is caused by defective reaction of some cone cells.

COMPLEMENTARY COLORS

Complementary colors are any two colors which produce the sensation of white when they are appropriately mixed. With the aid of a rotary disk it is possible to mix certain pairs of colors to give a white (gray) sensation (Experiment 7, p. 71). It may be said, in fact, that for any given color there exists a complement which, when fused with it in suitable proportions, gives white. If we confine ourselves to the spectral colors, we recognize such complementary pairs as the following:

> Red and greenish blue
> Orange and cyan blue
> Yellow and indigo blue
> Greenish yellow and violet

The complement of any color or shade, such as cerise or magenta, may be determined by a person with normal color vision by staring at it intently for a few seconds, then covering the eyes to exclude all light. Presently, the after-image (page 99) on the retina will appear in the shade of color that would complement the hue in question. Complementary colors are aesthetically pleasing, and the nurse should use them to decorate the table, tray or room of the patient whenever she can do so.

Achromatic Series

The achromatic color sensations are neutral or tone-free, such as white, black and gray. When an object absorbs all three primary colors, it gives rise to the sensation of black; when all three primaries are adequately reflected, they produce white. Colorless sensations may involve a continuous series from black progressively through lighter shades of gray to white.

The Sense of Hearing

The ear has a twofold function: it serves as the *receptor of sound waves* and as the end-organ of *equilibrium*. Sound waves, which are vibrations of the air, are received by the nervous mechanism and transferred to the brain by the acoustic nerve (eighth cranial nerve). *The sound waves are interpreted and distinguished in the temporal lobe of the cerebrum.* The ear is highly developed in man and is an important medium for acquiring knowledge. All vertebrates have an ear in some form or other. In the lower vertebrates, there is an inner ear that is used chiefly to orientate the animal, and as a means of equilibrium. The fish has ears, but no middle or outer structures for the perception of sound. Frogs and toads have inner and middle ears, which are rather well developed, and an outer ear, which consists of a thin membrane. These animals have good hearing. Instead of the three bones of the middle ear that are found in man, the amphibia and the reptiles have a column of hardened tissue, which works like a piston and carries the vibrations from the eardrum to the membranous openings of the inner ear, where the sensory nerve endings of the acoustic nerve receive the sound waves.

Regions of the Ear

There are three regions of the ear, the *outer, middle* and *inner* ear. The outer ear is so constructed as to receive the vibrations of the air and to carry them to the eardrum, where they are received by the bones of the middle ear, the *malleus, incus* and *stapes*. The stapes is attached to a membrane at the *fenestra ovalis* which vibrates a fluid, the *perilymph*. This fluid, in turn, vibrates the *endolymph* within the saclike structure of the inner ear. The nervous mechanism within the membrane consists of: (1) the *organ of Corti* on the floor of the cochlea, which receives the sound waves by means of sensory hair cells that transfer the sensation to the auditory center in the cerebrum by the cochlear branch of the eighth nerve; (2) the nerve cells in the ampulla of the *semicircular canals* that carry the impulses to the cerebellum by the vestibular branch of the eighth nerve.

The vibration, after agitating first the endolymph and then the perilymph, passes out of the inner ear to the middle ear by means of the *fenestra rotunda*, then down the *eustachian tube* to the mouth and the nose.

The organ of Corti has nerve endings that are the receptors of hearing. These *sensory nerve cells of Corti are the end-organs of hearing*.

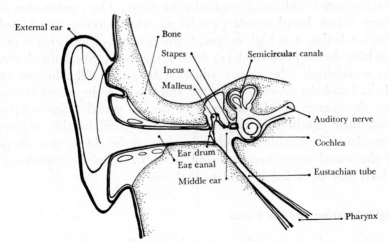

Figure 14.   Diagrammatic structure of the ear.

Equilibrium

Man has a number of senses to give him a sense of balance. The receptors of *touch* in contact with the ground, the sense of *sight*, *muscle* receptors, and finally the *semicircular canals* of the ear constitute the *organs of balance* (Experiments 5, 6, p. 71). However, the chief organs responsible for equilibrium are the *semicircular canals*. The semicircular canals are supplied with nerve receptors that are stimulated by the endolymph. They occupy three different planes and the combined stimuli received by all three ampullae make it possible to detect any shift in position, and so to initiate the muscular response suitable for the maintenance of equilibrium.

Sound, usually vibrations of the air, is the proper object of the sense of hearing. The hair cells of the organ of Corti receive the vibrations, which are coordinated in the auditory center of the brain.

Hearing

Sound is a kind of energy moving through matter, usually air. It will not move through empty space as light will. Sound of no definite wavelength that falls irregularly upon the ear is *noise,* while vibrations repeated with exact regularity are *tones.* The combination of many sounds heard together results in either *harmony* or *discord.* *Pitch,* whether it is high or low, is the number of vibration waves reaching the ear per second; i.e., other things being equal, the shorter the wavelength (the greater vibration frequency) the higher the pitch. *Loudness* depends upon the amplitude of the sound waves; i.e., the greater the displacement of the air particles (molecules) from their equilibrium position, the louder will be the auditory sensation. The quality or *timbre* depends on the character or shape of the sound waves involved, and secondly, upon the "overtones" which may be added to fundamental tones.

Sight, Hearing and the Nurse

Bright and moving lights annoy the sick. Normal light, however, consoles the sick, soothes the restless, and encourages the listless and unhappy. A dull room has a weird effect, and a darkened room gives the sensations of severe illness or death. The nurse, then, should avoid the extremes of excessive brightness or darkness. Some colors, too, affect the sick. Ordinarily, blue and yellow are to be preferred to red in decorating the sickroom. The thoughtful nurse can blend a variety of colors by using flowers and table decorations to make the room cheerful.

Such little considerations as watering the flowers, straightening the linen, keeping the bedside unit tidy and seeing to it that he is comfortable make the patient feel much happier. The nurse should check the room after she has finished morning care to make sure that everything is neat and pleasing to the eye.

Loud and sudden noises annoy the sick and the well. The good nurse is on her guard to check sounds that irritate the nerves of her patient, such as continued sounds of running water, squeaking shoes and chairs, walking on tiptoe instead of a quiet firm step, rattling dishes, slamming doors, whispering conversation with visitors. The room should be quiet and restful.

Internal Sensory Mechanism

Interoceptors

The *interoceptors* are nervous organs located in the lining of the *digestive system,* and are stimulated by the condition of this system.

The interoceptors deal with the sensations of *appetite, hunger* and *thirst.* No doubt, these three sensations influence our disposition. On some mornings we awaken with an abundance of zest and vigor, and accomplish a full day's work with satisfaction, while on other days we feel "logy" and out of sorts. This seems to be due in great measure to the interoceptors, though the exact nature of these nervous mechanisms is unknown.

The sensation of *appetite* is definite. It has been described as the "memory of food enjoyment," and is brought about by internal changes in conjunction with external stimuli, such as sight, odor and taste of food. It is one of the sensations of pleasure.

The sensation of *hunger* is an unpleasant sensation brought about by the muscular contraction of the empty stomach, and stimulates the whole being until food and water remove the condition.

Thirst is a sensation stimulated by the demand of the mucous lining of the throat for water. This sensation disappears when citric acid is applied to the throat, as the athlete realizes when he is supplied with a bit of lemon instead of a glass of water. Injection of water into the tissues also removes the sensation of thirst. Thirst, then, seems to be a demand of the tissues to replace the loss of water.

Proprioceptors

Proprioceptors are nervous organs located in the deeper regions of the body, especially in the muscles.

In order to get the sense of *weight* of an object, it is necessary to lift it—to test by muscular resistance the pull of gravity which the earth exerts on it. The nervous mechanisms concerned in such a test are the muscle, tendon and joint receptors that transfer the stimulus to the brain.

These receptors are responsible, in correlation with other senses—especially the semicircular canals—for maintenance of posture and body attitudes. Any motor activity like writing, dancing, speaking or driving a car requires the perfect functioning of many receptors, chiefly, the correlation of the kinesthetic or proprioceptors.

SUMMARY

1. The mind, which is the source of mental activity, is the directing force controlling human action.

2. The nerve cell is the unit structure of the nervous system. A stimulus is carried from one cell to another by means of the synapse, which consists of the linkage of the dendrites of one cell with the axon of another.

3. The brain is the central station of nervous activity, and is divided into three parts, namely, cerebrum, cerebellum and medulla oblongata. Each region contains important nerve centers.

4. Some functions are localized in definite regions of the brain.

5. The spinal cord carries out some reactions independently of the centers of the brain. The simple reflex depends on the cord as

its center of reaction. Stimuli ascend the cord in the dorsal or ascending tracts, and other stimuli descend in the cord principally by the ventral or descending tracts. Association bundles of nerves connect one region of the cord with the other regions.

6. A conditioned reflex is a reaction produced by an inadequate stimulus learned in association with an adequate one.

7. The S-R bond hypothesis explains some motor skills and simple reflexes, but fails to explain the basis of unit reaction.

8. The senses are classified according to the type of stimuli that are received by the end-organ or receptor.

9. Cutaneous sense organs are grouped together and divided into those of touch, thermal sense and pain.

10. Touch has to do with receptors of mechanical disturbances that are in direct contact with the skin, while pressure refers to stimulation that is sustained beyond transient contact.

11. Stimulations of touch are received by free nerve endings and modified nerve endings.

12. Thermoreceptors transfer heat and cold, which are specific stimuli; the cold receptors are superficial in position and the heat receptors are deep. Thermal sensations are relative.

13. Pain is received by definite nerve receptors and is distinct from touch.

14. The olfactory epithelium is localized in the superior-posterior part of the nose, near the nasal septum. There are many kinds of odors, but they may all be classified into six categories.

15. Taste is localized in definite nerve buds located along the papillae of the tongue. Taste is a sensation influenced by odor, but grouped into four stimuli, namely, sour, salty, sweet and bitter.

16. The eye is a specialized sense organ of sight. The end-cells are the rods and the cones of the retina. There are three primary colors and many complementary colors. Some people are color blind and cannot detect certain colors.

17. The ear detects vibrations that are interpreted into sounds. The hair cells of the organ of Corti are the specific receptors of sound. The length, number and quality of the vibrations give various stimulations. The ear is also the end-organ of equilibrium.

18. There are nerve endings located in the deep muscles and these give one the sense of weight and of balance. The nerve endings associated with the alimentary tract give the sensation of hunger and thirst and influence indirectly the sensation of well-being.

Suggested Experiments

1. Purpose: *To identify the location of sense receptors.*

   (*a*) Map out an oblong area (measuring 1 inch by ½ inch) on the back of the subject's hand.

   (*b*) Using a cold dry needle, explore the cold spots. The subject sits with eyes closed, and with hand loosely closed.

   (*c*) The needle should be applied lightly, moved in the same direction. When the subject states that he feels a cold sensation mark place with colored ink.

   (*d*) Warm spots are explored with a warm needle.

   (*e*) Let the experimenter lightly touch, with finely pointed needle, the bent knuckles of a finger of the subject. The spots that receive touch sensations are distinctly localized. The touch sensations are followed, after an obvious interval, by a radiating diffused unpleasant sensation of pain.

   (*f*) Touch a hair of the hand with the needle and the sensation is immediately noticed. Cut off the hair and re-stimulate the area.

2. Purpose: *To show that the sensation of cold depends upon the number of receptors stimulated.*
   Place the finger in cold water for a minute. Plunge the whole arm into the water. Note the difference.

3. Purpose: *To show that thermal sensations are relative.*
   The subject places a finger of one hand into water at 50° F. and the corresponding finger of the other hand into water

at 110° F. He should note the gradual changes in sensation. After a few minutes transfer the two fingers to water at 80° F., in which he moves them about, observing the temperature sensation.

4. Purpose: *To demonstrate the existence of the blind spot.*
   Look at Figure 15. Close your left eye and focus on the head of the nurse. Move the page of the book slowly toward your face and then away from your face. At a certain distance the mouse will disappear. When the picture is moved closer or farther away, the mouse will reappear. Close your right eye and focus the other eye on the mouse. The nurse will disappear when the picture is moved. Why?

5. Purpose: *To determine that sight is involved in balance.*
   Have the subject close his eyes and stand on one foot for one minute.

6. Purpose: *To test the sight and muscle receptors and semicircular canals involved in balance.*
   A student standing about 10 feet from the blackboard gazes at the tip of a 3-foot rod that he holds over his head. After turning around rapidly ten times, the student tries to put the tip of the rod in the middle of the "bull's eye," a circle, drawn on the board. The experimenter should be prepared to support the student if necessary.

7. Purpose: *To test the primary colors and complementary colors.*
   With a revolving disk and different colors, test the colors that give the sensation of white when the disk is revolved.

Figure 15.   Test for blind spot.

QUESTIONS FOR REVIEW

Essay Type

 1. Describe how the mind acts in regard to external objects.
 2. Sketch a typical nerve cell and label all the parts.
 3. Define dendrite, axon, cell, synapse, nucleus.
 4. What are the three regions of the brain?
 5. Where are the following centers located: sight, sensory, hearing, olfactory, motor area, respiration?
 6. Where are the Sylvian and Rolando fissures?
 7. Describe a simple reflex.
 8. Define and give two examples of each of the four types of reflexes.
 9. List a few procedures in pediatric nursing that are based on conditioned reflexes.
10. What are the four reasons some authors contend that conditioned reflexes are not true reflexive actions?
11. Describe the reactions of each of the three levels.
12. Define stimulus, response, receptor, gray matter, ganglion.
13. Describe the S-R bond.
14. Classify receptors according to stimuli.
15. What are the cutaneous sense organs?
16. Differentiate between touch and pressure.
17. Is the sense of touch uniformly distributed in the skin?
18. Where are Meissner's corpuscles?
19. Why is the sense of touch important for the nurse?
20. Why is the sense of heat and cold differentiated from touch?
21. Is the sense of cold absolute or relative?
22. Is it easy to localize the exact point of origin of pain?
23. What are the six categories of odors?
24. What practical suggestions would you give to the nurse in regard to the patient's olfactory sense?
25. What are the four kinds of papillae on the tongue?
26. Describe the position of the taste buds.
27. How does odor influence taste?
28. Comment on the phrase, "A nurse should taste the food before serving the meal to the patient."
29. Sketch the structure of the eye, and label all the parts.
30. Define cornea, sclera, blind spot, pupil, iris.
31. What is the function of the retina, of the ciliary process, of the fovea centralis, of the lens, of the iris?

32. Why do we call red and bluish-green complementary colors?
33. What are the primary colors? Name the colors of the spectrum.
34. Why can we distinguish a blue sweater from a red one?
35. Describe color blindness.
36. Trace a vibration into the ear, naming the structures that it must pass.
37. What is the end-organ of hearing? The end-organ of equilibrium?
38. Define noise, pitch, loudness, timbre, harmony.
39. Where are the interoceptors located?
40. Distinguish between proprioceptors and interoceptors.

Matching and Completion Type

Fill in the correct words:

1. The region where the end-fibrils of the axon of one nerve interlinks with the dendrites of another nerve. ....

2. A deep indentation of the brain. ....

3. The source of mental activity that is the directive force controlling human actions. ....

4. The color of the region of the cord or brain that is made up chiefly of axons. ....

5. A convolution of the cerebrum is called. ....

6. The type of nerve that carries an impulse toward the brain or spinal cord. ....

7. The name of the region of the brain where the center of equilibrium is located. ....

8. A nervous swollen area that is made up chiefly of dendrites and synapses. ....

9. The name of the lobe of the brain where the center of vision is located. ....

10. The lobe of the brain in which the auditory center is situated. ....

11. The term used for the fatty sheath that surrounds the axon and is inside of the neurilemma. ....

12. The name of the fissure of the cord along which the important ascending tracts are located. . . . .

13. A type of reflex, the action of which takes place entirely in the cord. . . . .

14. The bulblike modified nerve ending that is very sensitive to touch, and is located chiefly in the fingertips. . . . .

15. The name of the physiologist who first formulated the conditioned reflex theory. . . . .

16. The horizontal fissure on the lateral side of the cerebrum is termed: . . . .

17. The end-organ of a nerve that receives a specific type of stimulation. . . . .

18. The name of the gyrus located posterior to the fissure of Rolando, and in which the sensory area of the cerebrum is located. . . . .

19. The cranial nerve which supplies the organ of Corti. . . . .

20. The depression in the retina that is the place of best vision and is made up chiefly of cone cells. . . . .

21. The type of reflex that is produced by an inadequate stimulus learned in association with an adequate one. . . . .

22. The outer layer of the eyeball that is frequently called the "white of the eye" is termed: . . . .

23. The end-organ of hearing is located on the floor of the cochlea of the ear and is called: . . . .

24. The location in the brain of the centers of respiration, and the vasomotor action. . . . .

25. The name of the chief organs of the inner ear that are responsible for the sense of equilibrium. . . . .

26. The nervous system tends to react in the same way when a similar situation occurs, and this tendency of an impulse to take the same pathway at the synapse is termed: . . . .

27. The name of the region where the optic nerve enters the eye, and where there are no rod or cone cells. . . . .

28. The four papillae of the tongue are:

    a . . . .   c . . . .

    b . . . .   d . . . .

29. The three primary colors are: . . . . , ... and . . . .

30. The papillae of the tongue which have no taste buds are: . . . .

TOPICS FOR CLASS DISCUSSION

1. Impressions from external objects are received by the nerves and carried to the center of activity, the brain, and then I, the Ego, interpret these stimuli. That which reacts, then, is not the brain tissue alone; it is the mind, the Ego, the person herself—a psychosomatic human being.

2. The exact location of the motor centers of mental activity.

3. The different types of reflexes: simple, cortical, acquired, conditioned, and the levels of each.

4. The reaction hypothesis assumes too much. It fails to explain the higher powers of the mind, such as the action of the intellect and the will.

5. The cutaneous senses: (1) The thermal receptors can become negatively adapted to the thermal stimulus; (2) pain is a friend of man and not his enemy; (3) supplementary examples in regard to the cutaneous senses and the patient.

6. The nurse should endeavor to serve the food hot and attractive to whet the appetite of the patient.

7. As color does not reside in the object but is a psychologic phenomenon, then "Grass is not green because it contains the color green, but because we see it as green."

8. The image of an external object is "up-side down" on the retina, but we learn from experience to interpret the objects we see as "right-side up."

SOURCES AND REFERENCES

Bugelski, Bergen R., *A First Course in Experimental Psychology* (New York: Holt, 1951).

Fulton, John F., *Howell's Textbook of Physiology*, 17th ed. (Philadelphia: Saunders, 1955), Chap. XXIV.

Garrett, Henry E., *Great Experiments in Psychology*, rev. ed. (New York: Appleton-Century-Crofts, 1951), Chap. I.

Kuntz, Albert, *The Autonomic Nervous System*, 4th ed. (Philadelphia: Lea & Febiger, 1953).

Morgan, Clifford T., *Introduction to Psychology* (New York: McGraw-Hill, 1956).

Woodworth, Robert S., and Schlosberg, Harold, *Experimental Psychology*, rev. ed. (New York: Holt, 1954), Chaps. XI, XV.

4 • ACTIVITIES OF THE MIND

A casual observation of our own thoughts, actions, feelings and tendencies reveals that our mind is busy with many forms of different reactions and is complex in its action. We realize that the mental activity an interesting scene stirs up in our minds is entirely different from the reactions we experience when we study our lesson in anatomy. Again, it is a different form of mental process to memorize a scientific term than it is to imagine that we have just returned home after receiving our diplomas of graduation. The mind works differently when we choose a definite hypodermic needle from a box than it does when we feel the "hypo" of sterile water find its mark from the nervous hand of the "probe." These mental reactions are evidently distinct, and we must classify the subject matter of psychology according to the kind of reaction.

Though the mind is a unit, we study psychology according to the types of reactions. In anatomy we divide our study of the human body into systems, and by understanding different structures and their functions we obtain knowledge of how the whole body is constructed and acts; so, too, in psychology we divide our study into various powers of the mind, and by studying each form of reaction we may know more thoroughly how our mental life expresses itself.

MODES OF REACTION

In our study, however, the activities of the mind are divided in a logical manner according to the power that is manifested in each act. There are at least nine evident modes of reaction of the mind: *sensation, perception, imagination, memory, emotions, inclinations, habits, abstract thinking,* and *voluntary choice*. Each of these shall be explored in the succeeding chapters. Each different activity does not occcur to the exclusion of other reactions. For example, when a nurse is studying anatomy, she is using her power of the intellect to form judgments and to reason about the subject matter, and at the same time she uses her imagination to represent objects of former experience. She perceives the printed words on the page of the book, and she also employs the power of the will to continue to study, though other objects may attract her attention. All these activities are distinct mental reactions, yet the mind works as a unit, and the mind itself is not divided.

In our study of these forms of reactions many problems confront us at the very beginning. Up to the present we have considered the sense organs that receive the external stimuli, and have found that each organ is specific in its type of activity. Now we must consider how these impressions from external objects are made over in the mind into mental reactions; what type of mental activity is involved in such actions as reception of sensory stimuli, which we call *sensations;* how an actual object takes on meaning, which is the function of the central sense and results in *perception;* what type of mental reaction occurs in such activity as picture formation and imagery, which is the function of the *imagination;* how it is possible to retain past experiences and recall them to the surface of consciousness, which is the act of *memory;* what happens when a complex mental state stirs up untold body activities in glands, muscles and tissues, which we call *emotions;* how *inclinations* influence our instinctive actions to urge us to react in a particular manner toward some special goal and motivate our cravings and desires; what process the mind undergoes in forming ideas, judgments and reasoning, which are activities of the *intellect;* how repeated acts wear stimulus-response bonds in the neural mechanism so that we tend to react in the same way given the same situations, which occurs in *habits;* and finally, what takes place when we choose to do something or not to do something, which is the action of the *will.*

AWARENESS

Awareness is the *immediate consciousness of mental experiences.* We are aware of ourselves at every moment of our waking hours—of our mental states and of the fact that we exist. Man is either *conscious* or *unconscious.* When he is asleep he does not perceive what is going on in his mind; he is not aware of the external happenings around him. Often after an operation the nurse remarks that the patient has regained consciousness. She means by that, that he is now aware of himself; that he knows who he is, where he is, and can recognize those about him. Thus we are conscious when we see, we hear, we think, we move, we are on duty; in other words, when we are aware of our own existence.

It is clear, however, that only an infinitesimal part of an individual's knowledge can be in consciousness at any given moment. Part of the function of memory is to store all the knowledge a person has accumulated in various ways through the process of growing up and living through numerous experiences. This vast storehouse upon which one can call for information when he requires it, must contain a fantastic number of past experiences and the feelings they arouse, as well as a tremendous mass of factual material about the nature of the external environment.

FREUD'S CONCEPT OF MENTAL ACTIVITIES

CONSCIOUS, PRECONSCIOUS AND UNCONSCIOUS

We will consider briefly the theory of Freud's dynamic system of psychic energies at this time, as his division of the activities of the mind has radically modified the traditional meaning of the unconscious.

Freud divided the mind into three zones: *(1) conscious; (2) preconscious;* and *(3) unconscious* (Fig. 16).

Conscious

The conscious level of the mind is that part of mental life of which the individual is aware. The conscious mind consists of thoughts and feelings that shift from moment to moment, thought to thought, image to image and situation to situation. This idea of consciousness has not been changed from the traditional concept of consciousness.

Preconscious

This level of the mind contains experiences and sensations that may have been recorded by the senses but which are not here and now brought to the surface of the conscious mind. It is in this way, for instance, that memories are present in the mind when they are not actually being remembered. There are some aspects of mental life of which we are consciously aware only at certain times; at other times these experiences are present in latent form. This preconscious is not in fact conscious, but it can easily become conscious; we can become aware of its existence with some slight effort of memory, and we can visualize and talk about its content. One pronounced difference between the preconscious and the unconscious is the fact that one can readily bring the content of the preconscious to the conscious level, but it is extremely difficult to become aware of the unconscious phenomenon except by fantasy, dreams and free association.

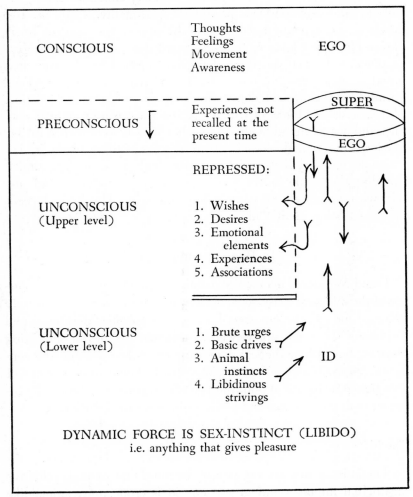

Figure 16. Graphic representation of the mind according to Freudian layer theory.

1. Three layers of the mind: *Conscious, Preconscious, Unconscious.*
2. Three dynamic systems: *Ego, Superego, Id.*

Unconscious

The unconscious is the third layer of the mind. The region includes psychic material which, under ordinary circumstances, is unable to enter the conscious part of the personality. There are two levels of the dynamic unconscious: the *upper layer* and the *lower layer*. The upper layer includes repressed desires, experiences, associations, and emotional traits that were rejected by the conscious mind at some period of one's life. This dynamic strata is supposed to influence behavior, feelings, decisions and interpersonal relationships. Emotional forces of which a person is unaware may be in conflict and act on the individual in such a way as to influence his behavior, even though consciously he knows nothing about it. For example, one may have a violent fear of high places without understanding the reason for the fear, or one may be inclined to like any girl with a stubby nose without knowing why. The lower layer is discussed below as the "id."

Id, Ego and Superego

Freud considered man as a dynamic system of energies. The powers of the mind are constructed of three main systems: (1) *the id;* (2) *the ego;* and (3) *the superego.* Each is to be considered as forces and functions. They are not viewed as concrete realities or self-acting entities, but as hypothetical dynamic powers that work on the conscious, preconscious or unconscious levels. These three systems of psychological forces—the id, the ego, the superego—dynamically interact with one another and produce the individual's behavior.

The Id

The id is the unconscious part of the mind that contains primitive instinctual impulses and urges. The id is crude, raw, animal-like and is not acceptable to society. The id is constantly putting out such emotional and instinctive basic urges as those for food, for sexual satisfaction, for aggression and for the gaining of immediate goals. The id is always in action, seeking to penetrate the conscious area and the upper level of the unconscious. The *superego,* however, checks its activity and ordinarily regulates its conduct. The personality of a newborn child is said to consist of id drives. At that time of early life, no other matured personality structure is present, as the ego is derived from the early interaction of the id with realities of the external world.

The id is the only source from which all psychic energy (libido) of the individual flows. *This dynamic force, the libido, is the sex drive, which is broadly interpreted as any function that gives satisfaction and the sense of pleasure.* Many psychologists oppose this view of Freud's. They contend that the driving forces of human nature cannot be limited to mere sex, as there are many other forces that drive human nature to activity, such as the desire for power, for happiness, for recognition, for security and for personal gain. Many other motives influence behavior. Freud, however, contended that the motive force (libido) is the sexual drive alone. His term, however, would include any function that gives pleasure; whether it be eating a candy bar, putting on make-up, giving a glass of cold water to a patient; each act gives pleasure and, thus, is sexual. Freud's idea of the libido, the sex drive, as the only psychic force of behavior, and his emphasis on sex and its role as the dominant force in conduct, is unrealistic and unwarranted.

The Ego

The ego is the force that brings us into conscious relationship with our environment. It receives instincts, wishes, impulses and strivings from the id. The ego has the function of conscious control and redirects the id-impulses in such a way that personal harmony is maintained with the external world. The ego is the conscious part of the human psyche, the center of human personality, the source of conscious thought, perception, feeling, and voluntary movement. The ego works chiefly on the conscious and preconscious levels.

The Superego

The superego is often referred to as the "conscience." It was previously called the *censor* and is the mentor, the watchman of morality, the subjective moral norm. It consistently warns: "This is wrong." "That is not permitted." "That is not allowed." The id wants to gratify all of our instinctive drives, but the superego refuses. The ego then decides how these desires can be expressed or repressed so that they can be accepted by members of society. Thus, the superego prohibits, postpones, directs the drives that come up from the id. The superego works on the three levels of conscious, preconscious and unconscious.

A child is told by its parent not to do this, not to do that. The parent rewards or punishes a child for his conduct. The child is continually under the direction of the parents and adults, and is taught what to do and what not to do. As a consequence, there gradually evolves in the child the *superego*, a system of restraining and inhibitory forces upon basic impulses. The superego admits, refuses, rejects, approves, disapproves and punishes. The superego becomes, in time, the internal substitute for the external forces of parental and environmental controls. One must, however, keep in mind the traditional meaning of conscience as a judgment by the intellect, here and now, of the goodness or badness of an act. Freud has assumed that this function is done by the hypothetical force that he calls the superego.

We are indebted to Freud for popularizing the theory that human personality is a dynamic unity and that the unconscious active elements influence behavior. This theory is very useful and some parts of it are indispensable, especially in treating mental disorders. Although the theory of Freud has been presented in order to explain the terms used, one should realize that the term "the unconscious" is used for convenience. There is no such thing as the unconscious as an entity or a segment of the psyche. The unconscious is simply a collective noun representing the sum of dispositions, experiences and memories of the mind.[1]

[1] VanderVeldt, James H., and Odenwald, Robert P., *Psychiatry and Catholicism,* 2nd ed. (New York: McGraw-Hill, 1957), p. 131.

THE MIND AS A UNIT

Our mind reacts upon objects in different ways and even has the power to reflect upon itself, but that substance that is acting is still the *ego, I, myself*. This underlying substance never changes but remains the same person acting throughout the individual's existence. The nervous mechanism may change, the tissues of the body do change, but still throughout its life the substance acting persists and coordinates all activities. The mind, then, is so closely united with the body that we say: "I see," "I hear," "I feel." It is not the eye that sees, nor the ear that hears, nor the receptor of touch that feels. The person is the one who sees, or hears, or feels. In every instance of human behavior the action undertaken is always the action by the *total person,* and every reaction of the individual is a *total reaction* of a single person. Illness, disease or mental disorder, regardless of the kind, is a reaction of both the body and the mind. Body and mind are so inseparable that whatever affects one affects the other.

Man's mind, will, judgment, principles, ideals and conflicts are without extension and are activities of a single person. They may not therefore be subjected to the special limitation imposed by the threefold division of the psychic life described by Freud. Man's psychic life is immaterial and inextended.[2]

SUMMARY

1. The mind, complex in its action, is busy with many different forms of reactions.

2. The sense organs receive external stimuli and are the bases of nine different kinds of mental activity, namely, sensation, perception, imagination, memory, emotions, inclinations, habits, abstract thinking and voluntary choice.

3. The activity of the mind is manifold, but the mind is one.

4. Awareness is the immediate consciousness of mental experi-

[2] Cavanagh, John R., and McGoldrick, James B., *Fundamental Psychiatry,* 2nd ed. (Milwaukee: Bruce, 1958), p. 83.

ence. Sensations are continually flooding the mind during waking hours.

5. The Freudian layer theory of the mind is described to enable the student to understand some special terms used in modern psychology.

6. According to the Freudian theory the mind is divided into three layers: conscious, preconscious and unconscious.

7. Man's mind, will, judgment, principles, ideals and conflicts are without extension and cannot fit in stratified layers as implied by the Freudian theory.

8. The ego is a hypothetical dynamic power which is the source of conscious thought, perception, feelings and voluntary movement.

9. Hypothetical forces work on different layers: the ego works chiefly on the conscious material: the superego is supposed to be the watchman of morality; the id is the lower unconscious libidinous dynamic force seeking to surge to the conscious level but is held in check by the superego.

10. Freud's idea that the sex drive is the only psychic force in behavior is unrealistic and unwarranted. Other forces, such as the desire for power, for happiness, for recognition, for security, and for personal gain, motivate our actions.

Questions for Review

Essay Type

1. Name nine evident forms of reactions of the mind.
2. Differentiate: ego, superego and id.
3. What psychic effects may result from a serious injury of the hand?
4. List the three layers of the mind as explained in the Freudian theory.
5. Distinguish the preconscious and the unconscious.
6. Define awareness.
7. Explain: the mind functions as a unit but its activities are distinct mental reactions.
8. What psychic reactions are included in the conscious mind?
9. Name the three dynamic systems of the Freudian theory.
10. What methods are used to bring an emotional element from the unconscious to the conscious level?

11. Describe the assumed activity of the id. How is the id controlled?
12. How does the lower level differ from the upper level of the unconscious?
13. What is the traditional meaning of the unconscious? How does this differ from the Freudian concept of the unconscious?
14. What is the function of the superego?
15. List the reasons why many psychologists do not agree with Freud's theory that the sex drive is the only psychic force in behavior.

Matching and Completion Type

Fill in the correct words:

1. The immediate consciousness of a mental experience is: . . . .

2. The three zones of the mind according to the Freudian theory are:

    a . . . .   c . . . .

    b . . . .

3. The layer of the mind which includes psychic material a person may readily recall to consciousness is: . . . .

4. The id is that unconscious part of the mind which contains:

    a . . . .   c . . . .

    b . . . .   d . . . .

5. The power of the mind by which we choose to do something or not to do something is: . . . .

6. The three dynamic systems of the Freudian theory are:

    a . . . .   c . . . .

    b . . . .

7. The reactions of the conscious mind are:

    a . . . .   c . . . .

    b . . . .   d . . . .

8. The content of the upper level of the unconscious includes repressed:

    a . . . .   c . . . .

    b . . . .   d . . . .

9. The power of the mind which forms ideas, judgments and thoughts is:

    a . . . .

10. The traditional psychologists contend that the unconscious is not a segment of the psyche but is a collective noun representing:

a .... c ....

b ....

TOPICS FOR CLASS DISCUSSION

1. Our mind reacts upon objects in different ways, and even has the power to reflect upon itself. It is always the mind by which I see, or hear, or feel.
2. Freud's theory of the mind and the various hypothetical powers.
3. The power of retention and recall of the memory in relation to the preconscious layer of the Freudian theory.
4. Compare the activity of the superego (conscience) with the activity of the practical intellect (conscience) which decides here and now the morality of an act.
5. The assumed activity of the id.

SOURCES AND REFERENCES

Brennan, Robert E., *General Psychology*, rev. ed. (New York: Macmillan, 1952), Chap. VII.

Cavanagh, John R., and McGoldrick, James B., *Fundamental Psychiatry*, 2nd ed. (Milwaukee: Bruce, 1958), Chap. VII.

Graham, Thomas F., *Dynamic Psychopathology* (Boston: Christopher Press, 1957), Chap. III.

Nuttin, Joseph, *Psychoanalysis and Personality* (New York: Sheed & Ward, 1953), Chap. III.

VanderVeldt, James H., and Odenwald, Robert P., *Psychiatry and Catholicism*, 2nd ed. (New York: McGraw-Hill, 1957), Chaps. VIII, IX.

5 • EFFECT OF SENSATIONS ON THE MIND

SENSATION

Sensation is the *reaction of the mind to sensory stimulus.* It may be described as awareness resulting from stimulation of the sense organs. There are as many types of sensations as there are classes of sense organs, namely, visual, auditory, cutaneous, gustatory, olfactory, intero-sensations, and proprio-sensations. Sensations are entering the mind all the day. These sensations come from every object in the world around us. We receive stimuli from the environment in which we live. Each avenue of the senses has its own particular stimulus. Every object around us may give many sensations such as: color, shape, size, heat, cold, touch, sound or even taste. In each case the sensation depends on the object, which may stimulate one or many sense organs. We see those about us; we hear various sounds throughout the day; we are continually experiencing reactions from touch and sensations of pressure from the clothes we wear, and from the contact with the external objects we must handle during the morning and night routines. All these multiform sensations are recognized by the mind and made over in the mind as images, and recognized as the representation of the objects that cause them.

The sense organs receive a stimulus from some object, and the sensory nerves transport the impulse to the central area of the cerebrum; *the mind in some unknown way is aroused to activity.* Thus, the sensation is not merely the reaction of the nerve ending to the stimulus; is also a mental state of consciousness that results from sensory stimulation. For example, if a fly touches the hand of a nurse, the stimulus is received by the receptors of touch, carried to the brain by the sensory nerve, and the nurse's mind is aware of the existence and properties of the insect that touched her. An object gives many sensations—pressure, heat, cold, texture, touch—since each quality of the object has a specific stimulation. The mind interprets these sensations and forms a mental picture of the external object, and the *process of the mind whereby the sensations take on meaning is called perception.*

PROPERTIES OF SENSATION

All sensations are not the same. They differ in *quality, intensity* and *duration*.

Quality

The quality of a sensation depends on the *nature of the stimulus.* There are as many sensory qualities as there are types of sense organs. Color, sound, touch, pressure, pain, taste, heat, cold are distinct and each gives a different sensation. The sensation of sound is different in its quality from the sensation of pain, and each has its particular effect on the mind. Even in regard to the same sense organs, sensations differ; for instance, blue causes a different feeling than red. A bright cheerful room in the hospital creates a different reaction than a somber room. One inspires hope, while the other suggests serious illness and even death. A clean uniform gives a different sensation than a soiled one; a new dress produces a different atmosphere than the dress a girl is accustomed to wearing. A reasonable amount of make-up in the morning causes a different sensation than the pale ghost appearance. A permanent wave gives a sensation unlike that of "dendrite-like" hair. A smiling face gives a different sensation than a scowling one.

Intensity

By intensity of a sensation is understood its degree of *strength in consciousness*. Thus sensation may be weak, mediocre or very intense. A loud sound is more intense than a faint sound. A bright light is more intense than a dim one. The intensity of a sensation depends on two elements: (1) *the amount of attention bestowed on the object,* and (2) *the force of the stimulus.* The intensity of a sensation may be greatly increased if one places her attention on the object. Thus, to a nurse who is listening for a sound from the nursery, the faint cry of a child becomes an intense sensation. A nurse waiting for her roommate to return from the city, detects her footsteps as soon as they come on the floor. A patient with an infected finger trembles even if a nurse merely touches his shoulder. As intensity is also increased according to the force of a stimulus, moving objects, bright lights, and loud noises are readily perceived, even though many other sensations are presented at the same time. A student is quickly distracted by a fly moving on the desk, or by two other students whispering while the instructor is at the blackboard.

Duration

Duration is the *length of time* the sensation persists. A patient rarely notices a slight noise, but if the sound is repeated a number of times, it becomes a strong sensation and may irritate the patient. Repeated similar stimulation increases the effect of the sensation and seems to wear a neural pathway in the nervous mechanism. Visual objects are distinguished as separate if the stimulus is presented not more than five times a second. Each object becomes a definite mental picture. A more frequent presentation of stimuli results in a continuous sensation. The individual pictures of the moving picture film become active objects as the small images are presented more than five times per second. The ear can ordinarily distinguish fifteen vibrations per second as distinct sounds. A more frequent presentation of auditory stimulation is heard as one continuous sound.

PERCEPTION

Perception is the *process of the mind interpreting and giving meaning to sensations of a particular object.* Any stimulus that is received by the sense organ initiates a neural impulse that is brought to the brain; consciousness is aroused, and the mind becomes aware of the sensation. A sensation, then, is the first reaction of normal activity aroused by neural stimulation. Thus far, the sensation has little meaning. But sensations never occur alone. They reside in the object and many sensations result from each object; for example, a hospital pin has many qualities such as color, shape, symbols, letters and numbers. When a nurse glances at such a pin all these sensations are received by the receptors, carried to the brain by the sensory nerves, and her mind then interprets these sensations as belonging to a definite object by comparing sensations of the external object with the mental picture she already has in her mind of a class pin. Perception takes place; the mind gives meaning to the new sensations. Each quality of the object gives different sensations and each sensation is always related to other sensations. *The mind reacts to each sensation and compares related sensations with past experiences.* Finally, the incoming sensations are related in the mind to similar sensations of the past and they are interpreted. *This process of the mind interpreting and giving meaning to sensation is perception.*

Perception commonly involves more than one type of sensation. The objects we perceive often possess tactual and auditory qualities, as well as visual and other qualities. Usually, we have no difficulty

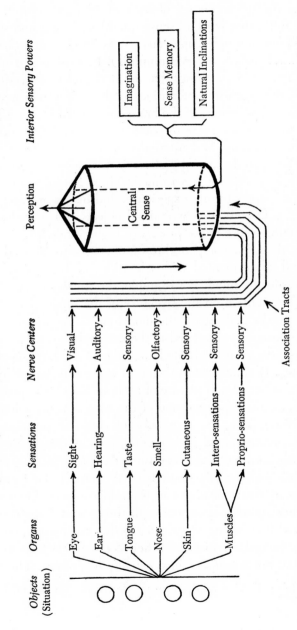

Figure 17.   Graphic representation of sensory perception. The central sense, compared to the central board of the telephone system, organizes and correlates the sensations from external objects with knowledge and images of past experiences in the process of perception. Most animals have the interior sensory powers which include the central sense; man has these powers and also the intellect and the will.

in identifying the proper source of each in the same object. This power of the mind that joins all sense qualities of sight and sound, of taste, smell and multiple cutaneous senses into a unit pattern, is called the *central sense* (sensus communis). It is the power of perceiving, in a sensible way, things that are here and now making an impression on the organism.[1] Sensations of the object, which stimulate the various sense centers of the brain, are carried by the association tracts to the central sense; this power then functions to correlate and to organize external and internal data into a unified pattern (Fig. 17). The central sense also stores in the memory and in the imagination the percepts it has formed. Thus, it unites and compares sensations, stores former experience, and makes an integrated sense picture, as it were, of new and old objects and related sensations for the mind to use in the process of higher knowledge.

Perception, then, is a compound result of sensations derived from the object and supplemented with sensations of past experiences already known in the mind. For example, the nurse studying anatomy places her attention on the structure of the lungs. The shape, form, color, and the make-up of the model are taken into the mind as individual sensations all related to the external object. Her mind compares these sensations with the knowledge of the lungs obtained in former study. Realizing that this model represents externally the same qualities as her mental picture of such an object, she perceives that this model is the representation of the lungs. Again, when she looks at a certain book, the sensations of color, shape, size, and printed words are registered in her mind, and by comparing such sensations with knowledge she has formerly obtained, she understands that this book is an anatomy book. When a nurse hears the voice of her roommate some distance away, she compares the quality, pitch, and other auditory sensations with those mental qualities she has experienced that belong to the voice of her companion, and she perceives that the girl at a distance is her roommate. *When one perceives an object the sensations must actually be present.* The mind

[1] Brennan, Robert E., *General Psychology* (New York: Macmillan, 1952), p. 160.

always compares the new sensations with former sensory experiences, then interprets the present sensations as belonging to something definite. When the nurse hears the siren of the ambulance, for example, she sees, as it were, the emergency call, forms mental images of the patient on the stretcher, the head nurse, the other nurses on call, the operating room, the doctor; she interprets the shrill tone of the siren with past sensations, and the sound takes on meaning. *There are no sensations without perception, and no perception without sensations.* Sensations precede perception as a necessary condition. The sensation is the first mental process caused by the external object; the mind, by the power of perception, compares, unifies, and interprets many present sensations in relation to former experiences.

All objects that are perceived are represented in the mind as definite objects and take form in some manner in the mind. Any word generally brings a definite object to mind. For example, in the process of perception we perceive a scalpel as a definite knife; a hospital as a specific hospital, generally our own; a nurse as one dressed in a uniform used in our school; a chair as a particular chair; a teacher as a definite teacher; a book as a definite book. The *percept is the representation that is present in the mind of an actual object.* For example, if we look at an orange, the shape, color, smell, and the entire make-up of the object give sensations, which are taken by neural pathways into the mind, then compared with past experiences of an object that we know as an orange, and interpreted correctly as a definite object. That mental picture of the external object is the *percept.* When we look at a building untold sensations of size, form, arrangement, space and distance come into the mind, and we perceive that structure as a definite thing. This process takes place in the mind as perception; the mental picture of the object, whether we continue to look at the object or not, is the percept. Thus the process of perception unites a great number of sensations of an object, and the object is understood in its correct relationship.

The nurse should cultivate the power of accurate perception. It can be *increased by close observation of details, concentration, attention to one's environment, intense effort and zeal for exactness.*

REACTION TIME

Reaction time is the interval between the onset of the stimulus and the beginning of the response. For instance, if a nurse were to receive a stimulus of touch, a period elapses from the time the stimulus is received to the time the subject manifests that she was touched. In a *simple reaction time situation,* there is usually a single stimulus such as a light, a sound, or a touch to the skin. In the *disjunctive reaction time experience,* however, two or more different situations are presented in a random order: for example, the subject is instructed to react to a green light, but not to a red one; or to put his foot on the brake when the red light comes on, but not to use the brake when the green light appears. Other stimuli could be introduced to make the reaction more complex, and thus increase the reaction time for any determined experiment.

In some people the reaction time is greater than in others. This difference depends on three factors: (1) *the characteristic of the stimulus,* (2) *the preparedness and attitude of the subject,* (3) *the intelligence of the individual.*

Characteristic of the Stimulus

The reaction time of the external senses vary; touch responds more speedily than hearing, sight, temperature, smell, taste and pain in this respective order. This variation of reaction time is due to the location of each type receptor, the speed with which each specific sense nerve reacts, or, probably, to the structure of the sensory-motor synapse. For instance, the receptors of heat are sunken deeper in the skin than the receptors of touch; hence, it takes longer for a stimulus of heat to activate the receptors than it would for a stimulus of contact to reach the receptors of touch.

The properties of sensations, namely, quality, intensity, and duration influence the reaction time within the same sense. For example, a loud, sudden noise has a greater magnitude than a weak one; a bright light takes less reaction time than dim light.

Preparedness or Attitude of the Subject

Our efficiency in coping with a situation is greatest when we are prepared for it. One who is on the mark set to run a race at the count of three, starts more quickly than one who is limp at the starting line; an experienced nurse in the emergency room reacts at once to the sound of the siren of the ambulance, differing considerably from the reactions of a nurse during recreation. One is "tuned" and "set" to receive the patient, the other is indifferent to the same stimulus.

Intelligence of the Individual

An intelligent girl who is attentive to a certain object will respond more rapidly than one who is mentally deficient. The mind requires a period of time to compare the incoming sensations with former knowledge, and this interval is increased or decreased depending on the efficiency of the receptors and one's mental alertness.

The analysis of reaction time between word stimuli and association concepts has long been used in the detection of guilt. By some, this method is called the "lie detector." A word list is prepared in which words related to the crime—for example, the names, color and location of objects stolen—are scattered through lists of items that have nothing to do with the crime. The subject is presumed to be guilty if his responses show unusual emotional disturbance that increases the reaction time for the critical words compared to the reaction time necessary to answer the unrelated items. Other tests, such as measuring the variation of the blood pressure, the change in respiration rates, and the increased moisture of the skin, are now used in conjunction with the reaction time.

It is obvious why this evidence is not acceptable in court. The increase of reaction time may be due to causes other than guilt. The subject may know the details of the crime from hearsay, reading, or from other knowledge, and is aware of the suspicion resting on him. These extraneous factors, and not the sense of guilt, may influence the results of the tests.

NEGATIVE ADAPTATION

If a stimulus is repeated too often, the sense organs become less sensitive, and the *sensation ceases to have its original effect.* This happens in everyday experience. It is the reason some people can sleep next to the clang of streetcars and the noise of traffic. This also explains why the nurse, when she first comes to training, will hear the bell at six o'clock in the morning, while the junior or senior merely rolls over in bed and never hears the bell. We become negatively adapted to the ticking of the clock, to the unpleasant odors of the hospital, to our own clothing and even to our own glaring faults. This process by which the mind becomes less sensitive to stimulation is known as *negative adaptation.*

APPERCEPTION

Apperception is the disposition of associating sensations according to past experience. It is a term used to emphasize one phase of perception. At birth the mind has no knowledge, and only by degrees does it learn the meaning of different sensations. Every new mental happening is stored in the mind, and gradually traces of experiences accumulate. The mind becomes, as it were, a storehouse of previous experiences. When an object stimulates the senses, it compares the neural reactions with something already known as belonging to a similar object, and forms its interpretation of the object. For instance, a child calls any moving object a "bug," and only later learns the names of differentiated animals. Since a learner develops a habit *of responding to objects or events in terms of his past experiences,* he tries to give meaning to all new stimuli, whether he can perceive them or not. When he is confronted with a new situation the meaning of which does not readily arise, he has a tendency, desire or craving to know what the new situation means. This added interest stimulates the learner to find the meaning and to understand the object, and thus increases investigation and closer observation. Generally, however, perception takes place immediately upon the reception of stimulus.

AFTER-IMAGE

Very often one notices that the *sensation persists after the stimulus has been withdrawn* from the sense organ. Such a sensation persists and lingers in the nervous system. This phenomenon, in which the activity of a sensation remains for a period of time after the stimulation has ceased, is known as an *after-image* or *lingering sensation*. If one looks at a light and then closes the eyes, the light persists and gradually changes color. The complementary color of the object remains as an after-image. For example, if one looks at a red object, and then turns his eyes on a white background, the outline and form of the object is seen on the white surface, but the color of the object changes to a green, and afterwards fades into other colors. If one looks at a colored light, the complementary color remains as the after-image when the eyes are closed, or when the lingering image is projected on a white or gray surface.

Certain tactile after-images linger for some time after the stimuli cease. *Kinesthetic* after-images remain long after one gets off a "merry-go-round," and after the "ride-for-life" at a carnival. Sensations from "swing music" remain long after the dance is over.

SUMMARY

1. Sensation is the reaction of the mind to sensory stimulus. Sensations are received by the mind from the sense organs of sight, hearing, touch, pain, heat, cold, taste, smell, proprioceptors and interoceptors.

2. Quality is the character of sensation that depends on the nature of the stimulus. There are as many sensory qualities as there are sense organs.

3. Intensity of a sensation depends on the force of the stimulus, and on attention.

4. Duration is the length of time that sensation persists.

5. Perception is the process of the mind interpreting and giving meaning to sensations of a particular object.

6. The central sense (sensus communis) is the power of per-

ceiving, in a sensible way, things that are here and now making an impression on the organism.

7. The mind always compares the new sensations with former sensory experiences, and then interprets the present sensations as belonging to something definite.

8. The percept is the mental representation that is present in the mind of an actual object.

9. All sensations involve a lapse between the time of the stimulus and the recognition. This is the reaction time.

10. We become used to a repeated stimulus, and become negatively adapted so that the stimulus fails to arouse the sense organs.

11. We tend to interpret sensations according to past experience. This is called apperception.

12. Lingering sensations are called after-images. The complementary color in visual after-images remains after the stimulus has ceased to act.

QUESTIONS FOR REVIEW

Essay Type

1. Define sensation, perception, apperception, negative adaptation, reaction time.
2. Cite three cases from your own experience of negative adaptation.
3. What is the quality of sensation? Its intensity? Duration?
4. What sensations may any object give? Give an example.
5. What is the value of sensation? What does it contribute to knowledge?
6. Is the reaction always proportionate to the force of the stimulus?
7. Describe how the sensations of a hospital pin are perceived.
8. How does the mind obtain a percept of an orange? Of a building? Of a nurse?
9. Describe the sensations you experience when called to the office.
10. What is meant by a conscious state?
11. What is the sensus communis?
12. What sensations do you experience on first-floor duty? Fourth-floor?
13. Describe the phenomenon of after-image.
14. Press a dime to the back of your hand for twenty seconds, then remove the coin. Does the sensation cease when the stimulus is withdrawn? Explain.

Matching and Completion Type

Fill in the correct words:

1. The reaction of the mind to sensory stimuli. . . . .

2. The disposition of associating sensations according to past experience.

   . . . .

3. The sense organ becomes less sensitive and the sensation ceases to have

   its original effect. . . . .

4. The process of the mind in interpreting and giving meaning to sensa-

   tions of a particular object. . . . .

5. The immediate awareness of a mental experience. . . . .

6. The property of a sensation which depends on the nature of the

   stimulus. . . . .

7. The time element involved from the moment that the stimulus is

   received to the instant in which the sensation is recognized. . . . .

   . . . .

8. The mental representation that is present in the mind of an actual

   object. . . . .

9. The power of the mind which unites and compares sensations during

   the process of perception. . . . .

10. The power of the mind by which we choose to do something or not

    to do something. . . . .

TOPICS FOR CLASS DISCUSSION

1. The mind in some unknown way is aroused to activity and interprets
   sensations.

2. A bright cheerful room in the hospital creates a different reaction than
   a somber room.

3. The intensity of sensation depends on the amount of attention bestowed
   on the object, and the force of the stimulus.

4. The sensation is the first mental process caused by the external object;
   the mind by the powers of the interior senses with the aid of the

intellect compares, unifies, and interprets many present sensations in relation to former experience. (Place special attention on the functions of the central sense, imagination, memory and natural inclinations.)

5. All objects that are perceived (perception) are represented as definite objects; all objects that are conceived (act of the intellect) contain the definition and meaning in general, and are not represented as concrete, definite objects (p. 264).

SOURCES AND REFERENCES

Brennan, Robert E., *General Psychology,* rev. ed. (New York: Macmillan, 1952), Chap. XIV.

Cunningham, William F., *The Pivotal Problems of Education* (New York: Macmillan, 1940), Chap. III.

Gaffney, Mark A., *Psychology of the Interior Senses* (St. Louis: Herder, 1942), Chap. III.

Gruender, Henry, *Experimental Psychology* (Milwaukee: Bruce, 1932), Chap. II.

Harper, Robert S., *Introductory Psychology* (Boston: Allyn & Bacon, 1958), Chap. III.

Krech, David, and Crutchfield, Richard S., *Elements of Psychology* (New York: Alfred A. Knopf, 1958), Chaps. II, III.

Moore, Thomas V., *The Driving Forces of Human Nature* (New York: Grune & Stratton, 1948), pp. 63-86.

6 • IMAGINATION AND DREAMS

IMAGINATION

All of us love to go to the land of reverie where we are the heroes in our thoughts and where the patients treat us with respect and are grateful for everything that we do; where the head nurse realizes that we are the best nurses on the floor; where the other nurses appreciate our good qualities, and are continually showering upon us words of praise and favors; where the doctors regard us as the "angels of mercy," and take the blame when a mistake is made. The *imagination is the power of the mind to form mental images or representations of objects in their absence.* This power to make mental pictures of past experiences and of future desires and fancy is called the imagination.

The image is the representation of an object in our mind. There are as many types of images as there are classes of sensations, namely: visual, auditory, cutaneous, gustatory, olfactory and motor. Some students have clear visual images, while others have strong auditory or distinct motor imagery. In general, however, there is a tendency for those rich in one kind of imagery to be rich in other kinds.

The activity of the imagination is twofold: (1) *reproductive* and (2) *constructive*.

Reproductive imagination represents images of objects of past experiences; for instance, we can see the lovely home that is waiting for us when we finish training; the corner drugstore where we spent a happy hour; the high school building, and many other objects of interest. *Constructive imagination* signifies the power of producing objects that are dressed in new circumstances and new associations and different features; for instance, we can place ourselves with Florence Nightingale on her visits to the sick, or see ourselves visiting the sick and the poor, or dress ourselves as Sisters of Charity in charge of the great hospitals doing the work of "White Angels." This activity of the imagination is possessed by the great inventors, painters, sculptors, scientists, doctors and leaders of the nursing profession.

Advantages

It is most important that a nurse develop a resourceful imagination during her days of training. An alert imagination will fructify her knowledge and add freshness to her studies by furnishing the intellect with materials for accurate and logical thinking. It will enable her to apply abstract theories and difficult techniques to practical cases by providing concrete examples. Furthermore, a constructive imagination makes it possible for a nurse to foresee what is expected of her while she is on duty. She is able to put herself in the place of the patient, anticipate his needs and render her service with kindness and sympathy, without becoming oversympathetic and foolish in her good work. She is able to aid her memory and advance in her studies, by learning to "see" the important topics of a printed page, the diagrams, the place for each scalpel and instrument necessary for an operation.

Disadvantages

The imagination is a power for good as long as it is regulated by right reason. Too often, however, it diverts attention from the essential to the trivial or fanciful; it takes one from reality to dreamy unreality; it clouds the judgment; it causes wasted moments of "day-dreaming" when the nurse should be studying and doing the required work. It leads to many complexes of action and feelings; it makes one lazy, listless, impractical and useless; and it may lead to dangerous thoughts and desires that have a tendency to weaken one's character.

Imagination Distinguished from Perception

The *imagination* differs from *perception* in the following ways: (1) Perception is the result of stimulation when the *object is present*, while the imagination produces images when the stimulus is *not present*. For instance, when I look at an apple, the perception is the result of the impression the object makes on my mind; when the sense object is not present, I call to mind and see by the imagination a mental picture of a red or green apple. (2) Percepts are vivid, clear, and distinct; images are faint, unstable and transitory in comparison to percepts. (3) Percepts are dependent on external objects; images are not. (4) The will generally has no influence over percepts, while images normally come under the control of the will.

✻ DISORDERS OF THE IMAGINATION

There are three common disorders of the imagination: (1) illusion, (2) hallucination, (3) delusion.

Illusion

Illusion is defined as false perception or as an inaccurate perception of an actual object. The timid nurse who must pass down an ill-lighted corridor at night sees cats and rats when a piece of paper moves on the floor; the nurse who listens to ghost stories and weird hospital experiences feels strange sensations when a cricket chirps, or when she hears a noise in the corridor; the one in charge of the nursery thinks that a child is crying in high "C" when the slightest noise is heard; the nurse who is visiting on a different floor imagines the head nurse is coming down the corridor whenever rosary beads jingle in her pocket. All illusions are inexact interpretations of external stimuli.

The chief causes of illusions are: (1) defective sense organs, (2) emotional strain, (3) errors of interpretation on account of surrounding objects.

Defective Sense Organs

Since perception depends upon adequate sensations from external objects, the receptors of sight, hearing, touch, taste and smell must be free of serious defects. A nurse who is partially deaf or one who has a bad cold often fails to carry out orders of the head nurse because she is unable to hear what she was told. A nurse with poor eyesight is inclined to misinterpret anatomic sketches drawn on the blackboard because she cannot perceive clearly the various lines and labels of structures. Normally, the sense organs receive the stimulus accurately, but if a sense organ is defective, illusions result from confused and obscure stimuli.

Emotional Strain

Expectation, desires and fear are mental states that have the largest share in the production of illusions. When a nurse is expecting her parents to visit her at school, she may think that each car that stops in front of the residence is the family car. If she is waiting for a telephone call, she may answer the telephone when she hears a bell ring, although the sound may be from an alarm clock in the next room awakening the nurse on relief. A nurse who has a "blind date" is subject to numerous illusions when a well-dressed young man ascends the dimly lighted front steps.

Errors of Interpretation Because of Surrounding Objects

Optical errors due to the surrounding objects are frequent (Fig. 18). The length of a given line is overestimated; parallel lines may appear bent to the eye; two railroad tracks seem to come together at a distance; faces and forms are made out on the wall or in the flowers; the chair with a towel or robe draped over it in a peculiar way could be interpreted as a visitor. If one places one's index fingers together, holds them about 2 inches in front of the eyes, and then looks over them at the wall, they appear like the nodes of Ranvier. If a nurse will roll a sheet of paper into a tube and place it before the right eye, and hold her left hand alongside the tube, then look at the wall with both eyes, it will seem as if she is looking through a hole in her left hand at an object on the wall.

In all cases of illusions the actual objects are present, but perception is inaccurate. Generally the mind realizes this inaccuracy and can correct the senses of perception by closer observation and by common sense. The patient, though, may often detect peculiar objects, which should be removed by the nurse without question or explanation.

Hallucination

Hallucination is the act of perceiving an object as present when it does not exist. Hallucinations are entirely subjective, whereas illu-

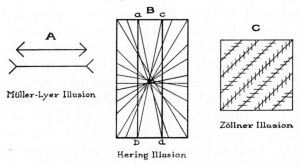

Figure 18. *A,* Both lines are of equal length. *B,* Lines *ab* and *cd* are parallel. *C,* Diagonal lines are parallel.

sions are objective. The source of a hallucination originates in the mind of the patient, while the source of an illusion is in the outer environment. In some nervous disorders of the cerebrum caused by poisonous substances, such as excessive morphine and alcohol, the patient is unable to distinguish between actual objects and mental fantasies. In ordinary language these patients are described as "seeing things," or as being delirious. Some patients imagine that the nurse and doctor are their enemies, ready to poison them; others see angels flitting over the bed, while others hear loud blasts and mighty screams when the room is perfectly quiet. These experiences are very real to the patient, and are to be taken seriously by the nurse as indications of sick behavior.

This condition may be temporary and the patient may become normal. If it is permanent, the patient is described as having a psychotic personality.

Delusion

A delusion is a false belief that is groundless and extreme. It is caused by an exaggerated use of the imagination. A delusion may arise from false information or from false perception. Most delusions come from the tendency to accept ideas that agree with our own pet ideas, and to reject the facts that do not please us or that cause us inconvenience. Anything we like to believe, we are inclined to believe without seeking all the information necessary to form a correct judgment. We take for granted that a pleasing thought is true. On the other hand, we tend to reject an idea that we fear, hate or abhor, even though it is true. This tendency is due to the fact that we are inclined to have a high sense of value of ourselves, and we do not like to hear any remark that lessens our estimation either of ourselves or of our friends. All of us tend to misinterpret and distort the evidence in regard to anything that we dislike or fear. We neglect to examine carefully or reason clearly when we are confronted with situations that may increase or decrease our self-esteem. Reason is clouded, and untrue conclusions result.

False beliefs or delusions arise in the normal mind. The sense of guilt, when we are aware of some weakness in our character, distorts the significance of a remark or the indifferent attitude of those about us. The imagination often magnifies a small incident and the mind accepts the idea as true. Too often, nurses live in the imagination, accept rumor without evidence, exaggerate trivial circumstances, and become "worked-up" by mob psychology. The nurse should develop the tendency to accept truth as it is found in the light of reason, and thereby avoid all forms of delusions.

There is no clear division between the delusion of the normal mind and the delusion of the morbid, mentally deranged patient. Delusions are morbid as soon as they become so fixed that they cannot be corrected by appeal to reason. The Napoleons, Lincolns and George Washingtons of the psychiatric hospitals suffer delusions so real that the patients identify themselves with these characters.

The four main types of delusion are: *delusion of grandeur, delusion of persecution, delusion of inferiority* and *delusion of negation.*

Delusion of Grandeur (Complex of Grandeur)

An exaggerated sense of one's importance, position, or ability is called the delusion of grandeur. This is common among many normal people. Such a person "puts on airs," is haughty, vain and inclined to live in fantasy and unreality. The nurse who overestimates her intellectual ability or her attractiveness is said to have the complex of grandeur. Such a person is termed by the students as "high-hat," or snobbish, and is generally self-centered. A nurse who parades down the street to display her new hat or her new dress, is living in the imagination; so is the young preclinical student who continually seeks the plaudits of the class.

Delusion of Persecution (Persecution Complex)

This form of delusion is common in any hospital. Such a person bears a grudge against the world in general or someone in particular without sufficient reason. Every remark is interpreted as controversial, and the most indifferent actions are interpreted suspiciously.

This complex inclines the person to be supercritical, fault-finding and moody. A supervisor may exaggerate unimportant happenings, and at times she feels offended when trivial mistakes of conduct occur on her floor. She may think that the student nurses intend to cause her personal inconvenience, not realizing that the girls would do the same thing on any floor.

Delusion of Inferiority (Inferiority Complex)

At times the unreasonable complex of inferiority takes possession of the mind even in the normal person, and this idea leads to temporary sadness, bashfulness, hesitancy and loneliness. Such a person tends to withdraw from the company of others, as he lacks self-confidence and social poise. Generally, this complex is accompanied by emotional strain. Such feelings of inferiority can be reduced by recalling occasions of past success and of opportunities that are to be gained by courage and self-reliance.

Delusion of Negation (Negation Complex)

The temporary false belief that a person lacks friends, or sufficient material objects such as clothes and money, or opportunities, is often experienced in the normal mind. A nurse, confined to her room by sickness, at times feels neglected because her classmates do not visit her, though she knows that it is difficult and sometimes impossible to obtain the necessary permission from the nursing office. Sometimes, too, a nurse is under the impression that she will fail an examination when she should realize that she can easily pass the examination since she has been studying her classwork daily.

We must be on our guard to look at things as they are, and overcome these complexes that cloud the mind and distort reason.

DREAMS

Dreams are the thoughts, images and feelings that pass through the mind during sleep. While we are asleep the imagination has full sway, unchecked by the external senses, so that a series of incoherent thoughts, visions and feelings move along in the mind under the guidance of association. The content of dreams is largely determined by the experience, occupation and conversation preceding sleep.

Dreams are probably universal in their occurrence, although some nurses contend that when they come off the floor they are too tired to dream. Apparently their dream comes so close to the waking state that they think they are awake in reverie. Other nurses dream whenever they go to sleep, even during class periods. Most people dream during short naps, during the early part of sleep and just before they awake. It is estimated that each person dreams about four times during the night. His eyes move during an active dream, and the dreamer witnesses his own dream even though he may not be conscious of doing so. As "brain waves" are different when a person is dreaming from those waves in sound sleep, it is possible to investigate the periods of dreams during the night by observing the kind of waves recorded on tape. The duration of a dream is generally only a few seconds, although it may seem to last for hours or even all night. Some dreams, however, may last a much longer period of time, perhaps for ten or thirty minutes. The kinds of dreams vary with different people: 90 per cent of dreams are visual (some of these are "colored television" type, while others are "black and white"); fewer are acoustic; a few dreamers experience tactile and kinesthetic sensations; an olfactory or a gustatory dream is rare. Logical sequence of events is generally lacking, since the images move through the imagination unchecked by reason and sense knowledge.

Causes of Dreams

Dreams may be due to physical and internal causes. Sickness, pain, hunger and external sensory impressions, such as a cool draft or local sounds, cause various forms of dreams. The nervous disposition predisposes the person to exciting and weird dreams, while other dreams are due to anxiety, anger, worry, fear and pleasant memories.

Dreams Compared with Illusions

While we are asleep the unconscious mind accepts the images as real objects since the external senses and reflection do not aid the dream-mind to test the reality of the pictures. The mental association flows incoherently from one locale to another; from the operating room to the diet kitchen; from the O.B. room to the first-floor clinic. All these representations seem real, as one having an illusion or hallucination, until one awakens, opens his eyes and feels only the pillow. At times one is pleased that the experience was but a dream, while at other times he closes his eyes to return to the banquet table of dreamland.

Interpretation of Dreams

Most dreams are mere continuations of imagery that has been taking place during our conscious life. In our waking life our thoughts are associated with perception of objects; in sleeping, however, these sensations are replaced by images reproduced in the imagination. Sometimes the dreams are associated with incidents that received little attention at the time they occurred.

According to Freud, dreams are fulfillments of wishes, especially of desires that we would disown and repudiate in our conscious state. The unconscious mind allows the desires and emotions of hatred, vengeance, envy, and other repressed urges to come to the surface during dreams. Many dreams are in the nature of wish-fulfillments that have been put into the background of consciousness by the reality of waking life. This truth, obvious enough in itself, was given too much of a sexual emphasis by Sigmund Freud and his earlier pupils, the Freudian analysts. According to this group, practically every dream is wish-fulfilling, and almost every wish is traceable directly or indirectly to the sex instinct. These theories are rejected almost universally by leading authorities in psychology and psychiatry, including the neo-analysts and Carl Gustav Jung. Although some dreams may be found that fit the description of the Freudians, it is certain that the majority of dreams do not fall into this class.

Any unsatisfied longing may, in fact, become the theme of wishful dreaming.[1] Many nurses have dreams about food, home, social entertainment and their mothers, which in reality are wish-fulfillments but have nothing to do with sex instincts. Many other dreams, such as those of frightful experiences and nightmares, are not wish-fulfillments. Dreams may at times give rise to representations of repressed emotions, but generally they are a continuation of the experience and association of the previous days, and are incoherent and inconsequential imagery of the imagination.

SUMMARY

1. The imagination is the power of our mind to form representations of objects in their absence.

2. Images are the pictures or representations of the imagination.

3. These mental images are objects of past experience as they appear in reality, or are objects placed in new associations.

4. The activity of the imagination is wholesome and good if directed by right reason and reflection.

5. Imagination is different from perception.

6. Delusion is a false belief not based on facts, while an illusion is an inexact perception of an actual object.

7. Expectation, desires, fears and physical errors due to the surrounding objects, cause illusions.

8. Hallucination is the act of perceiving an object as present when it does not exist.

9. The imagination, when unguided by reason, leads to many harmful consequences, such as complexes and impractical, listless actions.

10. Dreams are caused by the activity of images and thoughts that pass through the mind during sleep. They represent the objects as really present and are like illusions. They are caused by physical and mental conditions and deal with experiences that occurred during the waking hours. Incoherence and lack of logical sequence of

[1] Harmon, Francis L., *Principles of Psychology*, 2nd ed. (Milwaukee: Bruce, 1951), p. 350.

imagery are their chief characteristics. At times they indicate a suppressed desire, but generally they are a mere continuation of association experienced during the previous days.

QUESTIONS FOR REVIEW

Essay Type

1. Define imagination, image, dream, hallucination, delusion.
2. Describe the activity of the imagination in regard to fancy.
3. What are the advantages of the imagination for the nurse?
4. Distinguish between imagination and perception.
5. Define illusion.
6. What are the usual causes of illusions?
7. Differentiate: illusion, hallucination, delusion.
8. Why is it necessary for right reason to guide the activity of the imagination?
9. What are the disadvantages of the imagination?
10. What are the causes of dreams?
11. Why do dreams seem so vivid and real?
12. Describe in detail the different forms of delusions.
13. What are the causes of delusions?
14. Criticize the statement: "All dreams are the fulfillment of wishes."

Matching and Completion Type

Fill in the correct words:

1. The activities of the imagination are twofold, namely:

    a . . . .

    b . . . .

2. An inaccurate perception of an actual object. . . . .

3. The thoughts, images, feelings that pass through the mind during sleep. . . . .

4. A false belief that is groundless and extreme. . . . .

5. An act of perceiving an object as present when it does not exist. . . . . .

   . . . .

6. The chief causes of illusions are:

   a ....

   b ....

   c ....

7. The power of the mind to form mental images or representations of objects in their absence. ....

8. An exaggerated sense of one's importance, position or ability. ....
   ....

9. The type of imagination that represents images of objects of past experiences. ....

10. Two disadvantages of the imagination are:

    a ....

    b ....

11. The type of imagination that has the power of producing objects that are dressed in new circumstances. ....

12. A type of delusion when a person bears a grudge against the world in general without sufficient reasons. ....

13. Four physical causes of dreams are:

    a ....   c ....

    b ....   d ....

14. Four internal causes of dreams are:

    a ....   c ....

    b ....   d ....

15. A temporary false belief that a person lacks friends or sufficient material objects such as clothes and money. ....

TOPICS FOR CLASS DISCUSSION

1. The value of a constructive imagination for a nurse; for a doctor; for a dietitian.

2. Imagination and cheerfulness.

3. Personality defects which may result from an uncontrolled imagination.
4. Differentiate perception from imagination. Give personal examples concerning each.
5. Causes of illusions from the point of view of personal experiences.
6. Delusions of the normal mind compared to the serious delusions of a paranoiac patient.
7. Comment: Dreams are fulfillments of wishes, especially of desires we would disown and repudiate in our conscious state.
8. There is a tendency for those students who are rich in visual imagery to be rich in other kinds of imagery.

Sources and References

Bittle, Celestine N. C., *The Whole Man* (Milwaukee: Bruce, 1945), Chap. VIII.

Brennan, Robert E., *General Psychology*, 2nd ed. (New York: Macmillan, 1952), Chap. XV.

Gaffney, Mark A., *The Psychology of the Interior Senses* (St. Louis: Herder, 1942), Chap. III.

Harmon, Francis L., *The Principles of Psychology*, rev. ed. (Milwaukee: Bruce, 1951), Chap. XI.

Murphy, Gardner, *An Introduction to Psychology* (New York: Harper, 1951), Chap. XVI.

7 • MEMORY

GENERAL CONSIDERATIONS

Its Importance

A nurse should possess a good memory and common sense. She should be able to recall important knowledge with ease, regularity and assurance. For this reason, every nurse interested in self-improvement ought to understand and use the principles that increase her ability for memorizing and remembering. The ability to retain, reproduce and recognize previous experience must be put into practice continually, and the nurse must strive to improve her ability so that the acquired knowledge of facts, faces, names, symptoms and theory is available with readiness and facility. Throughout her course she endeavors to obtain the necessary knowledge of her profession, and then she depends on her memory to retain and recognize the material when the situation occurs in her own life. She

117

depends on her memory to recall facts she has studied, faces and names she has seen and heard, the proper method of treating patients, the correct time to give certain care, and the manner of performing certain actions. The possession, then, of a good memory means success or failure in many situations in life, and sometimes may even mean the difference between life and death.

Its Nature

Memory is the *mental power of retaining, recalling and recognizing previous experiences.* According to the definition, then, memory includes three activities, namely, *retention, recall* and *recognition. Retention* is a faculty of the mind to store in a systematic manner the various percepts, images and ideas of one's experiences. *Recall* is an act of the mind, bringing back to consciousness some image or event that happened in the past. *Recognition* is another act of the mind whereby one realizes that the present perception has been experienced before. Each of these three phases of memory, and the ways of improving the power of retention, will be studied in detail.

Memory is a living, active process of reviving images acquired through past experience. Knowledge comes back into consciousness through the familiar processes of either recognition or recall. It is usual to perceive several objects in a given experience, for each object leaves its impression. Our reaction to the whole experience is laid away in a set of images and ideas which are associated in so natural a way that the return to consciousness of one image or idea has the effect of bringing back a large proportion, or even all, of the images or ideas related to it. Memory is more than an absorption of the past experiences, for it *involves sensory stimulation, imagery, perception, thought, volition and even external manifestation.*

This ability varies in different individuals. Though all normal people naturally possess memory, some have perfected it by care and practice. Children's memory is not better than that of adults. The memory attains its greatest capacity in one's early twenties, and continues at approximately the same level or declines almost imperceptibly until one reaches the age of fifty or thereafter. *The will to learn, desire* and *change of interest,* however, affect a person's ability to memorize, no matter what his age may be.

Rote and Logical Memory

There are two types of memory: *rote* and *logical. Rote memory is mechanical learning of material by repetition.* One need not understand the meaning of the content that he endeavors to commit to memory. *Logical memory* is that form of memory in which *the person understands the meaning of the material* he studies and assimilates for future use. Everything we learn should be associated with something we already know. It should be organized with our existing mental life. For example, we should coordinate the study of a bacteria in microbiology with the disease it may cause, with the symptoms, prevention and treatment of the disease. This logical association is the only kind of retentiveness worthy of educational consideration. This type of memory requires clear thinking, comparison of ideas, and comprehension of the relationships of the new material to the previous associations.

THREE PHASES OF MEMORY

There are three phases of memory to be considered, namely, *retention, recall* and *recognition.* What is meant by each phase, how can we improve our ability in each, and what method should be adopted in memorizing and in studying?

RETENTION

Retention is an ability of the memory to store in a systematic manner the various percepts, images and ideas of one's experiences. Sensations are continually coming into the mind from the external world; we focus our minds on some of these sensations, but allow others to pass through the mind without attracting our consideration. In order to memorize, one must first record in the mind the sensations one is experiencing. Such recording is not a mechanical process comparable to the watching of television. Seeing is not necessarily observing. One must pay attention to the picture. One must see, hear, and understand what is happening and concentrate on the details of the drama that is taking place. The temperament, interest, ability and attitude of the spectator determine how much he remembers.

In the process of observation and understanding the person must, above all, be active if the content is to be remembered. He must be alert, attentive and willing to learn; otherwise, there is no possibility of remembering. Often when we are talking to our classmate she is not listening to a word we are saying; her mind is far away and she is thinking of some patient in the hospital or of a boy at home. Again, a professor can lecture most learnedly to a class of student nurses, but unless the students are listening and paying attention, the vibrations of his words merely hit the wall, and are unrecorded in the minds of the students. There is little possibility that the student will remember the teacher's lecture unless she is actively listening to and thinking of the subject matter of the lecture. The meaning of the expressed ideas often passes over the heads of the students because of inattention. Actually, then, *learning cannot be acquired without the cooperation of the learner.* The material to be remembered must be assimilated with previously known material, and through the interest of the person, incorporated into an organized unit. Memory is not mere reproduction; the processes of condensation, exposition and invention are also activated, making the act one of construction and systematic organization with past experiences.[1] Memory, being a living process, involves the general attitude and interest of the person. As these change from time to time, they also affect the manner and content of what is remembered. Briefly, then, *attention* and the *will to remember* are the essentially subjective elements of retention.

We listen to and learn those things that arouse our *interest.* Interest makes concentration much easier. The more interest one has in a subject, the easier it will be for her to intensify and increase the span of attention. Then, too, one should thoroughly *understand*

[1] Fox, Charles, *Educational Psychology*, 4th ed. (London: Routledge and Paul, 1951), p. 147.

the material before attempting to memorize it. *The clearer the understanding, the greater is the possibility of remembering.* It has been demonstrated that meaningful subject matter has a natural attraction for the mind, and the ideas and words that are understood can be retained easily and for a long time. Uninteresting and confused ideas make no impression and cannot be remembered. Thus, interest, attention and observation must be established if one hopes to impress the image of the object securely in the mind.

Methods of Increasing Retention

Three general factors influence retentive powers of the memory:
1. *Vividness of impression* of the experience.
2. *Repetition* until the impression is firmly established in the mind.
3. *Review* of newly acquired knowledge as often and as soon as possible, in order to revive or refresh the material when the impression starts to fade from the mind.

Vividness of Impression

A vivid impression is necessary for good memory. The deeper, the more perfect and the more intense the original impression, the more lasting will be the retention. We remember those events that had an overwhelming vividness and intensity. All of us recall the death of a good friend, the first day we spent in training, the day we received First Communion. *To impress an object deeply in the mind it is necessary to focus one's attention on the object, and to secure as complete an impression as possible.* The reason that impressions made by experiments performed in the laboratory or in practicing nursing arts are more lasting is due to the fact that we see, feel, hear and sketch to make the impression vivid.

In order to remember names and faces, we must pay strict attention to the persons whom we are meeting. We must make certain that we hear the names correctly, as we cannot hope to remember what we do not know. Next, we observe closely the appearance of the individual. We notice whether he is tall or short, thin or stout. The color of his eyes and hair is observed. We notice the kind of mouth, chin, nose. We fix upon some characteristic or expression and exaggerate this feature, as a caricature does, so that an intense impression becomes fixed in the mind.

Repetition or Drill

To remember an experience for a long time and to recall it at any particular moment, one must mentally repeat often the replica of the original impression. This strengthens old bonds of association, and the original impression is welded into an intimate union with former knowledge. For example, the names of the bones of the body are soon forgotten unless one recalls them from time to time. It is constant repetition, the act of doing or saying something again and again, that establishes the bond permanently in the memory.

Review

Immediate and systematic reviews of the essential ideas improve retention. Knowledge of a subject tends at first to fade very rapidly from the memory; it gradually diminishes unless one consolidates one's ideas and skills by frequent repetition. Thus, a student should review frequently the knowledge she has recently learned before the original impression fades from her mind; then she should review the entire subject matter at regular intervals to make the impression lasting.

RECALL

Recall is an act of the mind in bringing back to consciousness some image or event of past experience. It is a specific act of reproducing past experiences. Recall is of two kinds: spontaneous and voluntary. Recall is *spontaneous* if an experience comes back to us without any effort on our part. Recall is *voluntary* when we make deliberate effort to bring back to our mind what we have seen, heard, said or known, and we succeed in the effort. This voluntary process works in an orderly manner and is not haphazard. We want to recall, let us say, the name of a certain medication. We begin with a somewhat vague notion of what we wish to remember and try to go back to something connected with that notion. We endeavor to place ourselves in the mental situation of the original incident when we learned of the drug, and used it. Then a new set of images comes into the mind, related by similarity, contrast or contiguity. By repeated selection and rejection of specific concepts, we gradually come closer and closer to the name of the drug until finally it flashes upon us with a more or less lively feeling of satisfaction. We do not know the manner in which the past experiences, feelings, sensations, perceptions, impressions, ideas and judgments are stored in and retrieved by the mind. The task is so gigantic that it defies all powers of the imagination. Far less do we understand the intricate mechanism that operates to bring the material pertinent to any given problem to consciousness without appreciable delay and with few errors when the central sense and the intellect function at a particular time.

The process of recall *involves reflection, comparison, and active knowledge of relations.* The will controls and directs the course of images that are reproduced, freely accepting or rejecting various ones until the appropriate image is finally reproduced. This "searching power" of the intellect and the will within the process of recall is termed *reminiscence.*

RECOGNITION

Recognition, the third phase of memory, *is an act of the mind whereby one realizes that the present perception has been experienced at some previous time.* When a student says, for example, "I have seen that patient before; I notice that Mary is wearing her roommate's formal; I have heard that voice previously," she recognizes the patient, the dress, the sound of a voice. In recognition, one identifies the present perception as having been a matter of past experience. This identification may be definite or vague. *The essence of the process of recognition is judgment and not reproduction as in recall.* Recall and recognition are two different processes of memory. It is not necessary for recognition that the previous situation in which the patient, the dress or the voice were experienced, should be reproduced in the mind, for vague recognition often takes place when the previous situation does not return to consciousness and cannot be recalled. In definite recognition one is certain that he has seen, heard, experienced the same perception that is now repeated. In vague recognition, however, one is doubtful whether or not he can identify the present stimulus with the past experience.

The efficiency of recognition depends upon how well the material was learned originally, the amount of time that has elapsed since the original learning, and the nature of the activities in which one has engaged during the interval of time. Thus, recognition implies three facts: (1) knowledge of the past, (2) realization of one's past, (3) judgment that the object of the present stimulus is identical with the original impression.[2]

Recognition is an easier and a more dependable process than recall. It is used extensively in objective examinations, which are the popular standardized tests given in the armed forces and in all schools. In such a test a number of similar situations or statements is listed and the student is required to recognize each statement that is correct.

The way the mind acts in recall and in recognition enables us to reduce its acts to a few principles, which are the *Laws of Association.* These same laws of association are considered by some authors under the title of *Conditioned Reflexes,* and by others as the *Laws of Learning* (p. 284).

Laws of Association

There are primary and secondary laws of association. The primary are: (*a*) *Law of Similarity,* (*b*) *Law of Contrast,* (*c*) *Law of Relationship in Time and Space.* The secondary are: (*a*) *Law of Recency,* (*b*) *Law of Frequency,* (*c*) *Law of Vividness.* These laws express in a few words the manner in which the memory functions

[2] Gruender, Henry, *Experimental Psychology* (Milwaukee: Bruce, 1932), p. 196.

and also the way we correlate one thought with another. By the action of the mind in association we can recognize accurately our own street from many others, our friends' names, and past experiences.

Primary Laws of Association

Law of Similarity

Mental states suggest or recall their like in past experiences. For instance, a nurse's uniform reminds us of those with whom we live, or of the hospital; a song reminds us of a similar air of long ago; a friend reminds us of her mother, brothers, or other friends.

Retention of knowledge in the memory is aided by associating one type of knowledge with ideas related to it. Artificial aids that have no relationship to the material should not be used, as they put the mind to unnecessary labor in handling two kinds of material that have no natural relationship to each other. For example, the three layers of the eye: retina, choroid, and sclera should be labeled R., Ch., and Sc., and not 1, 2, 3. The serial number has no relationship to the term, but the first letters of the word recall the name of the structure.

The custom in some nursing schools of learning a verse as an aid in memorizing the twelve cranial nerves is a waste of time. It is easier and more desirable to memorize the nerves in the first place, and later the mind will not be forced to go through a double process in recalling each nerve.

Law of Contrast

The mind tends to recall images that represent experiences of an opposite kind. For example, heat suggests cold; black suggests white; virtue, vice; wealth, poverty; health, sickness.

Law of Relationship in Time and Space (Contiguity)

The mind, in the presence of an object or event, whether real or ideal, tends to recall other objects and events formerly *connected in time and space* with that now present. If a nurse happens to meet a girl friend from her home town, immediately thoughts spring up in her mind of home, mother, high school, teachers and other girl companions at home. The conversation is always concerning past events connected in time and space. Thoughts, desires, emotions and pictures recall similar states in former times when similar mental conditions prevailed. The memory is so closely bound to thoughts and events that are related in time and space, that it recalls each idea in circumstances similar to those which made the original impression.

Secondary Laws of Association

Law of Recency

The more recent the impression, the more easily it is retained, revived and recognized. This stands to reason. It is easier to repeat a lesson the next day than it is to do so the next month. It is comparatively easier to recall the name of a patient who visited the clinic last week, but almost impossible to call him by name a year later if one has not seen him in the meantime.

Law of Frequency

The law of frequency states that the more frequently an impression is repeated, the easier it is to recall or recognize. This law is a restatement of the principles of repetition in relationship to retention or memory. This law, too, is the basis of learning. Drill and reviews establish the bonds of association permanently in the mind (p. 122).

Law of Vividness

The law of vividness expresses the principle that objects and events that make a deep, vivid and intense impression at the time of observation are more likely to be retained, recalled or recognized.

This is the reason visual aids, diagrams, demonstrations, charts, pictures and case studies are used to increase attention and to make a lasting impression (p. 121).

FORGETTING

Forgetting is the inability to recall something at a given time. Forgetting is the converse of retention and, like retention, it varies in degree. We may forget some knowledge completely, partially, or not at all. There have been many observations made in regard to forgetting; they are summarized here:

1. The rate of forgetting is at first very rapid and gradually tends to slow down. It is estimated that we forget within a week approximately one half of the material we learned in one day unless we use the knowledge, or we repeat, restudy or review the new material we have acquired. We retain about three quarters of our knowledge at the end of a course of studies, less than one half after one year, and about one quarter after two years.

2. The rate of forgetting is greater for meaningless than for meaningful matter. Therefore, if we wish to remember, it is necessary to comprehend the subject matter thoroughly. We do this by reading over carefully the definitions, by repeating the ideas to ourselves in our own words, and by understanding the underlying principles of the subject we are studying.

3. The rate of forgetting is greater for recall than for recognition.

4. The effects of a period of study are to some extent diminished when, just after a period of study, we introduce a second period of mental activity rather than quiet relaxation.[3] This manner of studying that affects forgetting is called *retroactive inhibition.* The associations of new material tend to interfere with the bonds of associations of the material previously learned. The factors that influence retroactive inhibition are: (a) *Similarity:* If the new material is similar to the old material retroactive inhibition is greater. (b) *Time:* The study of new material *immediately after learning,* or *immedi-*

[3] Moore, Thomas V., *Cognitive Psychology* (Philadelphia: Lippincott, 1939), p. 436.

ately before recall causes greater interference. (*c*) *Degree of Learning:* The greater the degree of learning of the original material, the less the interference. (*d*) *Previous Experience:* The more familiar a person is with the new material, the less the interference. (*e*) *Meaningfulness:* Interference is lessened to the degree that the material lends itself to understanding and organization.

5. The rate of forgetting depends upon the amount of overlearning and repetition. The better the material is learned the better is its retention.

6. The forgetting of ideas is much more rapid and complete than the forgetting of motor skills. The reason for this difference is that motor reactions are usually repeated countless times, whereas a lesson is studied only a few times. Spaced repetition and reviews lessen the tendency to forget.

7. The rate of forgetting shows marked individual differences. These differences depend upon the capacity of the individual to remember, on the interest, the age and the attention of the individual.

8. Forgetting is probably never complete, although it may be impossible to bring the matter into consciousness at will. It may happen that some event one cannot recall returns to the mind in a dream or during a time of reverie.

9. Forgetting is a blessing in disguise. It is nature's method of relieving the mind of trivialities, sorrows and griefs. This would be a hard world to live in if we remembered all our difficulties, our struggles, our worthless and unpleasant experiences.

Although we may forget a large amount of the material of a subject we are required to study during our years in nursing, we should keep in mind that each study in the curriculum is worth our time and effort. What has been learned, however difficult it may be to recover, influences our conscious life all the time. *Past experiences have a permanent effect on our thoughts and actions,* even though conscious recall may not be possible. Although much of what is learned in school is forgotten, it does not, in the least, follow that it has no influence on our subsequent life. On the contrary, it may affect the whole of our thinking even if little of it is consciously recoverable.[4] A nurse who has been through a course of training has a changed outlook by virtue of that training, for her judgments are permanently influenced.

The forgotten facts are of little significance and can be recovered if one has the desire to do so. What is of lasting worth is the attitude of mind engendered during the acquisition of and the consequent effect of the knowledge, though forgotten, on future activity.

DISORDERS OF MEMORY

The memory may function improperly in two ways: (a) *by defect,* i.e., the past experiences fail to reappear (amnesia), or (b) *by excess,* i.e., the past reappears with unusual brilliancy (hypermnesia), or appears falsely (paramnesia).

Amnesia is the loss or serious defect of memory. It may be temporary, due to excessive strain or violent shock, or permanent, due to infection of the cerebrum. A person so afflicted cannot recall such common material as his own name, home, family.

Hypermnesia is an excessive and exaggerated activity of the memory involving many or even all events of the past. This is said to occur during periods of intense emotional excitements and at the time of death.

Paramnesia is a false memory, a fanciful remembrance of things that never occurred. For example, a person may relate an experience that never happened, and tell it so often that he believes it himself. Such a person loses the ability to distinguish between imagination and memory.

QUALITIES OF A GOOD MEMORY

A good memory has the following characteristics: (1) *facility of acquisition,* (2) *tenacity of retention,* (3) *ease of reproduction* and (4) *accuracy of recognition.*

A student who possesses these four qualities has an excellent

[4] Fox, Charles, *Educational Psychology,* 4th ed. (London: Routledge & Paul, 1951), p. 149.

memory. A student who may have some difficulty acquiring knowledge, however, may be considered to have a good memory if she has the other three qualities, namely, tenacity of retention, ease of reproduction, and accuracy of recognition.

The four qualities of a good memory are developed by applying the methods and aids that we have considered in Chapter 2, The Art of Study. The average student, by improving her study habits, increases her ability to acquire knowledge with ease, to remember for a long time what she has learned, to recall readily the information she needs, and, finally, to recognize accurately that the important points that she recalls are essentially without error.

SUMMARY

1. Memory is the mental power of retaining, reproducing and recognizing previous experiences. It is one of the great contributing factors to success in life.

2. Memory is more than absorption of past experiences, for it involves imagery, perception, thought, volition, and even external muscular manifestations.

3. The will to learn, desires, and changes of interest affect the ability to memorize.

4. There are two types of memory: logical and rote. Logical memory implies understanding, whereas rote memory is mechanical memorization.

5. There are three phases of memory, namely, retention, recall and recognition.

6. We listen to and learn those things that arouse our attention.

7. Retention depends upon vividness of impression, repetition and frequent reviews.

8. Recall involves reflection, comparison, and active knowledge of relations.

9. The essence of recognition is judgment, and not mere reproduction.

10. Recall and recognition are orderly processes of association by which a well-trained mind refers the notion of the present to the

impression of the past. The primary laws of association are threefold: similarity, contrast, and relationship in time and space; the secondary laws of association are: recency, frequency and vividness.

11. Forgetting is the inability of the mind to recall a former experience.

12. The four qualities of a good memory are: facility of acquisition, tenacity of retention, ease of reproduction and accuracy of recognition.

QUESTIONS FOR REVIEW

Essay Type

1. What is memory?
2. Why must a nurse train her memory?
3. Name the three phases of memory and define each.
4. Why is a vivid impression essential to memory?
5. How can you improve your memory for names and faces?
6. What functions do attention and observation play in the process of memory?
7. Discuss: "Repetition establishes the bond permanently in the memory."
8. When is the best time to memorize? Why?
9. Describe the process of the mind in the act of recall in relation to the laws of association.
10. What is recognition?
11. List five facts about forgetting.
12. Describe the disorders of memory.
13. Give an example of each of the primary laws of association. Of the secondary laws of association.
14. Distinguish between recall and recognition.
15. What is retroactive inhibition? What factors influence retroactive inhibition?
16. What are the four characteristics of a good memory?

Matching and Completion Type

Fill in the correct words:

1. The activity of the memory to store in a systematic manner the various percepts, images and ideas of one's experience. . . . .

. . . .

2. The inability to recall something at a given time. . . . .

3. An excessive and exaggerated activity of the memory. . . . .

4. The mind tends to recall images that represent experiences of an opposite kind. . . . .

5. A serious defect of the memory. . . . .

6. The mental power of retaining, reproducing and recognizing previous experiences. . . . .

7. The three primary laws of association are:

    a . . . .

    b . . . .

    c . . . .

8. A false memory, a fanciful remembrance of things that never occurred.

    . . . .

9. The type of memory in which the person understands the meaning of the material to be studied. . . . .

10. The three secondary laws of association are:

    a . . . .

    b . . . .

    c . . . .

11. An action of the memory whereby one knows that the object experienced now is similar to or identical with the impression previously received. . . . .

12. The term used to express the "searching power" of the intellect and the will within the process of recall. . . . .

13. The five factors which influence retroactive inhibition are:

    a   . . . .   d . . . .

    b . . . .   e . . . .

    c   . . . .

14. The four qualities of a good memory are:

    a .... c ....

    b .... d ....

15. Four reasons a nurse should have a good memory are:

    a .... c ....

    b .... d ....

TOPICS FOR CLASS DISCUSSION

1. Children's memory is not better than that of adults.
2. Seeing is not necessarily observing.
3. Learning cannot be acquired without the cooperation of the learner.
4. The clearer the understanding, the greater will be the remembering.
5. Memory is more than absorption of past experiences; it involves many other factors.
6. Each student should make out a detailed chart of her classes, study time and hours on duty.
7. There are at least four qualities a student must possess, which determine how much she will remember.
8. Voluntary recall involves many functions of the mind other than memory.
9. Recognition requires judgment; recall is mere reproduction.
10. The rate of forgetting is influenced pronouncedly by overlearning and repetition.
11. Whatever has been learned, however difficult it may be to recover, influences our conscious life all the time.
12. A comparison of conditioned reflexes with the laws of association.

SOURCES AND REFERENCES

Fox, Charles, *Educational Psychology*, 4th ed. (London: Routledge & Kegan Paul, 1951), Chap. VIII.

Gaffney, Mark A., *The Psychology of the Interior Senses* (St. Louis: Herder, 1942), Chap. IV.

Garrett, Henry E., *Great Experiments in Psychology*, 3rd ed. (New York: Appleton-Century-Crofts, 1951), Chap. VI.

McGeoch, John A., and Irion, Arthur L., *The Psychology of Human Learning* (New York: Longmans, Green, 1952), Chap. X.

Moore, Thomas V., *Cognitive Psychology* (Philadelphia: Lippincott, 1939), Chap. IV.

Mursell, James L., *Psychology of Modern Education* (New York: Norton, 1952), Chap. VII.

Woodworth, Robert S., and Schlosberg, Harold, *Experimental Psychology*, rev. ed. (New York: Holt, 1954), Chaps. XXIII, XXIV.

8 • FEELINGS AND EMOTIONS

Life would be uninteresting and colorless if there were no feelings of pleasure and pain, of excitement and depression, of tension and relaxation; or if life were one monotonous course without love, joy, surprise, merriment, admiration, awe, mingled with sadness, sympathy, fear, anger, and all the forms of emotional states that we notice in the people about us. The motivating force of activity is the urge for happiness and pleasure, which stimulates not only the mental powers but the whole body in some way or other. The feelings and the emotions influence our whole lives. Pleasure results ordinarily from the normal activity of the senses, and is a powerful incentive in even the hardest form of work. The feelings of pleasure and pain are indexes of bodily health, and as such should be of special interest to the nurse who observes them every day.

FEELINGS

Feelings are states of consciousness, known as pleasure and displeasure. They are reactions of sensations. Thus, there are as many

135

kinds of feelings as there are sensations experienced by the individual. Most psychologists limit the term *feelings,* however, to the most simple, elementary and unanalyzed phase of consciousness to which the word *feeling* can be applied. For example, suppose you say that a feeling of pleasantness accompanies the hearing of a certain familiar song; then suppose you undertake to describe the state of pleasantness that you experience. It is likely that you will be inclined to say, "It is most pleasant, and that is all I can explain about it." Like the sensation of hearing that it accompanies, the feeling of pleasantness is too elementary and simple to admit of analysis.

All activities that are *conducive to the well-being of the body* are accompanied by the sense of *pleasure,* while activities that are *excessive or detract from the well-being of the individual* are accompanied by *displeasure.*

We must remember, however, that feeling is always based on something perceived. It never appears alone in consciousness as mere pleasantness or unpleasantness. The mind is aware of the sensations, and the affective state of feeling accompanies this knowledge. The degree of the pleasantness or unpleasantness depends on the type of activity and on the instinctive traits which have been modified as one's own by experience, memory and volitional effort; thus, it varies with different persons, and with the same person at different times.

Pleasure

The satisfaction of hunger and thirst, the use of the senses of sight and sound, of touch and balance, recollections and desires, are all sources of pleasure. When a nurse completes her work for the day, she experiences a sense of pleasure. When she is given a word of praise or when her hopes are satisfied, pleasure is sure to follow. This feeling of well-being accompanies all activities that are the *result of favorable sensations,* such as eating, drinking, dancing and recreation.

There are different kinds of pleasure, depending on the activity itself and on the energy that is expended. Satisfaction derived from

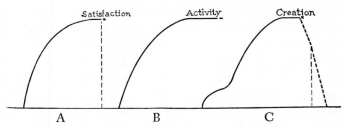

Figure 19. A line graph showing increase and fall of the sensation of pleasure. *A,* Pleasure of sense; *B,* pleasure of activity; *C,* pleasure of creation.

the exercise of the senses, such as eating, drinking, quietly resting in a comfortable chair, is qualitatively different from that pleasure one feels when listening to music, in playing some game or creating some artistic work. Pleasure derived from activity of the senses, for example, the gratification of one's appetite for food, increases steadily and once satisfaction is reached, there is a sudden cessation of pleasure (Fig. 19 *A*).

Compare this reaction with the pleasure of playing a game of tennis. The individual starts to play in an indifferent mood. Gradually the pleasure increases until there is a continuous source of pleasure, which consists in continuing the activity. The feeling would have no end if it were not for the fact that fatigue checks the activity (Fig. 19 *B*). The third kind of pleasure is derived from creative work. At first there is a period of unrest, until the idea is formed in consciousness, and then pleasure mounts until the goal is obtained; when the object is completed pleasure gradually goes down until a new idea is born (Fig. 19 *C*). There is no pleasure without activity. The nurse who does her work and takes reasonable recreation is the one who is generally the happiest; she experiences greater pleasure than the one who saves her energy.

Displeasure

Whatever is out of harmony with the well-being of the individual causes displeasure or pain. Whenever an activity is forced or excessive the feeling of dissatisfaction arises. This is *caused either by defect or excess* in the exercise of the senses. A popular song, at first, is pleasant to hear, but if your roommate continually sings it, displeasure replaces the original feeling. When a form of exercise is repeated too often, or the degree of the exercise of any of the senses is too intense, displeasure results. The abnormal exercise of any of our senses produces pain. This is the reason we welcome variations of any form of activity in order to lessen the sense of fatigue and at the same time exercise multiple sense organs, rather than just one or two.

Moods and Sentiments in Relation to Feelings

The sum total of all the feeling accompanying the various sensory and thought processes at a given time results in *temporary feeling called a mood, which soon fades away.* Any nurse who has been in training for even a short time has had the feeling of lonesomeness, of the "blues," followed by joy, "pep," exultation and the happiness of mere existence. At the present time we can hear the clatter of distant noises, the passing of traffic, and a hundred other additional sounds. At the same time the eye is appealed to by an infinite variety of lights, colors and objects; the skin responds to many contacts and temperature; add to these the reactions of the autonomic nervous system of respiration, of digestion, of circulation. And then, finally, add our conscious needs and desires, as well as the processes that accompany images of memory, imagination, thinking and the purposeful activity of the will. Thus, we see how complex our feelings are, and how our moods depend on multiple sensations.

Beside the more or less transitory states, which we call moods, there exists a class of *mental attitudes that contain intellectual activity linked with feelings.* These attitudes are called *sentiments.* Our sentiments, closely allied to emotions, are complex mental states that we name friendship, loyalty, sympathy, patriotism and the like. Sentiments have their origin in concrete experiences in which feeling is a predominant force, and gradually develop from repeated experiences and appreciation of values. It is true that sentiments cannot be reduced to mere feelings, as there are present cognitive and volitional factors of values fostered by repeated experience; nevertheless, feeling is so dominant a part of sentiment that it exercises almost a controlling influence.

It is well known that *moods and sentiments influence judgment and volition.* Motives that entice us when the world seems bright and gay fail to move us when we are sick. What appeals to us as a good proposition one day looks entirely different when we are ill and out of sorts. It is easy to do our work when everything is pleasant, but how difficult it is to do the same work when something goes wrong on the floor and everyone seems to be in ill humor. Although an efficient nurse performs her duty under all circumstances, it is a fact that she can accomplish the same work without mental strain when the shadow of discouragement is removed from her environment. For these reasons, a nurse should carefully consider the moods, attitudes and sentiments of her patients, endeavoring to create a pleasant atmosphere by her cheerfulness, and, at the same time, remove any object that would tend to irritate the sick.

EMOTIONS

The emotions are complex mental states that arise in response to the meaning of sensations and are accompanied by stirred-up body conditions. Mental states that arise in response to sensations are feelings; mental states that arise in response to the meaning of sensations are emotions. Emotions have two elements: a *psychic* and a *somatic* component. From these two elements we derive the term *psychosomatic.* The *psychic* component is the sensory apprehension of the meaning of sensations; the *somatic* component is the motor responses of the body, such as the activity of the facial muscle, the change in rate of the heartbeat, the change in respiration, the activity of the endocrine glands which pour secretions into the blood, and even a disturbance in the function of the gastro-intestinal tract.

An emotion can express itself in every tissue of the body, although in many cases it seems to limit its manifestations predominantly to those organs and tissues supplied by the autonomic nervous system. When a person is emotionally excited his muscles become tense; he moves about and finds it difficult to sit still; his heart beats quickly, breathing increases, his speech is hesitant and faulty; he feels queer sensations in his internal organs and perhaps a lump in his throat; the skin becomes either warm and reddened or cold and clammy; the eyes become watery and sparkle. At times, in an emotional situation, he says things that he would not say under ordinary circumstances.

Autonomic Nervous System

The autonomic nervous system innervates those structures of the body that work automatically and are not directly under the control of the will. For instance, the beat of the heart, the breathing of the lungs, the flow of saliva in the mouth, the digestion of food by the stomach and the intestines, the excretion of the kidneys, the manufacture and distribution of the chemicals of the endocrine system, especially those of the adrenal gland, are activities independent of voluntary control. The autonomic system carries out these functions without any effort on our part. Indeed, as long as this system functions normally, the individual does not even know he has these nerves inside his body.

The two divisions of the autonomic system, important in relation to the emotions, are: the *parasympathetic* and the *sympathetic. Each division works antagonistic to the other.* While one set of nerves contracts the pupil of the eye, the other set dilates it; one slows respiration, the other increases it; one slows the beat of the heart, the other stimulates it. When the two work in perfect harmony, as they do under normal conditions, their antagonistic action is not observed to any degree. However, when an individual becomes emotionally aroused, the autonomic balance is disturbed. The excessive activity of the sympathetic division causes the body to become stirred-up. Let us compare the activity of these two divisions in a nurse who is calm and a nurse who is angry. The calm, efficient nurse is regulated more by the *parasympathetic* division. She is satisfied with her existence, the heart beats in a smooth, regular way, respiration takes care of itself, digestive juices flow with rapidity when she eats. In the nurse who is angry the *sympathetic* division acts contrariwise. The activity of the *sympathetic* nerves causes her breathing and the beat of her heart to increase; her throat becomes somewhat dry; her eyes shed tears profusely, and her appetite decreases because of the retarded flow of digestive secretions. Interestingly, these are the same reactions a nurse in love would experience. An increased amount of epinephrine in the bloodstream stimulates the liver to release its stored sugar, and the above symptoms of the sympathetic system are activated.

The autonomic system reacts in a similar way in all forms of emotions, although such states as fear, anger, horror, sorrow, courage or love certainly "feel different" to the individual who experiences them. The great difference from one emotion to another is the *intensity;* that is, one can be fearful or just worried, angered or merely irked, scornful or displeased. The changes become more profound, more widespread with each increase in intensity. The physical core seems to be identical for the same degree of fear, anger, love and the other emotions. The explosive force of each motion depends on the way the individual perceives and interprets the situation, rather than on the stimulus itself. An emotion is essentially a state of generalized excitement that expresses itself both in the way we feel and in the motor responses of the body. When we are angry, we feel angry all over, and our classmates are aware of the fact. In addition, we feel queer sensations internally, cold chills, and a lump in our throats. These reactions are caused by the sympathetic division of the autonomic nervous system.

The following table summarizes the action of the autonomic system on some of the important structures of the body.

TABLE I. AUTONOMIC NERVOUS SYSTEM ACTIONS CAUSED BY EMOTIONS

Structures	Sympathetic (Angry Student)	Parasympathetic (Calm Student)
Heart	Stimulate	Check
Respiratory Organs	Stimulate	Check
Salivary Glands	Check	Stimulate
Digestive Glands	Check	Stimulate
Adrenal Gland	Stimulate	No action
Lacrimal Gland	Stimulate	Check

James-Lange Theory

This theory teaches that the *emotions are the result of the stirred-up body condition* and are not due to the mental state. As so often expressed, "We are afraid because we tremble, and we do not tremble because we are afraid." It is a question then of whether the stirred-up body condition is the cause of the emotion or whether the psychic (mental) state is the cause. This theory was very productive of research, and it is of value for this reason. It seems, however, since the work of Walter B. Cannon[1] on the effect of adrenalin on the emotions, that the perception of danger precedes the visceral changes of the body.[2] Therefore, the old concept that the mental state, not the stirred-up condition, as James-Lange contended, is the cause of the emotions, is more plausible. The mental state causes the autonomic nervous system to work, and the physical effects are due to the action of adrenalin in the blood and tissues.

Facial Expression

The expression of the face changes with different emotions, and it is possible for the nurse to accustom herself to reading the face to learn how the patient feels. States of attention, reflection, pain, horror, disgust, astonishment, joy and laughter may be read in the face. When a student in the class is called on to exemplify these emotions, the other nurses usually recognize the specific emotions by studying her facial expressions. The nurse should also learn to recognize bodily and postural signs of emotion, such as restless feet, tapping with fingers, and sudden jerks of the body.

KINDS OF EMOTIONS

All attempts to classify emotions into neat categories have failed. The reasons are that the emotions are not fixed qualities when ob-

---

[1] Cannon, Walter B., *Bodily Changes in Pain, Hunger, Fear and Rage* (New York: Appleton-Century-Croft, 1929).

[2] Moore, Thomas V., *The Driving Forces of Human Nature* (New York: Grune & Stratton, 1948), p. 127.

served by others, and one emotion seems to merge with others when observed in ourselves. For example, when you received your cap you rejoiced, yet you were fearful that you might make a mistake during the exercise, worried that your cap might not stay on your head or that your candle might burn out before you pronounced the Nightingale pledge. Emotions are complex states, and we must be satisfied to enumerate different forms as they are usually considered: (1) those emotions caused by objects the individual apprehends as *favorable and attractive,* such as love, affection, excitement, happiness and joy; (2) those emotions caused by objects the individual apprehends as *dangerous to his security,* and to be *overcome by fighting or aggression,* such as anger, jealousy, hatred and hostility; (3) those emotions caused by objects the individual apprehends as *situations to be avoided,* and to be *overcome by escape,* such as fear, worry, dread, sorrow, embarrassment, regret and disgust.

"Love is the fundamental element in all emotion. Love is the attraction of the mind toward something good, beautiful or desirable. If the object is in our possession, we *enjoy* it; if proposed to us merely as a future good, we *desire* it. When we lose an object we love, we become *sad.* We *hate* the evil that deprived us of good. If this evil only threatens to overtake us in the future, we *abhor* it and seek to avoid it. If the good appears attainable, we indulge in *hope;* if unattainable, we lapse into *despair.* If we realize that we can overcome the evil without danger to ourselves, we take *courage;* if we are threatened with an evil difficult to avoid, we *fear.* If the evil actually overtakes us, we become *angry.*"[3]

Anger, fear and love are native emotions. Under anger might be included rage, fury, revenge, irritation and vexation. Intense worry, anxiety, dread and terror are related to fear, while exaggerated pity and sympathy are variations of love.

Fear

One of the major problems that confronts the nurse is the anxious

[3] Barrett, Francis F., *Elements of Psychology* (Milwaukee: Bruce, 1931), p. 185.

patient. She should know how to cope with anxiety and how to help the patient keep his mind off his worries. Reassurance and confidence in herself, in the hospital and in the patient's doctor should be expressed to the patient.

Often the patient who comes into the hospital is troubled. In the first place, his sense of security is lost as a result of leaving home and familiar surroundings. Confinement in a hospital is a new experience; the patient fears medications, pain, treatments; if he comes for major surgery, he is worried about the competence of his surgeon, about the effect of the anesthetic, about whether he will survive the surgery; every mother frets about her children at home; a young child seeks his parents, brothers, sisters and friends, and will pull away from the nurse or other strangers; a father occupies his mind about finances, insurance, or the possibility of losing his job even if he recovers his health.

As hospital life is a complete change from home life, it is only natural for a patient to feel ill-at-ease in his new environment. He is eager to understand the cause of his illness and know what can be done about it. The nurse may inform the patient what is expected of him while he is in the hospital, and thus help him to adjust to the hospital routine. She may also eliminate some mental strain by encouraging the patient to talk about his worries and his fears. She can build up his confidence by assuring him that his doctor is one of the best, and that an efficient nursing team is working with him. She may explain each procedure that she is going to do, and tell him why it is necessary. Sometimes the treatment is of such a nature that the patient is able to help the nurse; if so, she can encourage him to do so. This combined effort of nurse and patient can do a great deal to relieve his stress. Finally, the nurse can help the patient to relax mentally by being cheerful and confident, and by having a pleasant sympathetic attitude.

Method of Eliminating Fear

Fear develops when one is faced with a difficulty he cannot overcome. When the object one fears cannot be overcome at the moment, the only rational behavior is to escape from the object that threatens harm. In this reaction we concede that we are temporarily failures. However, this retreat from the object that causes the difficulty should pave the way to reflection as to the best method of conquering the object; when this has been decided, one renews the battle and overcomes the obstacle.

A summary of rules helpful in overcoming fear follows:

1. As a rule, the anxious person should be made to understand the cause of his anxiety. He should ask: "What am I afraid of?" "Why am I afraid of this?" and "What can I do to rid myself of this fear, or how can I turn it to my advantage?" When one realizes the true reason for his condition, he is frequently capable of overcoming his fear.

2. Do not fight your fear. Reasonable fear, which is in proportion to its cause, is a valuable means of protecting a person against danger. Fear makes one cautious of danger and warns him to stop fighting when he is getting the worse of the conflict. He fights the thing that makes him afraid by facing his own problems and by evaluating them with logical and constructive thinking. In this way he is able to understand the object that lies at the root of the fear complex, and by overcoming the object he is able to overcome the element of fear. At examination time one should not endeavor to directly overcome the anxiety; one must study and know the classwork that causes the anxiety.

3. Most fears are disguised, and are due to ignorance. Endeavor to bring the element of fear from the unconscious mind into the open and thus unmask the mystery.

4. Overcome the habit of fear and hesitancy by becoming successful in the work that causes anxiety. Nothing is difficult if you know how to do it. Success will follow if you form correct habits.

CONTROL OF EMOTIONS

Emotions must be controlled by the will, and a mature person is one who can regulate his emotions so that they do not cause harm to his own character, or cause embarrassment and harm to others. He has the ability to understand, tolerate, accept and respect himself and others. The emotions are good in themselves and the motive power of life. When they are directed into the right channels they lead to the highest forms of achievement. An emotion becomes harmful only when it grows unmanageable, becoming so excessive that it disturbs the physical and mental balance of the person concerned. There is nothing more noble than a dutiful, sympathetic and well-balanced nurse; nothing more humiliating than a nurse who is impatient, intolerant of discomfort, demanding immediate gratification of her every whim, primarily self-centered or explosive in her behavior.

Four Essential Ways of Controlling Emotions

Disorderly emotions may be governed by directing our natural drives and our emotional impulses into generous activities. This is done in the following four ways: (1) by *controlling the imagination;* (2) by *learning to wait for one's reward;* (3) by *learning to care for others;* and (4) by *looking at things as they are.*

Controlling the Imagination

The imagination should not be permitted to reproduce an object that arouses strong emotions. Situations are often grossly misinterpreted and magnified in the imagination. As we have already asserted when we dealt with controlling fear, an individual may prevent many an angry response by asking himself: "Why am I angry?" "Why should I be afraid?" "What does this person really want?" By transferring the situation from the imagination to the intellect, the intensity of the emotion becomes lessened and, often, the emotional response even fades away. Hypersensitive people, who are inclined to make a "mountain out of a molehill," must check the tendency to take an insult from a situation or statement where no offense is intended.

Learning to Wait for One's Reward

A person must regulate his immediate drives, needs, and desires if he hopes to control his emotions. This is done by learning to wait for one's reward by working for a more remote goal that is far greater than immediate aims. Generally, if a person waits to analyze his desires, he is able to get a clear view of the emotional situation. Some things that appear attractive at first lose their luster when one delays for a short time. An emotionally *mature patient* has the ability to control his immediate impulses, and he cooperates with the hospital staff so he may recover his health more rapidly. An *immature patient,* on the other hand, is self-centered, wants his own way, and insists on receiving medications and treatments before the nurse can take care of any other patients. Usually, he is hard to please and feels that the nurses and others of the staff do not give him adequate care. He protests against procedures; he is un-cooperative and intolerant. He does not accept responsibility, nor will he try to aid in his own recovery. It is a pleasure to take care of a patient who is kind and considerate.

Learning to Care for Others

An intense care for and a cautious respect for the feelings, rights and property of others should bring emotional harmony into one's life. Lifelong training and thoughtful, daily planning are required to establish desirable, harmonious relationships with one's associates; to play fair in all dealings; to respect one's parents, those in authority, the aged, and the sick; and to give aid to those in need. Essentially, a nurse can do this by being cheerful in her work, courteous and charitable to all her patients, respectful and kind to her classmates, and, finally, cooperative with those who are in authority at the hospital.

Looking at Things as They Are

Many an individual takes himself too seriously. He sets social, moral, and ideal standards for himself and for others that are un-realistic and impractical. He often expects too much of others and refuses to make allowances for human weaknesses. We must keep in mind that no one can be perfect in all respects. Thus, when we fail in some things—as everyone invariably must—we should be able to laugh at ourselves along with others. So long as one can laugh, things are not too bad. The ability "to laugh it off" has saved many an awkward situation in the classroom and in social activity. Laughter sweeps away the annoyances, worry, jealousy and disappointments of daily life. It is necessary for one who is developing emotional maturity to have a sympathetic understanding of human weaknesses and to form a practical judgment of the shortcomings of others.

EFFECTS OF EMOTIONS

On Health

Strong emotions have no place in the sickroom, and the nurse must take care that the patients are not subject to anger, fear, excessive worry or excitement. These emotions seek their expression in bodily resonance that affects the appetite, digestion and elimination. They retard recovery and lengthen the period of convalescence. The nurse, then, must be on guard that she is not the cause of word or action that may arouse a strong emotion in a patient. Kindness and cheerfulness, poise, and efficient service in taking care of the sick are the true safeguards for the nurse to observe in order to avoid unnecessary emotional reactions in the sickroom.

On Motor Skill

While under strong emotion a person loses partial control of his muscles and his motor skill suffers. At times, crude strength is increased, but technique and control are lacking. The mind is distracted from the efficient accomplishment of the immediate work to the fanciful object of the emotion, and the muscle effectors are disturbed and uncoordinated.

On Reason and Judgment

It is impossible to reason with a person who is excessively angry or in love. Such a one has her mind set on the object of the emotional resonance, and is like a prejudiced old woman who cannot see any point of view other than her own. A violent emotion partially destroys reason and judgment and, like a raging torrent, devastates all that comes in its way. Never argue with one who is wrought up, as opposition merely increases the emotion and greater harm results. When a nurse must deal with such a patient, she should endeavor to remove the cause of the emotion, but she must not reason with him or give excuses. Keep quiet and go about your work as if nothing happened. If you are the cause, leave the room as soon as possible, and let the head nurse take care of the case.

On Character and Training

All must strive for emotional maturity. So often it happens that a nurse is well trained in her profession, well educated and cultured, yet exhibits the emotional behavior of an infant. Character depends much on the control of the emotions, so that one is not easily piqued, flighty or egocentric. We expect children to be intolerant and explosive in behavior, to demand immediate satisfaction of every trivial whim, and to display "puppy love." When these same traits are displayed in the adult, there is something lacking in character formation. Endeavor to be tolerant of the other person's opinions and actions, to learn to endure inconveniences and sufferings when they are necessary, and to strive for a future good greater than an immediate lesser good.

SUMMARY

1. Feelings and emotions influence our whole lives, supplying the motive force of action.

2. Feelings of pleasure and pain depend on the form and intensity of the activity.

3. Pleasure results from sensations favorable to the well-being of the organism.

4. When an activity is forced and excessive the feeling of displeasure arises.

5. The emotions are complex mental states caused by the mean-

ing of the sensations and accompanied by stirred-up body conditions. This bodily resonance is due to the action of the autonomic nervous system.

6. The James-Lange theory teaches that the aroused body conditions, not the mental state, are the cause of the emotions. This theory has been refuted by the study of the adrenal body, which is influenced by psychic reactions and causes the stirred-up body condition. The mental state is the cause of the emotion and the body condition follows, contrary to the opinion expressed in the James-Lange theory.

7. There is no satisfactory classification of emotions. They are grouped at times according to the object: (1) tendency toward the object, or (2) tendency away from the object associated with danger or difficulty.

8. Emotions are good, but must be controlled by right reason.

9. Disorderly emotions must be directed into generous activities.

10. Strong emotions affect health, motor skills, reason and judgment. Character training must consider the emotions and develop the individual to emotional maturity.

QUESTIONS FOR REVIEW

Essay Type

1. Define feeling, emotions, autonomic nervous system, pleasure, displeasure.
2. Distinguish between feeling and emotion.
3. What five activities give the sense of pleasure? Why?
4. Discuss the statement: "The motive force of activity is the urge for happiness." Give three examples.
5. What are some of the things a person does when he is emotionally excited?
6. Describe the action of the two divisions of the autonomic nervous system.
7. Discuss the James-Lange theory of emotions.
8. Why should a nurse be able to distinguish the external signs of emotion?
9. Name at least ten kinds of emotions. Define each.
10. How can one control the tendency toward an unreasonable emotion?
11. What reactions do strong emotions have on health?

12. Describe the emotionally immature patient.
13. How would you treat a patient whom you have unconsciously offended?
14. Describe the emotional tendency of a child.
15. What suggestions would you offer a self-centered patient?

Matching and Completion Type

Fill in the correct words:

1. The feeling of well-being that is the result of favorable sensations.

   . . . .

2. A temporary feeling which soon wears away. . . . .

3. The type of feeling that results from forced or excessive activity.

   . . . .

4. The theory that states that the emotions are the result of stirred-up body conditions and are not due to the mental states. . . . .

   . . . .

5. The attraction of the mind to something good, beautiful or desirable.

   . . . .

6. The division of the nervous system that works automatically and is not directly under the control of the will. . . . .

7. States of consciousness, known as pleasure and displeasure, and are reactions to sensations. . . . .

8. The different kinds of pleasure depend on two factors, namely:

   a . . . .

   b . . . .

9. The term used to identify a class of mental attitudes that contain intellectual activities linked with feelings. . . . .

10. Complex mental states that arise in response to the meaning of sensations and are accompanied by stirred-up body conditions. . . . .

    . . . .

11. The four chief effects of strong emotions are:

a . . . . c . . . .

b . . . . d . . . .

12. The four essential ways of controlling the emotions are:

a . . . . c . . . .

b . . . . d . . . .

13. The six emotions that result from tendencies toward definite objects are:

a . . . . d . . . .

b . . . . e . . . .

c . . . . f . . . .

14. Four strong emotions that have no place in the sick room because they affect the patient's appetite, digestion and elimination are:

a . . . . c . . . .

b . . . . d . . . .

15. The emotions that denote danger or difficulty to be overcome are:

a . . . . d . . . .

b . . . . e . . . .

c . . . .

Topics for Class Discussion

1. The feeling of pleasure and pain are indexes of bodily health.
2. The psychic and the somatic components of emotions.
3. The control of emotions in relation to the personality of the nurse.
4. Identification of various emotions, as exemplified by the facial expressions and pantomime of one of the members of the psychology class.
5. List the kind of emotions you have observed in the conduct of others during the past two days.
6. The effect of moods and sentiments on your social relations with a definite nurse in your freshman class.
7. The antagonism of the sympathetic and parasympathetic nerves on the following structures: the heart, the lungs, the digestive glands, the salivary and lacrimal glands. (The increased or decreased stimulation of these structures, as evident in the reactions of an angry student or a nurse in love, are caused by the sympathetic nerves.)

Sources and References

Barrett, James F., *Elements of Psychology* (Milwaukee: Bruce, 1931), Chap. XI.

Bernard, Harold W., *Toward Better Personal Adjustment*, 2nd ed. (New York: McGraw-Hill, 1957), Chap. IX.

Cannon, Walter B., *Bodily Changes in Pain, Hunger, Fear and Rage* (New York: Appleton-Century-Crofts, 1929)

Cole, Luella, *Psychology of Adolescence*, 5th ed. (New York: Rinehart, 1959), Chap. X.

Guilford, J. P., *General Psychology*, 2nd ed. (New York: Van Nostrand, 1952), Chap. VII.

Kuntz, Albert, *The Autonomic Nervous System* (Philadelphia: Lea & Febiger, 1953)

Moore, Thomas V., *The Driving Forces of Human Nature* (Grune & Stratton, 1948)

Ruch, Floyd L., *Psychology and Life*, 4th ed. (Chicago: Scott, Foresman, 1953), Chap. V.

Woodworth, Robert S., and Schlosberg, Harold, *Experimental Psychology* (New York: Holt, 1954), Chaps. V, VI, VII.

9 • DRIVES, INSTINCTS, CHOICE AND MOTIVATION

GENERAL CONSIDERATIONS

Human nature is endowed with certain inclinations that influence all our actions. These impulses are unlearned and are inborn in our very nature. A newborn babe is not taught to breathe, to cry or to suckle; it has these abilities from the moment of birth. Instinctive fear, dependence, cries of pain and alarm, crawling and similar reactions transcend national boundaries and race distinction. Other tendencies are present in all men, such as the impulse to escape sorrow, and to enjoy perfect happiness. All of us love to be in the companionship of others; we like to move from place to place; to compete with others and succeed in competition. All of us seek food when we are hungry, drink when we are thirsty, rest when we are tired. We experience these drives in the presence of an actual opportunity to make use of any one of our natural abilities. Certain tendencies are universal in human beings, such as the desire to win the approval of those about us, to master certain techniques, to defend our rights. At other times we are attracted to objects that move, to bright and sudden-appearing objects. We call these tendencies "natural leanings," and we enjoy the opportunity of acting under favorable conditions while pursuing these inclinations.

We are influenced, however, not only by our natural inclinations but also by our *intellectual apprehension* of the value of certain plans in life that appeal to us. We have, for example, come to a school of nursing because we desire to obtain adequate knowledge and skills to be efficient nurses, although we could have decided that it would be much easier to stay at home, or go to another school for a different profession. Since we have chosen a specific plan of life we are daily choosing the intermediate means necessary for successful attainment of that ultimate goal—to be a registered nurse. We are on time for duty, for class, for meetings, and we do so deliberately and willingly. We are conscious at the same time that these acts are our own choice, and that we could do otherwise if we so desired. We are continually regulating our life in conformity to the rules and regulations of our school, influenced by loyalty, obedience and tact. This mental power whereby we choose to do what is necessary to obtain our chosen goal is the *will*, which is defined as *the power of the mind by which we choose objects intellectually perceived as something of value.*

In order to understand natural inclinations, choice, and motivation, we will study: (1) instincts, (2) instinctive behavior of lower and higher animals, (3) natural drives in man, (4) the power of choice in relation to the sense of value, and (5) motives and motivation.

INSTINCTS

An instinct is an internal sense by which one apprehends a corporeal object or sensation as beneficial or harmful, without knowing the ultimate reason for such dangerous or useful qualities.

It is an inherited tendency to perform a specific action in a definite way when an appropriate situation occurs. An instinct is manifested as a unit pattern of behavior common to all individuals of the same class, and is given by nature to secure the welfare of the individual and the preservation of the species. It is an *inborn type of reaction; it is not learned from experience.* Young spiders that are taken away immediately from the mother build perfect webs. Young kittens, blind at birth, will go easily to the mother at once even when they are scatterd in different directions. All animals of the same species act instinctively in the same way. The web of spiders, the cocoon of moths, the habits of mice, moles, deer, squirrels and many other animals give evidence of the presence of the definite species even if the animals are not seen. Our study of symptoms of diseases is based on the instinctive actions of the lower organisms, as each species manifests specific reactions to definite tissues and regions of the body.

Instincts present types of behavior admirably adapted to attain a valuable purpose, yet *the animal has no way to learn about the value of the reactions.* Many partial acts are required to bring about a useful goal, but the complete chain of acts is destined to bring about one and only one situation. If one partial act is disturbed, the complete pattern of action is repeated instead of the animal adjusting that phase that is temporarily checked. A certain type of wasp, for example, places a caterpillar near a hole prepared in the ground, paralyzes it and drops it in the hole; finally the wasp deposits her eggs deep in the soft tissues of the caterpillar so that the young may have a source of food when they hatch. If it happens, however, that an observer disturbs the unit plan of action by covering up the hole before the wasp returns with the caterpillar or after the wasp has paralyzed it, the wasp will dig another hole and re-enact the whole series of behaviors instead of repairing the hole or using the material already obtained. It seems that each partial act stimulates the insect to continue the next action in the series and if one part of the series is broken, the necessary stimulus is lacking, so the wasp repeats the entire chain of reactions.

Instincts in Lower Animals

Instinctive activity in the lower animals *is practically unchange-able, as time and distance have slight influence on their behavior.* Termites now build houses the same as termites did years ago; migratory birds flock north each spring and south in the fall to keep near the source of food. Each species acts in a definite way to protect itself in case of danger. Chickens hatched in an incubator have the same arrangement of instincts as those raised in a natural way. Orioles and canaries warble the same melody whether they come from Texas or California. So perfect are most of the instinctive actions of animals, that everywhere they are the admiration of observers. We see in these actions a perfect adaptation of means to an end; a minimum of effort is expended, and the maximum result is produced. And when we reflect that these instinctive actions are carried to perfection prior, it may be, to all experiences, this admiration becomes even greater.

Instincts in Higher Animals

It should be noted that sometimes *an instinct in higher animals may be modified,* but only by appealing to some other instinct. For instance, the tendency of wild ducks to migrate to the south as winter approaches may be checked by appealing to their instinct for food. If an abundance of grain is easily accessible to these wild fowl, the instinct to migrate is overcome by the stronger instinct for food, even though their staying in the north would involve considerable hardship.

We may note, also, that instincts in some animals are not as precise as a machine because sense learning often tends to obscure instinctive patterns of behavior. To realize this, one needs only to compare the behavior of certain domesticated animals with that of the same species in wild life. Then, too, certain animals can be trained to accomplish certain actions that are associated repeatedly with specific situations. The horse, the dog, the elephant furnish us with extraordinary examples of instincts modified by training.

Certain actions, such as a dog's rising on his hind legs, are linked up by the trainer with a very definite word ("up, up") or movement (a snap of the fingers), and in turn, this word or movement is associated with the memory of some particular sensory reward or punishment. Instincts in the higher animals are susceptible to modification and control by training in proportion to the learning capacity of the animal, and in all cases depend on association with sense memory and sense imagery of another instinct capable of being satisfied by a certain particular object.

Function of Instincts

Instincts in animals are essential for their very existence, for without this ability to recognize objects as harmful or useful they would have a short-lived existence. The species would be exterminated even before it could propagate its kind. The author of nature implanted instincts, therefore, *to secure the development of the individual* and *the perpetuation of the species.*

NATURAL DRIVES IN MAN

A natural drive is an impulse to exercise an ability when an opportunity presents itself. Many synonymous words are used to express the same concept as natural drive, namely, *urge, impulse, inclination, trait.* Each term has a similar meaning and they are often used interchangeably. These drives are similar to instincts, and yet are not to be identified with them, as knowledge, reason and volition alter an impulse to such a degree that it is difficult, if not impossible, to find even one pure instinct in human conduct. This difference between impulse in human conduct and instinctive activity in animal behavior is evident when we consider the fact that *an impulse in man is a tendency to an action of a specific nature in relation to a definite goal apprehended in consciousness, and the atttainment of which involves former experience, reason, memory and volition.* An animal instinctive action, however, is *a mechanical performance of a series of acts useful to the well-being of the organism,* but the animal itself is unaware of the usefulness and purpose of its action, as we have seen in our former discussion of instincts. Thus, the term "drives," not "instincts," is used to describe certain tendencies that are present in all people at some time or another in a greater or lesser degree, although they do not manifest themselves at the same period in life.

Impulsive actions of man, other than those of babies and idiots, are modified by the interaction of perception, acquired skills, imagination, likes and dislikes, memory, intelligence, volition and emotional states. "Man's intellectual power exerts such a remodeling influence on instinctive beginnings that many authors decline to say man has instincts. Actually, he has as many as the brute, but they are covered over by an incrustation of mental life."[1]

DIFFERENT DRIVES

Inasmuch as a drive is an impulse to make use of an ability, there are as many different kinds of drives as there are abilities. Indeed, it would be an impossibility to consider all the organic urges of the individual to action. Thus, we will limit our study to the essential, and especially to the social, drives of human nature.

Self-Preservation

Self-preservation is the urge to oppose any threat that may deprive an individual of his position, his possessions, or even his life. Although man desires to live in peace and security, he will fight for his rights and will oppose any force that would unjustly deprive him of his home, his family, his valuable property or his standing in the community. If any violence threatens his life, he will try to escape by running away from the danger if there seems to be no possibility of overcoming it, or he will use adequate means to protect himself. The drive for self-preservation is the fundamental reason a patient desires to enter a hospital when he is seriously sick or injured, or when he needs an operation to improve his health. This urge is

[1] Gaffney, Mark A., *The Psychology of the Interior Senses* (St. Louis: Herder, 1942), p. 189.

intensified when the health of a person has been affected. The nurse can play an important role in this drama of life by encouraging the patient to struggle bravely to regain his strength. The patient must be convinced that the goal of better health is worth much of his time and effort. She needs to encourage him to accept inconvenience, pain, and even intense suffering for a short period of time under medical supervision so that he may improve his health and eventually make a complete recovery. When a patient loses his will to live, his chances of recovery are greatly reduced. Since the nurse is with the patient more than any other person during the time of serious illness, she can be influential in inspiring his spirit of confidence. She should encourage him to accept his present aches, pains and the treatments necessary to make him well. The nurse, too, should appeal to the patient's spirit of cooperation to do what the doctor has prescribed, so that he may go back soon to his family in excellent health and be able to return to his regular job, and resume his usual social activities.

Motor Activity

The healthy body tends to be physically active. This drive is evident in an active child, who keeps his mother and the "baby sitter" continually on the alert lest he injure himself. When the mother finds the child quiet, she begins to worry that he is either sick or in some trouble. The urge to move is innate. If a cat or dog is held tightly, it will struggle frantically until it is set free.

The nurse must be aware of this trait in tending her patients. Anyone who has been active throughout his life endures torture when forced to remain in bed. This is relieved temporarily by massage, which helps to overcome the muscle tensions preventing sleep and rest. The position of the patient should be changed frequently to relieve the restlessness. Motor activity in post-operative care is encouraged by many doctors. It lessens the possibility of complications that sometimes occur after surgery. The patient may not like this type of treatment at first, because he may fear that he will have to endure pain. The nurse should explain why it is necessary for the patient to move about, and thereby appeal to this latent impulse to motor activity.

The patient, too, should do whatever he can for himself, such as feeding himself, taking his bath, combing his hair aand brushing his teeth. These activities tend to increase his spirit of independence. Appealing to the drive of motor activity is especially necessary in caring for elderly patients, amputees, rehabilitation patients and the chronically ill. The ability to dress and to feed themselves is something in which they take pride.

Curiosity

A sign "fresh paint" attracts us to experiment with our hands to learn whether it is fresh or not. *Curiosity is an urge to seek knowledge of something that attracts our attention.* A father at Christmas time often plays with the trains and toys more than does the young man for whom they were purchased. A small child is curious to know what is inside a new toy, a clock or his father's new electric shaver. The nurse, while shopping, is not satisfied until she handles and tries on all the hats of her proper size. There is a tendency for us to look at and handle everything before we are satisfied. When something happens, we want to find the cause of it. If we are told to do something for no apparent reason, we are driven by our natural urge to find out why. When we see groups of people together, we desire to discover the reason. We are naturally curious to learn the reason of all things. Thus curiosity, directed by sensibility and training, can be cultivated to the highest form of success and should be encouraged.

Numerous questions arise in the mind of a hospitalized patient. Naturally, he wishes to know how, why, what, where, and when he will undergo different treatments. The nurse has the responsibility of satisfying the curiosity of the patient by explaining each treatment before it is carried out. This explanation is particularly important when the treatment is going to be painful. She explains why diets are prescribed and why special diagnostic procedures must be undertaken. She suggests beneficial effects of the treatments and she interprets the orders of the physician. The worry and anxiety that sometimes accompany curiosity are reduced when the nurse takes time to answer the patient's questions. The patient will feel more at ease, more cooperative, and more trustful of the nurse.

Association with Others

Association with others is a natural tendency, and man finds satisfaction in companionship, especially in a group. When a patient is alone or confined to his room for a long period, he becomes restless and lonesome. Everyone needs companionship each day and needs to talk to someone. Good company and visitors are always an aid to one who is convalescing. A visit by friends breaks the monotony, time seems to pass more quickly, tension is released and the patient becomes restful.

Vocalization

The first cry of the normal babe proclaims its tendency to use its vocal cords. The babe later takes pleasure in muttering and babbling. Talking and laughing start when a child gets a little older. Children love to talk, laugh and shout without restraint. Crying and laughter are forms of vocalization. In the adult crying is rare, and when it occurs it usually results from a mental state of helplessness. Crying sometimes can make a person sick and very nervous. Laughter, however, is one of the most healthy forms of expression. Laughter, an indicator of merriment, is associated with physical well-being, and it seems to stimulate the whole body. Normal laughter and jolliness generally reflect a wholesome atmosphere of kindness and good will.

Imitation

A child obtains most of his knowledge by imitation. He watches and listens to others and then tries to imitate those about him, especially his parents or the people with whom he lives. The baby talk of the child is the direct result of the words he hears, and is not children's language. This imitation drive, united with the imagination, accounts for the boy soldier, Flash Gordon, Space Man, Maverick, doll life, and even for Annette of the Mickey Mouse Club.

Good things attract us, and we strive to acquire their good qualities. Education depends in a great measure on this trait urging us to attain the perfection we see in others.

Social Approval

We want others to think well of us, and we avoid their scorn and disapproval. We need love, friendship and affection to fight off loneliness. We need the strength that makes us believe we are secure and independent. Social approval impels us to do the right thing at the right time. A small child may try to show off by riding his bicycle without holding the handle bars, by standing on his head, or maybe by being a little tyrant trying to catch everyone's attention. As the child gets older, he may enter a contest in hope of showing his parents and friends that he is doing something outstanding. Adults will go to great excess and effort to win the good will of the community. This drive is an aid in the pursuit of the good and a restraint on wrongdoing. Public opinion, when based on truth, is conducive to good social order and high ideals.

Patients usually want to be liked by the nurse. They want to do what is expected of them and to cooperate with the nurses and doctors so that they will recover more rapidly. The nurse can show that she approves of and accepts the patient by being friendly and encouraging.

Self-assertion

Self-assertion is a normal impulse, which affects the nurse according to the way she uses it. This tendency may be a stimulus to earnest, persistent effort, to leadership, to wholesome independence of thought and action, to success in her career. It must, however, be regulated by right reason or it may degenerate into impatience of all restraint and a rebellion against authority.

The urge of self-expression is manifested by certain tendencies, namely, *mastery* and *competition*.

Mastery

The term "mastery" is used to describe the drive of human beings to dominate persons and things. Everyone likes to be a leader, and every nurse would like to be head of the hospital at least for a day. This tendency of dominating people is seen clearly in the juniors, who often initiate the lowly "probes" and freshmen who enter training. This impulse can easily be overdone when the desire becomes unruly, and may be the cause of sorrow and frivolity. A nurse must, by her very position, demand obedience and cooperation of the patient, and at times can permit no interference. But she should guard against being unnecessarily despotic about trivial and optional things. Too often the senior nurse forgets that kindness and consideration will bring her greater success with the nurses on the floor than a haughty and lordly attitude will.

The driving spirit of overcoming frustrations is expressed in the tendency to dominate things. Man is continually striving to obtain mastery over inert objects, and is gradually bringing even nature under his power. This tendency to master the conditions and forces of nature has steadily improved hospital equipment and modern scientific methods of treating disease.

Competition

Any game of competition stirs up interest, as we have a natural tendency to match our skill against others. This drive is the basis of energetic teamwork in all our sports. There is danger in all our native traits unless they are held within bounds. This is true of the competitive spirit. Jealousy, fraud, vanity and mob rule can develop from an excessive competitive spirit. It is better to have groups compete with groups rather than to have individual contests, or, better still, to have one compete with her own past record, especially in studies and hospital skills.

A nurse should teach a patient to compete with himself by encouraging him to do a little more and a little better each day in his activities. This is a practical consideration in dealing with rehabilitation patients, where progress extends over a long period of time. The nurse could make a competitive game out of treatments, and thus keep up the patient's interest and enthusiasm to continue to strive to improve.

Native Emotional Response

We have already stated in the chapter on the emotions that there are three native emotions, namely, *fear, anger* and *love*. A child will withdraw from sudden and loud noise and will give evidence of the *emotion of fear* by *crying*. This tendency is later manifested in worry, which is fear of the future. The nurse should be on guard not to stimulate the fear response in the patient, taking care that she knocks on the door, avoids sudden and unexpected noise in performing her duties, and that she handles trays quietly.

The urge to nourish, cherish and protect the offspring is universal in human nature. This impulse is called the maternal urge, which is sometimes termed the parental urge or the *sex drive*. The mother's love is the epitome of sacrifice, devotion and the supreme love that makes life beautiful and endearing. This same love, ruled by right reason and decorum, is imitated by the young at puberty, and accounts for the loveliest virtues in mankind, namely, kindness, affection, sympathy, gentleness, mildness, loyalty, sweetness, mortification and self-sacrifice. The tendency of this urge, when ruled by modesty, is the greatest motive force for good; it fills life with happiness and strengthens character to the highest degree.

POWER OF CHOICE IN RELATION TO THE
SENSE OF VALUE

Our whole system of justice, civil and domestic, is built upon the notion that man is responsible for some of his acts. In conformity to this persuasion we make laws, enact sanctions, reward and punish; acts which would have no meaning or effect unless man has the power to determine his actions. The supervisor on each floor appoints certain nurses to take care of the medical needs of certain patients, and the head nurse holds each girl responsible for the treatment, charts, records, and case histories of those particular patients. Each girl accepts the respective patients as her responsibility. She realizes that she can follow or not follow the orders that were given originally by the doctor, and then relayed to her by the supervisor and the head nurse. Her reason and good judgment inform her that she should follow all the doctor's orders. The *will* is the mental power by which one chooses to act or not to act.

In any decision we make, there is a consciousness that the Ego, I myself, is doing the action, and we hold ourselves responsible for the action. In all voluntary actions there are two or more impulsive inclinations of the will to do or not to do a certain thing, and I, myself, act as an arbiter as to which of the conflicting motives is to prevail. I am conscious that I am the one acting and I express this same fact by such phrases as: I consent, I decide, I agree, I accept, I resolve, I disapprove, I make up my own mind. We realize that we are free agents, and that we are doing the act and are willing to give testimony that we are the ones who should be held responsible for our voluntary acts.

In our ordinary daily lives we choose those activities we think will make us happier, better, and more contented with ourselves. We are striving continually to improve our condition. We do this with the power of the will by choosing objects and ideas that appeal to us as having special value for our own individual personality or particular goal in life.

We will analyze briefly a voluntary act. Suppose one of our classmates, while window-shopping in the city, notices a distinctive dress in one of the show windows of a store. She is taken by its color, style, beauty and attractive pleats. She would like to have the dress. First she finds out the cost of the dress, and then the size; she tries it on to ascertain whether or not she looks well in it. The dress fits her perfectly and she wants to buy it at once; yet she considers the cost of the dress. Is it worth the price? She hesitates at the thought of going into debt or of leaving the dress until she can redeem it when her allotment is due. Still keenly aware of her desire and with visual and tactile images to symbolize the value of the dress, she half persuades herself that it would be better to purchase it. This process of deliberation may be a matter of seconds only, or may continue much longer. Eventually, it leads to a decision by the girl; she either has the clerk put it away and save it for her, or she declines to buy the dress. Whatever she actually does, she will be well aware that she could have elected to act otherwise. If she buys the dress, it will not be as if she were impelled in a purely reflexive manner to do so. It was her own deliberate choice to buy or refuse to buy. The motives were there for buying or for not buying.

Psychologically, the nurse's voluntary behavior involves the following factors.

1. *Organic drive* caused by the attractiveness of the dress.
2. *Rational inclination* to have the dress.
3. *Sensory representation* of the means to satisfy the organic drive. The nurse examines the texture, the size, the make of cloth.
4. *Representation, partly by sense image and partly by intellectual concept* of consequences attendant upon each alternative of purchasing or of not purchasing.
5. *Deliberation.* Several motives are abstracted from the situation: "to gratify a natural craving," "to go into debt," "to wait for the next allowance."
6. *Choice.* After evaluating the various motives from the standpoint of the good they represent, our classmate consciously expresses a choice; she consents to a certain course of action, thereby making the choice her own.

We experience such situations each day and designate our reactions as *desiring, wishing, intending, choosing, approving, disapproving, deliberate yielding, preferring, permitting, commanding.* What is common in all these experiences is a conscious inclination toward the object apprehended as desirable, or a conscious aversion to the object apprehended as unsuitable. Such actions involve a comparison of something desirable or undesirable, and generally we choose deliberately the object that seems better to us. The choice, however, varies according to: (1) the individual's *personality*, which would include her abilities, attitudes, impulses, traits, habits, training, as well as her physical characteristics; (2) the amount of *attention* she places on the object, which would determine the vividness and attractiveness of the desirable qualities; and (3) *the object itself*, because some objects are valuable and others are worthless.

MOTIVES AND MOTIVATION

A *motive* is the reason an act is performed. A person's motive can be discovered by the question: "Why did I do a certain act?" The answer to the "Why?" of the question reveals the motive for acting.

If one should ask a classmate, for example, "Why are you studying?" she may answer in a number of ways, but each response implies some value she hopes to obtain by studying rather than by not studying. There is always a reason behind a deliberate act. She may have various motives, such as to obtain knowledge, to pass an examination, to keep out of trouble, to fulfil a duty, to make up a quiz; each reason contains some value that inclines her to study. Each answer reveals some desirable end that moves the will to choose a specific type of activity. The answer to the question "Why?" then, indicates the motive that is the source of a particular action.

Wishes and Desires

The sources of motives are twofold, namely, *inclinations* and *desires*. Natural inclinations (drives), such as self-preservation, motor activity, curiosity, self-assertion, mastery and many others, are modified by the interaction of the intellect, the emotions and the will. These drives are motives to act in a given situation. When we are able to carry out these inclinations by suitable activities, we derive a pronounced sense of pleasure. When we cannot satisfy these inclinations because of other conflicting urges, lack of opportunity, insufficient time or restricting ideals and principles, there arises in the mind the appetitive sense of wishing or desiring.

A *wish* is a conscious inclination to have a certain thing that would give us pleasure, realizing at the same time that we have only a slight chance of acquiring it. A great sum of money, an extended vacation, a trip around the world, the opportunity of falling in love with a charming, kind millionaire are some of the wishes that might flash through our minds. Such inclinations are most agreeable, but ordinarily one makes no great effort to fulfil one's wishes.

A *desire*, however, is a distinct *yearning* in consciousness to produce a situation in which impulsive tendencies may be satisfied. The cause of a desire is a temporary or permanent block of impulsive inclinations. A desire arises in consciousness each time we are unable to exercise an ability. We are inclined to arrange the time when, and the place where we will have a good opportunity to obtain what we want when an impulsive inclination is held in check. There are as many desires as there are human abilities. Desires may have their origin in any of the five senses, in organic wants, drives, tendencies, aptitudes, and in other physiologic and psychologic causes. A very popular classification of social desires is that of William I. Thomas, which summarizes the natural inclinations of man considered from the point of view of the "four wishes." [2]

Thomas' "Four Wishes"

The most fundamental and universal social motives, according to Thomas, are: (1) *the desire for new experience,* which includes the yearning for motor activity, curious things, travel, adventure, books, games, new friends, new clothes and membership in groups; (2) *the desire for recognition,* such as social approval, to be known by others, to be prominent in class activities, to be a power in the group; (3) *the desire for security,* such as the desire for economic status, physical health, friendship with the group, affection from parents, friends, acquaintances and the opposite sex; and (4) *the desire for mastery* or the "will to power" exemplified by success in schoolwork, social skills, athletics and nursing techniques.

[2] Thomas, William I., and Znaniecki, Florian, *The Polish Peasant in Europe and America* (New York: Alfred A. Knopf, 1927), Vol. I, p. 73.

Sensory and Intellectual Desires

The division of desires into two general types, sensory and intellectual, is a very clear classification for nursing education.

Sensory desires are inborn, involuntary, and they arise no matter what we do; they come and go according to the condition of the body. We experience this type of desire in hunger, thirst and pain; from excessive pressure and abnormal temperature; during the periods when the ordinary wants of the body are not satisfied.

Intellectual desires, or the contrary, are acquired, subject to voluntary control, and they may be modified by a system of training. They abide continually with us and are readily built up into systematic plans of activities. The organization and coordination of one's desires into a uniform pattern under the influence of the will have a pronounced effect on one's personality.

MOTIVATION AND THE NURSE

Most of our actions are spontaneous and habitual. They take place with ease and proficiency. The motives of these activities, however, are the result of training, experience, and the influence of others. This influence is referred to as *motivation*. The original acquisition of our habits has been achieved through conscious effort and constant repetition, until a set pattern of action has been developed.

Continuous motivation is necessary in the nursing profession, as a nurse is required to learn new techniques, to supplement her knowledge, to increase her interest and to develop a pleasing personality. For a nurse motivation is supplied in the principles and ideals set up by the nursing profession. She is encouraged by her profession to present appropriate and intellectual ideals of action both to the patient and to her associates. These ideals are expressed in the Florence Nightingale pledge of duty which the preclinical student repeats during the capping exercise, and which become the regulating principles of her years of training and her whole nursing career. She is directed to control her emotional, social, personal and physiologic drives and cultivate the intellectual motives of trust, interest, loyalty, reliance, cheerfulness and devotion to duty. She is advised to govern her desires and other motives of action by the goals of the nursing profession she has chosen, realizing that the satisfaction she derives from a successful career is vastly more extensive and lasting than the immediate pleasure of whims and impulsive acts. The nurse, then, should cultivate these higher motives, first, in her own life, and then inspire these same ideals of behavior in the minds of the patients and in the lives of those with whom she lives.

SUMMARY

1. A natural drive is an inborn tendency to spontaneous action and is directed toward our well-being.

2. Drives in animals are called instincts.

3. These tendencies are essential to the existence, preservation and development of the individual.

4. Self-preservation is manifested in ordinary sensations of desire for food and drink, and response to touch, pressure and pain.

5. We tend to express ourselves in action, and motor activities become a means of expression of this tendency.

6. The tendency of curiosity urges us to seek the answer to the causes of things and may be used in scholarship.

7. Man is a social being and desires to be with others, deriving pleasure by imitation.

8. The urge of social approval is universal in the human race.

9. Self-assertion manifests itself by the tendency to overcome obstacles and to dominate things and persons, and by mastery and competition.

10. There are three native emotions: fear, anger and love. These tendencies persist in the adult, as do worry, pugnacity, maternal instinct and sex instinct.

11. Man's mental power of choosing suitable means to carry out a definite plan is termed the will.

12. Rarely will two individuals choose the same thing for the same reason, because the choice varies according to three factors,

namely: (1) the personality of the individual, which includes his attitude, habits and training; (2) the attention he places on the object; and (3) the object itself, as some things are relatively satisfactory while others are worthless.

13. A motive is the reason an act is performed.

14. Intellectual motives are necessary for proficency in any type of work. Motivation for a nurse is implied in the principles and ideals set up by the nursing profession.

QUESTIONS FOR REVIEW

Essay Type

1. Define a natural drive and distinguish it from an acquired tendency.
2. What drives do you experience most often while on duty?
3. Point out the dangers of self-assertion.
4. Discuss the tendency of overcoming obstacles in relation to ambition.
5. Why is it difficult for an "applause seeker" to become a popular nurse?
6. What difficulties are likely to be encountered by a nurse who has the urge to dominate others?
7. Select the nurse you admire most and defend that selection.
8. What drives are held in restraint by sickness?
9. List ten things nurses frequently do to secure social approval.
10. What natural and intellectual inclinations dominate your best friends?
11. Discuss native traits and interest.
12. Which of the drives listed in the chapter are most prominent in your life?
13. Which tendencies are likely to be gratified in the life of the nurse, the doctor, the head nurse, the teacher, the administrator?
14. What drives operate in the following: service room, diet kitchen, head of the floor, dance, class meeting, first floor, nursery, children's ward, attending a party, hiking, going downtown, examination, operating room, adverse criticism, receiving the cap, graduation, at the telephone booth, dressing for a party, a tennis game, praise of patients?

Matching and Completion Type

Fill in the correct words:

1. The type of impulsive drive to overcome a dangerous situation which

threatens to deprive a man of his possessions or his life. . . . .

. . . .

2. The power of the mind by which we choose objects intellectually

perceived as something of value. . . . .

3. An internal sense by which an animal apprehends an object as bene-

ficial or harmful. . . . .

4. The three native emotions are:

a . . . .

b . . . .

c . . . .

5. The urge to nourish, cherish and protect the offspring. . . . .

6. The reason an act is performed. . . . .

7. A distinct yearning to obtain something when we are unable to use

an ability at a definite time. . . . .

8. Thomas' four wishes are:

a . . . . c . . . .

b . . . . d . . . .

9. A tendency to exercise an ability when an opportunity presents itself.

. . . .

10. The type of drive that inclines us to be kind and considerate to others,

and to avoid the scorn of others . . . .

11. A drive that explains why good company and visitors are always an aid

to those who are convalescing. . . . .

12. The six psychologic factors in a voluntary act are:

a . . . . d . . . .

b . . . . e . . . .

c . . . . f . . . .

13. A conscious inclination to possess some pleasing object that we make

no effort to obtain. . . . .

14. The type of desire that is involuntary and depends on the condition

of the body. . . . .

15. Specific choices of different objects vary in different people because of these three factors:

a . . . .

b . . . .

c . . . .

16. The influence, guidance and direction given to support one in accom—

plishing a worthwhile project. . . . .

17. The type of desire that is acquired and that may be modified into a

unit plan. . . . .

18. Five ideals mentioned in the Nightingale pledge are:

a . . . .   d . . . .

b . . . .   e . . . .

c . . . .

TOPICS FOR CLASS DISCUSSION

1. Make a list of all the drives, intellectual desires, and motives responsible for your choice of a nursing profession.
2. Contrast two patients you know, one of whom tends to be influenced by natural drives, the other by intellectual desires.
3. The factors responsible for the diversity of things you choose contrasted to the multiple things your roommate chooses.
4. The extent that interest depends upon natural inclinations.
5. Diagnostic symptoms of septicemia and instinctive activity of the causative organisms.
6. The reasons a nurse may follow the prevailing styles in her choice of dresses and hats, even though the style may detract from her natural beauty.
7. List at least four powerful incentives used by the nursing staff to increase efficiency.
8. Psychologic factors involved in "choosing a husband."

Sources and References

Brennan, Robert E., *General Psychology* (New York: Macmillan, 1952), Chaps. XVII, XXV.

Harmon, Francis L., *Principles of Psychology*, rev. ed. (Milwaukee: Bruce, 1951), Chaps. XVI, XVIII.

Moore, Thomas V., *The Driving Forces of Human Nature* (New York: Grune & Stratton, 1948), Chap. XVIII.

Murray, Raymond W., *Sociology for Democratic Society* (New York: Appleton-Century-Crofts, 1950), Chap. X.

Mursell, James L., *Psychology for Modern Education* (New York: Norton, 1952), Chaps. II, III.

10 • FRUSTRATIONS AND ADJUSTMENTS

GENERAL CONSIDERATION

How do you act when things do not go according to your desires? Some complain immediately, rave about the injustice of life and magnify the sacrifices they must make; others stop trying to progress; some pout and act offended; others go to their rooms and become "moon-faced"; still others face the difficulty, endeavoring to substitute some other form of activity in place of the original desire.

Frustrations in life should stir up the best that is within us, and should contribute toward our mental development. It is not what difficulty may happen to a nurse, but how she takes it that is important. The main thing is not the problem, but that she meet the problem in a straightforward and acceptable manner. Frustration is always present and should be admitted. In ordinary life we meet all kinds of situations and we act differently in the face of each. One day we are too warm; the next day we are too cold. One moment we are hungry; the next we have eaten too much. One time we are tired; the next we are restless from inactivity. We might bump our heads on an unseen door, or stub our toes on the chair put there by our roommate; in each case we must adapt ourselves to the situation and change the environment according to each experience. We must face things as they are and adapt our methods to meet each circumstance in life.

Normal life is full of reversals, contradictions, disappointments and changing problems. A nurse, then, cannot expect the world to stand still and serve her. She must adapt her desires and her life to conform to her environment. She must choose the proper course and act accordingly. There is no use deceiving ourselves and acting as if we were the only ones in the world to have difficulties and troubles. Frustrations are sure to confront us throughout our lives. Living is adjusting. Every human being is constantly occupied with bringing himself into harmony with his environment. Frustration should not be used as an excuse to whine and give up, but as a challenge to do something different and an opportunity to receive the great pleasure that comes from the ability to meet an emergency successfully.

Frustration

The inability to obtain what we want is called frustration. Any intense interference with our desires and needs arouses in us feelings of helplessness, disappointment, inadequacy and anxiety. Two conditions are necessary for the presence of frustration: (1) an aroused need or drive or tendency toward an action; (2) some object that interferes with or blocks the satisfaction of the need. For example, a student nurse wants to accept an invitation to a dinner dance but cannot get anyone, not even her roommate, to go on duty in her place. The uncertainty and frustration produce a condition of increased pressure, which is referred to as *tension.* Tension is an impulse toward action. In each case of frustration, one endeavors to do something to break down the tension by removing or surmounting the obstacle that stands in the way, or by accepting a substitute goal. There is set up a regular series in a frustrating situation, namely: (1) need or desire; (2) blocking of this need or desire, which leads to frustration; (3) tension; (4) activity; (5) adjustment.

Frustrations constitute an intimate part of life. They add zest to living. This is evident in the description of a preclinical student's "First Days in Training": "When I arrived at the nursing school, I was thrilled and happy, yet somewhat saddened because I hated to leave my family, especially my baby brother. After my parents left, I began to wonder what the school would be like. I sort of felt lost. The Juniors, however, gave us a coke party that evening to help get us in the swing of things. After the party my roommate and I were so excited that we could not sleep and we talked until the wee hours of the morning. During the first few days I practically lived in utter confusion, never knowing exactly where to go or what to do. I soon straightened myself out and decided that this was not high school and that studies had to be taken to heart."

Barriers of one sort or another are continually cropping up and blocking or interfering with the satisfaction of one's needs and desires. Frequently the barriers are temporary and trivial and are passed over without an appreciable effect upon the individual. At other times, however, something may prevent the attainment of a longed-for goal, with the result that there is an accumulation of tension and resentment within the individual. This is what is called a *frustrating experience*.

CLASSIFICATION OF FRUSTRATION

As frustration is caused by barriers that check needs, motives or desires, it is possible to have as many frustrating experiences as there are external and internal obstacles—actual, imagined or anticipated. The barriers could be classified as physical, moral, spiritual, social and personal. A subdivision of each of these general classes could be greatly extended.

A simplified classification arranges the barriers into three general types, namely: (1) *privation,* (2) *deprivation,* (3) *obstruction.*

Privation

This type of barrier involves a *lack* in environmental, physical, social, and intellectual factors, which may affect the individual personally or which may influence his status in society. Lack of money, food, and rest necessary to fulfil one's desires comes under this classification. There are three kinds of privation to which all student nurses are exposed: (1) they are always hungry; (2) they are always tired; (3) they are always "broke." These same frustrations carry on long after the nurse enters her professional career.

Privation alone does not cause frustration. The person must perceive that his lack of some object interferes with what he needs or that its lack affects him personally. It is not frustrating when a nurse does not have a hypodermic needle when she does not need it. The lack is frustrating only when she needs the needle and does not have it. The lack of a boat, of fishing equipment, of swimming suits are barriers only when a person needs these supplies at a lake resort.

The loss of prestige or security increases the intensity and the strength of the frustrating activity. For example, many hospitals are limited in funds to add more space, laboratory facilities, modern operating tables, air-conditioning and improved kitchen equipment. This condition is only mildly frustrating to those in charge of the maintenance of the hospital until the overcrowded quarters and antiquated equipment threaten to endanger the continued accreditation of the hospital. The loss of accreditation would be a severe blow to the prestige of the hospital and the community. Thus, a former passive barrier of privation has now become an active one, and may be the cause of intense frustration, unless a community drive obtains the money necessary for the improvements.

Personal privation may include any defect, real or imagined, in the individual's physical, moral, spiritual or social make-up. Organic inferiority, such as weak eyesight, poor hearing, lameness, blindness, low mentality, undeveloped organic structures, physical weakness and disabilities are sources of personal frustration. A tongue-tied man can never be a brilliant orator, no matter how much he longs for the distinction. A one-legged man cannot enter into competitive sports. A withered limb, a blemish on the nose, a sore eye, a sore foot or finger may occasion a variety of frustrations. Such organic defects limit the person's activity. The manner of adjusting is to admit the frustration, and endeavor to accomplish alternative activities that may increase one's prestige and peace of mind. This is what generally occurs. The congenitally handicapped do get along without excessive frustration, provided, of course, they are not laughed at, ridiculed, slighted or snubbed by others.

Deprivation

Deprivation is the *loss* of something. The loss of health, wealth, power, reputation and security is the cause of the most severe frustrations of one's life. This type of frustration is more severe than privation. As one becomes accustomed to certain things in life and takes for granted that they belong to his personality, he feels that the loss of anything personal affects his very being. A person, for instance, who becomes blind some time late in life finds this affliction much harder to bear than would a person who was born blind. A person who has his leg amputated suffers greater frustration than one who has been crippled from infancy.

A few of these deprivations which may affect our lives sooner or later are: loss of health by sickness or accidents; loss of one's job; sudden loss of wealth from storms, hurricanes, fire and economic depressions; failure in business or any undertaking; loss of social recognition and security; breakdown of transportation; old age; and finally, death.

We witness this type of frustration in every hospitalized patient we attend. A cardiac patient, who has had a severe attack, faces unlimited frustrations and must make multiple adjustments if he desires to rehabilitate himself. He is required to take specific medications at particular times; use a planned diet; limit his activities and avoid any exercise or work that may cause chest pains, shortening of the breath, palpitation, or undue fatigue. These limitations may create a constant inner struggle until the patient is convinced that each regulatory procedure is necessary and essential, and that he must cooperate with the advice of the physician if he wants to continue to live.

Obstruction

Obstruction is a term used to classify *a group of barriers of a general nature that causes worry and anxiety,* such as the clash of moral principles, attitudes and social pressure. Some of these obstructions are physical in nature and cause a type of frustration that can easily be solved; others, however, are connected with emotions and are psychic in nature. They cause a mental state in which opposing desires and tendencies are present at the same time. These present very serious problems, which must be solved satisfactorily before peace of mind is restored. This latter type of frustration is called a *conflict.*

Physical Obstructions

Obstructions may occur at any time to block our wishes or plans and temporarily cause anxiety and tension; the car will not start; the door is locked and one is without her key; the time for examinations is inopportune; the schedule requires too much regularity and too much study; the rising is too early; the class hours are too long; there is not sufficient time allotted after a dance to get a hamburger and coffee before one must report back to school. These are the regular gripes of any group of nurses and indicate frustration of their desires in some degree.

Psychic Obstructions or Conflicts

The psychic obstructions are the greatest source of difficulty in life, and may build up intense worry and anxiety within the individual. This type of obstruction deals with the principles and ideals of life. Very serious obstructions that cause conflicts and demand careful adjustments are social pressure, social approval, security, self-respect, parental restrictions, religion, racial opinions, economic stress, sexual morality, early training, attitudes, loyalty, honesty, interest and the sense of value. Each of these concepts impose restrictions on desires and inclinations and on all motivation.

Often contradictory desires and principles are present in the mind at the same time and cause serious frustrations called conflicts. A conflict is defined as *an emotional mental state when two opposing desires are present in the mind at the same time, and the individual is forced to choose one of the desires in preference to the other.* One is drawn by an ethical principle and by an emotional need at the same time; yet he must make a decision to do one thing or another, or to compromise between the two opposing forces.

A well-regulated, normal person must choose the proper manner of acting each time a new situation arises; and, as man is placed in so many different circumstances of life, he must be restricted by thoughtful judgment to respect the rights and feelings of others. If one followed native desires and natural tendencies and each whim of the moment without limitation, he would establish a very strange world in which to live.

It is logical to expect that some frustrations, and at times, very serious ones, will arise when we deal with other persons who have had training different from our own. It is necessary for our peace of mind to get along with others and to meet their ideals and principles, moods and peculiarities with an open mind, and accept or differ on reasonable, rather than emotional, grounds. A nurse who is ready to adjust herself to a social situation, and yet has the strength to continue in her toilsome and demanding profession with her patients, will seldom find herself in conflict with herself or with others.

Types of Conflicts

There are four types of conflicts:[1] (1) *approach-approach,* (2) *approach-avoidance,* (3) *avoidance-avoidance,* and (4) *double approach-avoidance.*

Approach-approach

This type of conflict is one in which a *person is attracted by two different desirable goals,* but by the very nature of the situation it

---

[1] Lewin, Kurt, *A Dynamic Theory of Personality* (New York: McGraw-Hill, 1935), pp. 88-94.

is possible to fulfil one of his desires, but not both. A nurse is undecided which skirt to wear, which movie to attend, whether to choose pie or ice cream for dessert. Since all the possibilities are attractive, free of any serious factors of repulsion, the approach conflict is rare and trivial. The conflicts occur because it is not possible to fulfil both attractive desires at the same time, and a choice of one goal must be made. In the act of responding to one of the incentives, a person turns his back on the other. Ordinarily, in this type of conflict the period of indecision, tension and anxiety is of short duration. The person chooses one of the alternatives and forgets the other.

Approach-avoidance

The conflicts in this class have a pulling and a repelling power present simultaneously in the same situation. A desirable motive is present; but present also is a tendency to avoid the situation toward which the individual is attracted. A patient, for example, may desire an operation to restore her to good health; at the same time she fears the pain, distress, inconvenience of surgery and the period of convalescence. Another example is that of a nurse who wants to continue her education to receive her bachelor of nursing degree after she has obtained her R.N., but is reluctant to put in the extra years of required studies. The tendency to approach and the tendency to avoid counteract each other. This inner frustration produces indecision and vacillation of behavior, and the longer the indecision lasts, the greater the tension and stress become. The usual reaction to approach-avoidance conflicts is that of cessation of all activity. A typical conflict of this type is related in the Washington Evening Star by Judie in a letter to Abby: "I used to like a boy friend and he likes me. I don't like him any more. I like my girl friend's boy friend better, and he likes me better than he likes his girl friend. My girl friend still likes her boy friend. I don't want to hurt my old boy friend and I don't want to lose my girl friend, but how can I get my girl friend's boy friend without hurting any body's feelings? Signed, Judie." The answer was the following: "A girl can't help it if her girl friend's boy friend likes her better than he likes his girl friend. Be sure to let him do all the chasing and you'll have no apologies to make. Signed, Abby." (Washington Evening Star, Washington, D.C., June 27, 1958.)

This category of approach-avoidance is filled with instances of attractive objects that the person may desire but that are forbidden by the ten commandments, the laws of the state, the laws of the nation. A car may be very attractive to a person, but the car belongs to another, and thus the approach-avoidance conflict is quickly settled by an upright citizen. A delinquent would persist in obtaining what is forbidden. Many sex problems fall into this group of conflicts, but training in virtue and self-respect gives the satisfactory remedy to these conflicts.

Avoidance-avoidance

This type of conflict is present when *a person has a choice of two undesirable alternatives*. Neither of the situations are of his own choosing, and he is "caught in the middle" of two disagreeable situations. For instance, a cardiac patient must decrease his work load or he may have another attack; a nurse must study to pass her examinations or she will be dismissed; a patient must undergo an operation or continue to endure the sharp pain; a man must work overtime or lose his job. This is the type of conflict our soldiers experienced when captured by the Communists in Korea; they were either punished severely or forced to take the "brainwashing" lectures.

This type of conflict is prevalent in an atmosphere where a dictator or one with unlimited powers is in charge of a project and "swings the big club."

Double Approach-avoidance

This is a common type of conflict, as most attractive situations contain inherent elements of repulsion. The individual moves toward one goal and then away from it as he realizes he must lose the second goal if he accepts the first one. These negative factors cause him to doubt whether or not he should accept the object and he delays his choice for a time; this period of vacillation builds up within him and causes a stress that makes him uncomfortable to a degree that he must seek a remedy to overcome the uncertainty.

The double approach-avoidance situation is one in which *the individual is torn between two goals, which are both desirable and disturbing in some aspect.* Almost always there are undesirable factors working with desirable motives. The person is reluctant to make a final decision, but at the same time is forced to make one. For instance, a woman has a difficult time choosing a new hat since many styles appeal to her; she fears that she will regret her decision when she shows the "masterpiece" to her husband, or when she wears it for the first time. A nurse debates with herself whether to accept an invitation to a show, or to go to the country club dance on Friday evening. She would like to attend both the show and the dance. She knows that she would have a nice time at either, yet she must choose one or the other event, and she regrets that it is impossible to accept both invitations.

The double approach-avoidance differs from the approach-avoidance type conflict in this: the double approach-avoidance situations offer choice between two attractive alternatives, but involves elements of repulsion; in the approach-avoidance situation, one of the choices has positive attractiveness and the other has a negative, repulsive character.

REACTIONS TO FRUSTRATION

A child expresses various reactions when discomfort is present. The unpleasant situation may be caused by hunger, cold, restraint of his bodily movements, intense sounds or lack of emotional warmth. His instinctive awareness that something is wrong is expressed by rapid respiration, perspiration, waving of his arms, kicking and crying with no restraint whatsoever. Children cannot overcome a situation by their own effort, so they express themselves outwardly to attract the attention of others.

As the child grows older, he learns to fight by his own ingenuity if he is fortunate enough to have adequate training. The kinds of activity that increase discomfort are abandoned, and the growing child learns by experience to respect the type of behavior that gives satisfaction. The range of conditioned reflexes a child may learn is as wide and as complicated as life itself; yet those habits will persist that give satisfaction and pleasure, rather than those that cause difficulty and unpleasant sensations. The reflexes learned in childhood carry over into manhood and are present in the unconscious, and one is inclined to meet opposition in later life in the same way he did when he was a child (Subconscious Influence, p. 195).

When the environment fails to yield to a plan of attack, the sensible thing to do is to change one's tactics. Exactly how long to persist and when to change is indefinite. Experience alone can be the guide for particular occasions. Some people refuse to change and persist stubbornly even in the face of defeat. *Unreasonable persistence is stubbornness.*

MEETING CONFLICTS AND FRUSTRATIONS

There are two ways of meeting a conflict: (1) *direct method of facing life's problems;* (2) *defense mechanisms or substitution reactions.*

Direct Method of Facing Life's Problems

When one desires two or more things that are mutually exclusive, the sane thing to do is to admit the reality of the conflict and endeavor to solve the problem. This manner of acting is the rational method of readjustment and active repression, made under the influence of intellectual insight and ideals of conduct. If it is not possible to solve the conflict at once, the individual should delay and seek the reasons and circumstances that stand in his way. This delay is generally beneficial, as it gives him the opportunity to think of various things that might throw light upon the problem, and also allows time for circumstances to change so that his desire may be fulfilled. As one grows older, he learns from experience that the passage of time often changes the combination of circumstances. A child and an emotionally immature individual want things immediately; a person with a well-trained mind is willing to wait for a greater prize.

If, however, after due deliberation and waiting, one cannot satisfy the original craving without compromising his standards of conduct and the rights of others, then he should do something else that is becoming and reasonable. He thereby obtains success over his own cravings and strengthens his will to control future frustrations.

The direct method of meeting frustration implies the following series of activities: (1) *facing the problem,* (2) *admitting the reality of the difficulty,* (3) *seeking the facts of the situation,* and (4) *struggling to make the best possible adjustment in the light of reason.*

We should solve our frustrations by the direct method just described. But so many times we do not do this. We adjust more often through the emotional rather than through the intellectual process. In the struggle for personal adjustment, most of our efforts during our lifetime are directed toward devising methods to avoid anxiety, disappointment and tension. We often feel impelled to act in order to relieve the internal pressure built up by frustration, thereby hoping to procure peace of mind temporarily. The uncertainty, insecurity and anxiety accompanying frustration often forces the use of substitution reactions.

Defense and Substitution Reactions to Frustration and Conflicts

Defense mechanisms are adjustment reactions, usually unconscious, by which *an individual substitutes indirect futile means in order to avoid unpleasant situations.* If a person is to avoid anxiety, worry and frustration, he must defend himself against environmental demands and personal desires that cannot be satisfied, but that threaten his security and self-esteem. Since everyone uses defense adjustments at one time or another, and since they are obviously part of the mental life, it is essential that the nurse be aware of the most important ones, their names and how they are used.

Aggression

Aggression is the response to frustration *when a person strikes out against the apparent cause of the opposing force.* Aggression is essentially a form of reaction that seeks the reduction of tension and frustration by behavior that is demanding, overpowering and possessive. A child expresses a great deal of aggression by anger, biting, scratching, teasing, fighting and rebellion against the person causing his frustration. A head nurse who is angry at a supervisor whom she cannot attack takes out her spite on a preclinical student. Aggression is often expressed by anger ("letting off steam"), violence, sullenness, hostility and noticeable irritability. Generally speaking, those who face life with an aggressive attitude lack a real desire or the courage to solve their problems. They feel sorry for themselves and unconsciously endeavor to hide their inferiority complex from themselves and from others by engaging the attention of and promoting the embarrassment of others. Certainly, aggression serves to reduce the tension of frustration, but it complicates the frustrating problem instead of solving it. This is evident when a ball player disputes the decision of the umpire. He may rave and argue with the umpire, but his aggressive conduct will not change the decision that caused the frustrating situation.

Well-adjusted persons in all walks of life learn to control, tolerate and live with frustration. Yet it is sometimes necessary for them to resort to aggression in order to meet the demands of a situation. These dynamic people, although aggressive, do not disrupt their relations with others nor their feelings regarding them. We think ordinarily of these people as having initiative, drive and energy for the successful completion of important assignments.

Daydreaming

Daydreaming is *living in the world of fantasy rather than the world of reality*. Daydreaming is common to all ages and is practically universal in adolescence. Used to a discreet degree, it may be beneficial, as we considered under the Advantages of the Imagination (p. 104). But it is possible to form the habit of living in the imagination and not in reality, so that imagination becomes a refuge for the nurse when she is confronted with frustration. This kind of defense mechanism can lead to the fantasy of the "conquering hero" or the "suffering martyr."

The conquering hero type retreats from reality and allows her imagination full sway, like the child with its infantile fantasies. The subject becomes a heroine in her own mind, picturing herself in the headlines on the front page of her hometown paper, or as an "angel of mercy" administering to the dying at the battle front, or as becoming head nurse, or as living in the time when she obtains full control of the hospital. Instead of facing the frustration as it is, she retreats into her own imagination and becomes a great leader, not realizing that this form of action can easily lead to moroseness and delusions.

The suffering martyr type becomes the injured soul whom "no one understands," and who thinks that she is persecuted by others. This condition exists only in the mind of a person living in the imagination and not in the world. This form of unreality develops complexes of shyness, conceit and sadness. These types of patients are not uncommon, and the nurse must endeavor to keep the patient busy about other subjects of interest than himself.

Regression

Regression is a process in which *the individual escapes frustration and anxiety by returning to methods of adjustment that proved successful at an earlier stage of life.* When the individual is faced with present-day interferences, he may unconsciously adopt a pattern of reactions which were suitable for him when he was growing up. Many a nurse obtains what she wants from her classmates by regressive behavior such as pouting, refusing to speak to another or crying. These immature emotional reactions were successful when she was a child; they are often successful now. Wives sometimes dominate their husbands and husbands their wives by threatening, sulking and weeping. Very old persons, too, often regress to "second childhood" because they are no longer able to deal with the difficulties of changing ways in the modern world. Regression is generally an unsatisfactory mode of adjustment, as it is a retreat from the present-day situation, and it leaves present frustrations unsettled. Often, one will become involved in immediate, misleading objectives and, consequently, will not organize his activity to resolve his real problems. Tension and worry are prolonged by the method of regression when a serious problem is present that must be faced.

Some temporary value may come from regression, insofar as it releases us from the strain and tension of present-day problems. Sometimes we return to them refreshed, renewed and better able to handle them. The days of yore may be relived by an alumnus who returns to his alma mater for Homecoming Day or for commencement. Often he amuses himself by retreating to student days, by boisterous merrymaking and "horse play." This release from the tensions of everyday work and the pressing problems of everyday life is valuable.

Rationalization

We defend many of our actions by petty excuses; the individual selects *the most convenient reasons* for yielding to a dominant craving. A great number of people enjoy fooling themselves. Rationalization is an unconscious effort to cover up feelings of inadequacy, failure and guilt; the individual seeks to save his pride by conjuring up a credible excuse. This is false thinking by which a person justifies the things he has done, or has decided to do. One can observe this type of reaction every day when a nurse is too indifferent to study and gives the excuse that recreation and rest are necessary for health; she is late for duty because her roommate did not call her. She may bump her head in the dark and blame the door; spill a tray and blame the coffee pot; stumble going upstairs and blame the steps; miss a stroke in tennis and blame the racket. Each case reveals an inability to face the problem, admit the weakness and accept the responsibility. Rationalization is very common, and we must be on guard to avoid this form of unsatisfactory adjustment.

Some people lack the spirit of fight and give up with the excuse of not wanting a thing anyway, as if the object were worthless, whereas it is not. This is sometimes called the "sour-grapes mechanism." A nurse is taken off a case on account of inefficiency, but she convinces herself that it was a blessing in disguise because she couldn't sleep at nights. Another girl takes away her "boyfriend," but she states that she didn't like him anyway.

This form of rationalization is the cause of many false opinions: "pretty girl has no sense," as if beauty and intelligence were never united; "learned easily, soon forgotten" is a misstatement; "competent in one form of work, one is inclined to be weak in another" is often heard and is an overstatement of reality.

Weakness and self-deception are often portrayed in the attitude of accepting everything for the best. This tendency of accepting a thing because "it could have been worse" induces one to be negative instead of progressive. Too much optimism is a weakness.

Projection

Projection is one of the most frequently used forms of rationalization. Generally, individuals who suffer frustration resulting from personal inadequacy find it difficult to admit it. It is far easier to place the blame on someone else. This *unconscious process of blaming others for one's failures* is called projection. A person attributes his difficulties to someone else and feels relief by doing so. A nurse, for instance, who comes late regularly to class, blames the supervisor of the floor for giving her too much work to do, although the other nurses from the same floor are on time; another fails in an examination and finds fault with the teacher. Rarely do we hear a student blame herself for failing a class. Ordinarily, she ascribes her failure to poor health, to sickness or maybe to poor study habits learned in high school. Thus, by projecting the blame to something else, she relieves her ego of the emotional discomfort that comes with failure. It should be noted, however, that whenever a nurse blames another for her inadequacies, it is a good indication that she feels guilty and is blaming herself indirectly.

Faultfinders are generally covering up their own weakness. The hypercritical blame others for the very things they themselves do, or would like to do. They endeavor to soothe their own consciences by criticism and suspicion. Acting in the open and facing reality are the only sane ways of living. Openness and the lack of hypocrisy are two lovely traits in our youth, and should be cultivated and preserved.

Capitalization

This is a substitution reaction of taking advantage of the sympathy of others. A child will often cry profusely when slightly injured, in order to obtain the sympathy of the mother. The young will play sick, complaining of headaches or toothaches in order to stay home from school. This same tendency often carries over to the adult in whom slight injury is capitalized upon in order to take advantage of others. Some patients magnify their afflictions to become the center of attraction and to obtain extra service.

Identification

Identification is a mechanism by which *an individual regards the accomplishments, social standing, feelings and traits of others as though they were his own.* Identification is the opposite of projection. All of us are most proud of the nurses who were elected officers of the Student Nursing Association, as though their success was given to each one of us. The fact that our school is fully accredited gives each one of us an uplift that is felt personally. We identify with our school. This spirit of identification has its roots in childhood. A child, through his love for and his wish to be like his parents, automatically molds his actions, mannerisms and behavior to be like those of the parents. The boy imitates his father and the girl takes on the general actions of the mother. A little girl will play the game of "dressing up" with the discarded clothes of the adults, push around in high heels, and smear lipstick and rouge on her face; later, a young girl will copy the style of dress, mannerisms and hairdo of the movie actress she admires. Identification that leads to assimilation and further development of worthwhile traits has a salutary effect on adjustment and personality development. It may have adverse effects if the identification is based on undesirable qualities that could lead to juvenile delinquency.

COMPENSATION AND SUBLIMATION

Compensation is a form of reaction in which a person who finds it impossible to carry out his original desire, seeks to make up for the unpleasant situation by undertaking some new activity. The different activity is of the same level of satisfaction as the lost pleasure. A nurse, because of her hours of duty, cannot attend a dance, so she goes to the movie instead. A nurse who is too shy to be a social success compensates by getting the best grades in classwork. Actually, success in her studies may be only her second or third choice, but it is better than obscurity.

Compensation is on the rational level when one endeavors to do something worthwhile when it is impossible to carry out one's original desire. When a group of nurses cannot play tennis because the courts are being used, it certainly is most reasonable to substitute another game, or go for a hike, or take some other form of exercise. In this manner they compensate for the disappointment in not being able to play tennis, and at the same time use their stored-up energy by participating in another pleasant form of exercise. This compromise, while not giving perfect satisfaction, at least provides relief from tension and diverts the energy into harmless and useful modes of expression.

On the other hand, compensation is evident in many forms of the defense mechanisms: for example, when a nurse lives in the imagination instead of facing reality; when she uses sarcasm to hurt another who opposes her suggestions; when a patient exaggerates his suffering to obtain the sympathy of others. These forms of compensation do not give a satisfactory answer to frustration; tension and anxiety continue in the mind.

Sublimation is a special type of compensation in which satisfaction is sought in pleasures of a higher nature, rather than substitution of a new activity on the same level of satisfaction. Thus, a married couple who cannot have a child of their own adopts a child to take the place of the one for whom each has yearned. A nurse disappointed in love may devote her life to the care of orphans or to some necessary social service. Sublimation is most reasonable and brings happiness and contentment to those who cannot satisfy their desires in the ordinary manner.

SUBCONSCIOUS INFLUENCE

The subconscious is said to retain all past experiences and sensations recorded by the senses, but here and now, these events are not present in conscious life. The preconscious of Freud is sometimes used interchangeably with the term subconscious, but the subconscious is also used to include both the preconscious and the unconscious.

At any given moment we can recall very little of the accumulated experience held in the mind. The vast bulk of the content of the subconscious mind is beyond the possibility of recall. Yet the upper levels of it are available to consciousness. Almost every day we have the exasperating experience of being unable to recall a name, a face, or an experience. Later, an association of ideas may unexpectedly bring back the hidden memory we had been unable to recall. Another idea that passed through the mind unlocked the door of the hidden storehouse. The subconscious includes also those sensations of objects that are present at the time we are attending to something else and that receive slight notice in consciousness. Although such sensations, dimly perceived in consciousness, are not recalled to mind, they influence us in many ways.

We do many things for reasons of which we are totally unaware. Such actions produce strange results and much inner discord. Therefore, we must, whenever possible, bring such influences to the conscious level. We may be unaware of such activity in ourselves, but we can readily see evidence of it in the conduct of others. When we study our own reactions, we realize that these influences are also present in our own conduct and that we must bring them under control. When we like a nurse it is hard for us to see any fault in her; when we have an aversion for her it is hard to see any good in her. The usual expression is that such a person has a "drag" with us, or such a person is on the "outs" with us. If one of the nurses does a good job of assisting the doctor in an emergency, we say that she had everything prepared by others; if we do a good work, it is due to our acumen and skill. If one of the girls passes a difficult examination, it was due to luck; if we pass it our success is due to "brains."

Our attitude toward strangers is often colored by their resemblance to a friend or to someone we disliked, and immediately we like or dislike them. Prejudices for blondes, brunettes, redheads or crooked noses are probably based on some unconscious influence. The real motive for our attachment or antagonism is not based on reason, but on some intangible something beyond our reason. A person is tolerant of opposition when his beliefs are based on reality, generally intolerant when they are based on unconscious influences.

MENTAL HEALTH AND ADJUSTMENT

Human nature is complex. It is made up of countless tendencies, feelings, emotions, ideals, thoughts and reflexes. Frustration in life is certain, since one must deal with people and must live in an external environment. Each day brings changes and new problems. Peace of mind, however, will result if one limits his motives and desires when it is evident that realities of life will force him to do so if he does not. Theoretically, if one has something and does not want or need anything more, he should be extremely happy.

Adjustment is a process by which our internal demands and needs are brought into harmonious relationship with the demands of the people with whom we are dealing and with the reality of the environment in which we live. Everyone must realize that he is himself and nobody else. He has to accept himself as he is; not as the ideal self but as the real self, with its talents and its defects. It is necessary for him to accept the fact that some things are hard for him to do, and other things are easy for him to do.

The past, too, must be considered. Each individual must accept his past. Maybe some of his actions could have been more perfect, noble and unselfish. No matter what they were, he must accept the responsibility for these acts. He cannot rewrite the past, but he can *modify the present* and *reshape the future.* Self-acceptance, however, does not come overnight. There are many things about ourselves we cannot face. We must endeavor to accept what we can. Mental health and wholesome adjustment results from our acceptance of the external and internal demands of reality.

SUMMARY

1. Frustration is the result of the inability to obtain what we want.

2. Frustration in life should stir up the best that is within us, and should contribute to our mental development.

3. The sources of frustration may be classified under three main groups: privation, deprivation and obstruction.

4. Privation is the lack of something one needs at a particular time: for example, money, food, prestige, security, and health.

5. Deprivation is the loss of something one formerly possessed: loss of health, loss of wealth, loss of one's job.

6. Obstruction includes barriers of a general nature that block one's needs. These are of two kinds: physical and psychic.

7. A conflict is an emotional mental state when two opposing desires are present in the mind at the same time, and the individual is forced to choose one of the desires in preference to the other.

8. Four types of conflicts are: approach-approach, approach-avoidance, avoidance-avoidance, and double approach-avoidance.

9. Mental conflicts are challenges to do something different. When successfully met they bring happiness and pleasure.

10. Conflicts in life may be met in two general ways: first, by direct attack, which admits the reality of the situation and then does something about it; second, by the indirect method of defense reactions, by which an individual substitutes indirect futile means in order to avoid unpleasant situations.

11. Defense reactions are many: aggression, daydreaming, regression, rationalization, projection, and subconsciously influenced activity.

12. Mental health results from our reasonable acceptance of the external demands of reality.

QUESTIONS FOR REVIEW

Essay Type

1. What do you mean by the following: conflict, capitalization, rationalization, daydreaming, direct method?
2. What is the meaning of "tension"?
3. What are the three main causes of frustration?
4. What adjustments is it likely a cardiac patient must make to rehabilitate himself?
5. List five types of deprivations that may cause severe frustrations in life.
6. How would you treat a convalescing child, age ten, inclined to be stubborn?
7. Distinguish between each of the four types of conflicts.
8. How do children typically react to frustration?
9. Why do people differ in the way they meet difficulties?
10. Distinguish the double approach-avoidance type of conflict from the approach-avoidance type.
11. Describe in detail the direct method of facing life problems.
12. Describe "conquering hero" and "suffering martyr" types of people.
13. Describe the activity of an aggressive nurse.
14. Why is regression an unsatisfactory mode of adjustment?
15. What is the value of waiting in the presence of a difficulty?
16. What is the danger of waiting too long to solve a difficulty?
17. What excuses does your best friend generally use to "cover up"?
18. Describe the actions of a patient who demands his own way.
19. How would you treat a patient who demands his own way?
20. Describe the way the subconscious influences your conduct.
21. How do ideals conflict with drives?
22. What tendencies must be limited and what adjustments must be made by the following: (a) a moody spinster, (b) a mother who lost her first-born, (c) a nurse in the operating room for the first time, (d) a nurse having an untidy roommate, (e) a nurse on night duty?
23. List the frustrating situations you have encountered this past week.
24. Does worry indicate the wrong form of adjustment? Why?
25. Give two examples of each type of defense reaction.

Matching and Completion Type

Fill in the correct words:

1. Two necessary conditions for the presence of frustration are:

   a ....

   b ....

2. The three causes of frustration are:

   a ....

   b ....

   c ....

3. A group of barriers of a general nature that cause worry and anxiety.

   ....

4. The inability to obtain what we want. ....

5. The tendency of self-deception in accepting a thing because "it could

   be worse." ....

6. A defense reaction used by those who endeavor to obtain their desire

   by criticism and anger. ....

7. An emotional mental state that arises when there are opposing desires

   and tendencies. ....

8. Type of compensation when satisfaction is sought in activities of a

   higher nature. ....

9. Type of conflict in which an attractive situation also contains repelling

   factors. ....

10. Type of conflict in which a person has a choice of two undesirable

    alternatives. ....

11. Type of conflict in which a person is attracted by two desirable

    goals. ....

12. Type of conflict that has a pulling and a repelling power in the same

    situation. ....

13. The reason we find it difficult to find fault in a nurse we admire.

    ....

14. Indirect adjustment reaction designed to defend the individual from unpleasant situations. . . . .

15. The direct method of meeting frustrations implies the following series of activities:

a . . . .   c . . . .

b . . . .   d . . . .

16. Unconscious process of blaming others for one's own failures. . . . . . .

. . . .

17. Living in the imagination is called . . . .

18. Type of reaction characterized by petty excuses. . . . .

19. Unreasonable persistence is called . . . .

20. The type of reaction that uses the sympathy of others to obtain one's excessive desires. . . . .

TOPICS FOR CLASS DISCUSSION

1. List the natural tendencies and reasonable desires that are restricted during "years of training."
2. Many wholesome interests are necessary in facing the problems of life.
3. Personal subconscious influences.
4. Personal weaknesses and dynamic aggression.
5. Items of rationalization you have observed during the past week.
6. Your early training and philosophy of life that have influenced your inclinations and desires.
7. "A girl who is trained in religious principles has a stability that neither death nor calamity has the power to shake."
8. Frustrations and adjustments of a cardiac patient.
9. Mental health and the direct method of facing difficulties.
10. Frustrations and adjustments experienced during your first week at the nursing school.
11. Influence of conditioned reflexes on subconscious reactions.

SOURCES AND REFERENCES

Bernard, Harold W., *Toward Better Personal Adjustment*, 2nd ed. (New York: McGraw-Hill, 1957), Chap. IX.

Karn, Harry W., and Weitz, Joseph, *An Introduction to Psychology* (New York: Wiley, 1955), Chaps. VII, VIII.

Kimble, Gregory A., *Principles of General Psychology* (New York: Ronald, 1956), Chap. XVI.

Lehner, George F. J., and Kube, Ella, *The Dynamics of Personal Adjustment* (New York: Prentice Hall, 1955).

Lingdren, Henry C., *Psychology of Personal and Social Adjustment*, 2nd ed. (New York: American Book Company, 1959), Chap. IV.

Magner, James A., *Mental Health in a Mad World* (Milwaukee: Bruce, 1953), Chap. V.

McKinney, Fred, *Psychology of Personal Adjustment*, 2nd ed. (New York: Wiley, 1949), Chap. V.

Munn, Norman L., *Psychology*, 3rd ed. (Boston: Houghton Mifflin, 1956).

Noyes, Arthur P., and Kolb, Lawrence C., *Modern Clinical Psychiatry*, 5th ed. (Philadephia: Saunders, 1958), Chap. IV.

Ruch, Floyd L., *Psychology and Life*, 4th ed. (Chicago: Scott, Foresman, 1953), Chap. XII.

Sappenfield, Bert R., *Personality Dynamics* (New York: Alfred A. Knopf, 1954), Chap. IV.

Schneiders, Alexander A., *Personal Adjustment and Mental Health* (New York: Rinehart, 1955).

Symonds, Percival M., *Dynamic Psychology* (New York: Appleton-Century-Crofts, 1949).

11 • PERSONALITY

GENERAL CONSIDERATIONS

No two patients are alike physically or mentally. The nurse realizes early in her training that the sick differ from one another in their wants and desires, in their traits and tendencies, in their moods and temperaments, as much as they do in their facial and general appearance. All natures are not made from the same mold. Some patients are kind, generous and thoughtful, while others are unkind, ungenerous and selfish. It is a pleasure to take care of those who are simple, sincere, agreeable and hopeful; while others try the patience of the nurse by their domineering and vain, haughty mannerisms.

The patient's actions observed over a period of time disclose a unique relationship of thoughts, ideals, habits, tendencies and desires, which distinguishes him from anyone else. The tone of voice, the gleam in the eye, the natural poise, alertness and animation of the individual, and a thousand other external signs are distinctive in each of us. Although they are only passing manifestations, they connote certain abiding, permanent and unified inner qualities—personality traits. These traits, such as cheerfulness or courtesy, characterize an individual in a wide range of his activities, and are enduring specific tendencies of action in every situation and problem of life.

Personality is that combination of qualities, mental and physical, that distinguishes an individual uniquely from all others. It involves physical, mental and spiritual development in relation to the social environment in which one lives. It consists of the dynamic traits and tendencies, mental and physical capacities, habits, desires, temperament and behavior embodied in the individual. Personality designates the individual not only in what he essentially is, namely, his individual substance endowed with reason, but also in what he does and how he affects others. It embraces his appearance, his voice, his general intelligence, his manners, his habits, his likes and dislikes, his emotional make-up—everything, in fact, that can be ascribed to him.

Among our own classmates we can identify many types of personalities by the manner in which each girl responds to regular activities. Most of the girls we have met since we have come to training, we admire. It may be because their ideals agree with ours. Maybe it is because of their spontaneity, their dispositions, their cultured appearance or their constructive and affirmative activities. Whatever the cause may be, the self-evident fact remains that each girl has a definite personality that distinguishes her from all others.

PERSONALITY AND CHARACTER

Some modern psychologists use the terms "character" and "personality" synonymously. Others, however, make a distinction. The term personality, according to them, is applied to behavioral qualities that manifest certain inner traits of a person, while character designates those inner moral qualities that are developed by the implanting of ideals of conduct through the exercise of deliberate acts. Thus, if we say a man has a "dynamic personality but a very poor character," we mean that his external qualities are pleasing and forceful, but that some particular moral traits are not present. Inasmuch as personality is really the individualization of a human being, and a human being is a unit organism, then, basically, *personality includes the fruition of all training—physical, mental and moral.* Personality, in fact, is an integration of *all* abilities, impulses, habits, desires, as well as the physical characteristics of the whole man. Consequently, in our consideration we shall not place emphasis on the distinction of personality and character, but shall consider the two ideas under one term, namely, personality.

PERSONALITY TYPES

There is no single scientific, universally accepted classification of personality types, as yet, because human personality traits are varied and individual differences are great. Popular classifications tend to deal with two extremes, such as good and bad, strong and weak, stable and unstable, hasty and slow, efficient and inefficient, timid and brave. Another popular classification includes three predominating types: the *impulsive,* persons who act quickly without thinking; the *inhibitive,* who fret over trivialities and fail to act on time; and the *intelligent,* who act promptly and efficiently with due reflection.

Temperaments

One of the earliest noteworthy attempts to classify personalities was based on temperament. *Temperament is a persistent disposition of excitability which is manifested by the manner in which the individual reacts when an impression is made on his mind.* According to this classification, individuals are divided into four types of personalities, depending on their characteristic modes of excitability, vitality and motility. The four classic temperament types are: *sanguine* (lighthearted, vivacious, imaginative), *choleric* (impulsive and energetic), *nervous* (reflective, but prone to suspicion, envy and sadness) and *phlegmatic* (slow and deliberate).

The advocates of this theory of personality types contend that in any individual, definite traits of temperaments are likely to be manifested according to a theoretical curve, and it is impossible to point to a rigid type that has fixed boundaries. Certain traits predominate, but are continually modified by experience, training, habits, and especially by the influence of the will. Thus, each temperament has good qualities that are to be cultivated. The *sanguine* has his good humor, his candor, his cheerfulness; the *choleric* his inexhaustible enthusiasm and force; the *nervous* his delicacy and sympathy; and the *phlegmatic* his self-possession and prudence.[1]

INTROVERTS AND EXTROVERTS

Carl G. Jung, a Swiss psychologist, made the best-known classification of psychologic types based on temperamental tendencies of the individual. He started off by dividing people into two groups, introverts and extroverts. The *introverts,* who are characterized by subjective thinking, are the people whose interests are mainly within themselves. They hold themselves from group activities and are more interested in ideas than in their practical application to the problems of the world. Artists, writers, scientists and inventors are in this class. The *extroverts,* on the contrary, are characterized by objective thinking, and they find their predominant interest in objects and things outside themselves. They are men of action and leaders of crowd activities in the world about them. Salesmen, social workers and organizers evidently belong to this latter class.

This classification into two extremes, introverts and extroverts, fails to consider what is perhaps the largest aggregate of personality types, the middle group. It is evident that one cannot classify people by pointing out extremes any more than he can classify one group of nurses as brilliant and another group as dull students. The theory of Jung has been modified to include the middle group by the term *ambiverts.* But even this term is too extensive, because the measurements of human characteristics show a continuous distribution which approximates the normal probability curve. Most people, including

[2] Barrett, James F., *Elements of Psychology* (Milwaukee: Bruce, 1931), p. 225.

those we have mentioned above, combine both introvertive and extrovertive tendencies. The main objection to any classification is that types are too theoretical, abstract and artificial to be of much practical value.

SOMATIC TYPES

The popular belief that certain bodily characteristics are correlated with certain personality traits has been promoted in the movies and on the stage. The actor who represents "Prince Charming" is usually a tall, athletic and vivacious person, and the villain is either "lean and hungry" or is fat, broad and stumpy. This same thought that the physical make-up is of prime importance in one's personality was encouraged by the theory of *schizoid* and *cycloid* types advanced by Ernst Kretschmer, a German psychiatrist. His theory, however, was based on a study of abnormal individuals. He observed that a schizophrenic patient generally has a body build and constitution markedly different from that of a manic-depressive patient. The schizophrenic patients are usually tall and lanky with long arms and thin fingers and a loose muscular development on a narrow skeletal framework, while the manic-depressive patients are short, chunky and fat. He divided people into three groups: the asthenic, athletic and pyknic. The *asthenic* were described as tall, thin, long-armed individuals; the *athletic* as tall people with broad shoulders and well-developed muscles; the *pyknic* as short, plump and fat people. He claimed that each of these physical characteristics predisposes a person to a definite temperamental trend. The asthenic and athletic people develop along "schizoid" temperamental trends, in which inner emotional life is not manifested openly; the pyknic individuals reveal their emotional life freely (cycloid conduct) and are extremely sociable.

Although the theory of Kretschmer is not highly regarded in this country, his tendency types, schizothymic and cyclothymic, are widely used in psychiatry. The chief objection is the fact that normal persons, though influenced by constitutional factors, do not show personality traits in keeping with the theory, but are influenced chiefly by environmental and free-will factors. The correlation between physical size and mental ability is so small as to be negligible.

INFLUENCES ON PERSONALITY DEVELOPMENT

Personality develops gradually throughout life. It is the result of hereditary qualities, environmental influences and the will of the individual. Heredity provides the basic qualities, which are transformed and molded by the surrounding influences. Native tendencies, traits, temperaments, emotional characteristics, physical and intellectual capacities are given to a human being in the very beginning. These elementary qualities are acted upon by training, example of others, education and social experience, which, in cooperation with the dynamic, self-determining free will of the subject, make the personality of the individual actual. The raw material, as it were, is given by *heredity;* the adornment, beauty and perfection are offered by the *environment* and accepted and developed by the *will.*

It is extremely difficult to distinguish the pure hereditary traits from those tendencies which have been influenced by environment, because the individual is exposed from birth, and even before birth, to the influence of environmental factors. Physical constitution, personal experiences in terms of nursing and feeding, as well as the mother's love and treatment during the first two years of life, interrelations with playmates and friends—all leave such an indelible effect upon the person that it is impossible to say where hereditary capacities merge with the effects of environment. At least it is true that hereditary predisposition is probably always present. But this is molded and elaborated upon by the early impacts of environmental influence, so that it is neither possible nor useful to make a clear-cut line of demarcation.

Native Ability

The capacity for knowledge is given in the germ plasm. This will be considered later under the heading of Intelligence Tests. The ability to learn is chiefly a native capacity, but it must be developed by the individual within the limits possible for him. The moron and the idiot cannot pass a certain level, as they have not the wherewithal by which to develop. All normal individuals, however, have the ability to learn, to remember, to think and to reason; these qualities should be developed continuously.

Each nature is endowed with many constitutional traits and tendencies that will develop to excellent advantage if the individual governs himself and his desires according to good reason and judgment. In order to obtain a stable personality, a person must accept certain standards of conduct and have an inner conviction that self-discipline and generosity have a real value in themselves. For example, consider briefly the tendency of social approval. This stirs the individual to action and ambition, to superiority and efficiency. These are good qualities within moderation; but, on the other hand, the consciousness of superiority, the tendency to impose one's will upon others, and the attitude of "easy sailing" in life, can readily produce a selfish egotism and sterility in personality. The ability to regulate hereditary drives with persistency and moderation is highly regarded in society as the distinguishing mark of a stable personality.

Emotional Basis

Though nature has endowed all persons with feelings of pleasure and displeasure, each individual differs radically in his emotional resonance. Some people are easily irritated and annoyed; others are calm and serene under the same circumstances; some are high-strung and ready to manifest externally their emotional attitudes; others are inwardly affected, but control the outward expressions of pleasure or displeasure. Among any group of nurses personality varies from the calm to the hypersensitive. The primary emotional basis is found in the hereditary qualities of the individual, but the way of handling the emotions depends on experience and the will of the individual. Each one has a native tendency to react in a similar way to a frightening experience, for example. But the degree of action and the intensity of the response will depend on the previous experience of the person and on the strength of the will to control outward manifestations. *Individual differences are due largely to the degree of control of the emotions.*

Physique and Physiologic Reactions

The degree of physical perfection increases or decreases the opportunity of developing inherited traits and tendencies. When the individual possesses some physical perfection, he is inclined to exercise that trait which provides the greatest pleasure. For instance, the athletic girl finds great enjoyment in games that demand physical skill, while girls who have organic defects gain their pleasure in contests that do not demand physical activity. Different traits will be exercised and controlled in each case, and various substitutions and adjustments tend to bring out different habits and character formation. Those who have well-formed physiques generally endeavor to live up to the high expectation demanded of them; they are forced to control the natural tendency of domineering over others, and to subdue likewise the haughty, boastful attitude that is linked by the uneducated with physical perfection. Great strength of character often develops from organic weakness, which stimulates the individual to excel in traits that cover up the handicap. The blind man wins our admiration by developing his other senses; we admire him because he shows great strength of will by his patience and perseverance. Character depends largely on the power and control of the will, and often the individual who has some organic affliction shows great strength of character by adapting himself to various situations through a well-ordered mind and great force of will power.

Glandular activity influences the development of various traits of personality. A slight variation in glandular or circulatory activity sometimes accounts for some peculiar charm and force of personality, and at other times accounts for an unusual handicap of personality. Chronic indigestion, inadequate circulation and excessive or inactive glandular secretion modify the habits and experience of the individual and, in accordance with the degree of intelligence and will power, influence the development of personality variations.

Example of Others

The actions, words and demeanor of the mother and father have an indelible influence on the life of the child. Most children are hero worshippers, and their ideal heroes are the parents. During the impressionable years, when the child obtains its knowledge by example and imitation, the home is the only known world of experience for him. The atmosphere of the home, the association with brothers and sisters, the companionship of neighboring children influence the child to form social or antisocial attitudes that last indefinitely. For the child to achieve stability, it is necessary that he develop a deep sense of security and belonging; and this the home alone provides. During this period, respect for honesty, obedience, unselfishness, prayer and emotional control should be instilled into the naïve mind of the child. True character formation begins in the home, where the child imitates those with whom he associates.

The importance of the influence on character formation of the home, the school, the church, the playmates and the close association with many other intimate friends cannot be overemphasized. The child is inclined to ape the actions of others and to store in his mind all the experiences encountered in his limited sphere. His ideals of justice, citizenship and freedom are derived largely from his experience of neighborhood life. Every precaution, then, must be taken to see that the school life is wholesome, the playmates suitable and the friendships in the home and school above reproach, so that the child may develop tendencies that emerge into permanent qualities of character.

EDUCATION

Personalities vary according to the influence of training and education. The powers of the mind must be cultivated and controlled according to correct principles in order to form the ideal type of personality. Deviation from the correct principles of character will cause an inferior personality. Development of character requires years of training and instruction. The intellect must be trained to think correctly, to reason perfectly, to judge accurately. The imagination, the memory, the emotions and the native tendencies must be controlled by reason. Motives of good habits, correct instructions, adequate manner of conduct, and correct principles of behavior must be engendered in the growing mind in order to perfect the best character. A marked degree of difference in personalities results from different methods of training the mind. Education, then, is one of the most influential factors determining individual characteristics.

OTHER SOCIAL INFLUENCES

Poverty, wealth, wholesome or unsuitable social surroundings influence the life of the individual. Good, wholesome social gatherings should be encouraged; a human being instinctively desires to be with other persons; great mental enjoyment is to be obtained from social functions. Dances, banquets, entertainments, parties and plays have their place in the development of personality. Right reason and circumstances must regulate this phase of personality formation.

HOW TO DEVELOP ONE'S PERSONALITY

To be successful in life the nurse must develop a strong, competent personality that can overcome mental difficulties, face reality as it is, increase social approval, and keep happiness fresh in the heart. *Personality development is largely dependent upon the growth of emotional maturity and the feeling of security.* This requires the development of many traits of leadership such as self-confidence, sincerity, dignity, initiative, loyalty, dependability and cooperation with the staff, the patient, the doctor and the other nurses. *Leadership* is acquired through study, imitation and experience, and *is the ability of an individual to influence a large number of people.* To accomplish this aim the nurse should develop energetically the qualities of leadership by *having an ever-present ideal, by knowing herself,* and finally, *by having a plan of life.*

QUALITIES OF AN IDEAL NURSE

An ideal is necessary for any career of life. Of course the ideal is not an actual object that exists, but an image of perfection in the mind. This perfection can be some supernatural or imaginary condition that is above human endeavor. It would be better if one would not strive for something of this type. The ideal must be *human in every degree*, must be *practical* and, above all, must be *possible*.[2] Then, every ideal must have certain qualities in order that perfection be attained. These qualities are four—*tact, will power, amiability* and a *pleasing appearance.*

Tact

Tactfulness implies candor, openness, honesty, purity and straight-forwardness of character, regulated by sound moral principles. The rights and feelings of others are foremost in the mind of the nurse of sensitive mental perception. The moral virtues of obedience, meekness, liberality, temperance, chastity, humility and diligence should place the ideal leader on a high plane, and these qualities, united with good habits, should render her prompt and ready to exercise kindness and benevolence toward all patients. The nurse must know what ought to be done and how to do it. Prudence in dealing with the patient, with other nurses, with the doctors, and with those in charge of the hospital should be evidenced in her work. The nurse who is tactful knows when to keep silent and when to speak; she can guard a secret even from her closest friends; she can at all times avoid making undue criticism of those in charge; she can order other nurses with kindness and moderation, yet be strict with herself. Such a nurse can control her emotions by moderating her anger, pride, sloth and envy, by establishing peace, quiet, humility and alertness in her actions, and thereby obtain the cooperation and the esteem of all her associates. In short, a tactful nurse is one who has good common sense based on humility.

Will Power

The power of choice, which is the function of the will, is the characteristic and determining element of the ideal nurse. It is the

[2] Barrett, James F., *Elements of Psychology* (Milwaukee: Bruce, 1931), p. 226.

nature of the will to follow the intellect; thus, the nurse must know the best course to be followed before she can choose the ideal way. The choice a nurse makes to overcome difficulties and trials manifests to the world a strong, ideal character or a weak "pussy-foot" personality hiding under a veneer of paint, powder, permanent waves and a beautiful uniform. *The will is the element in personality that betrays what we are.* A weak-willed personality makes no impression on people and seems to express externally the lack of this inner quality. Such a one never attains leadership.

The ideal nurse has a strong will controlled by intellect. In all things she offends neither by excess nor by defect. She is ever steadfast in her duties, has a keen sense of humor and sympathy, and yields neither to force nor flattery. An order from the doctor is always regarded as a law; the fulfillment is accomplished with prudence. The nurse of strong character overcomes her tendency to domineer, is kind to all, and considerate to each nurse under her charge, endeavoring to keep perfect order first in her own life and then in the lives under her authority. She is firm and unmoved in cases of emergency and is master of the situation. The possessor of an ideal personality, then, is master of her will and regulates her choice by prudence.

Amiability

An ideal nurse possesses tact and a strong determination; she tempers these qualities with sweetness and friendliness—in other words, with amiability. Force of action is implied in the will; pleasantness and kindness reside in the feelings. A nurse will never be successful unless she strives for a sympathetic understanding of human weakness and suffering. The ideal nurse manifests amiability in her voice, in her manner, in her service, in the atmosphere of her surroundings. The sick expect to find amiability in every nurse, and the degree of this quality determines in a large measure the perfection of the ideal. The ideal nurse must be kind of heart, simple and easy in her ministration to the sick, and entirely free of ill humor. Her face must light up with a pleasant smile, which reacts more potently with the infirm than the medicine of the doctor. This smile should be natural, flowing from an overabundant heart of benevolence, and not artificial. Kindness, cheerfulness, and hopefulness should permeate her personality.

Pleasing Appearance

The ideal nurse, with character marked by tact, will power and amiability, appears externally in a manner becoming to her career. She pleases the eye. Her uniform is neat, clean and tidy. Her bib, apron and cap are spotless, well pressed, fresh. Her hands are soft, unstained, unchapped and unadorned. Her fingernails are well manicured but free of unseemly, bright polish. Her make-up of cheeks, of lips, and of eyebrows is sufficient to add charm to her features but lacks gaudiness, cheapness and tastelessness. Her step is firm and quiet, her gait graceful and unhurried. Her shoulders and head are held erect, without ostentation or slovenliness. Her demeanor bespeaks her high profession and it preserves the atmosphere of reserve, command and efficiency.

SELF-KNOWLEDGE

Self-knowledge is indispensable to one who wishes to develop leadership. All dispositions have certain favorable traits, tendencies, desires and habits that can be cultivated into outstanding personal achievements. On the other hand, every individual possesses certain defective tendencies that must be curbed and controlled. So often, these traits and tendencies are evident to everyone but ourselves. These hidden traits, then, must be known to the nurse herself, so that the advantageous elements may be developed and the defects may be restrained.

Self-examination is an important method of obtaining this self-knowledge. It discloses to the nurse what she really is, what she has to hope for, what her fears are from her natural disposition, what she desires that is becoming to her profession or what is contrary to her career, what her shortcomings are, what directions her effort must take, what her possibilities are, what her good and inferior habits are, and what she must do to increase her personal charm.

PLAN OF LIFE

In order to cultivate distinctive leadership, the nurse must continually strive to improve herself. The mere desire for improvement is not sufficient, however. She should endeavor to promote those situations that will exercise the wholesome qualities of her disposition. At the same time, she must note the circumstances in which certain weaknesses tend to supersede the wholesome traits and tendencies. A plan of life would be very helpful. This plan should include all the hours of the day when the nurse is either helping in the hospital on duty or associating with others during recreation or attending and studying classwork. The plan must be concerned with traits that are to be developed, and the weaknesses of personality that are to be restrained. It must allow, too, for occasions when she can enlarge her personality by endeavoring to increase her interests and reasonable desires through social and creative work.

The nurse, then, should endeavor to develop a pleasing personality by striving to make herself like the ideal nurse by cultivating the virtues of kindness, loyalty, cheerfulness, tact and amiability; by developing a firm will that can withstand trials and difficulties; by knowing her natural goodness and weakness; finally, by having a plan of life that tends to regulate the development of the desirable traits and to control the undesirable ones.

IDEALS AND THE NURSE

Ideals in life supply the motive of success. Whatever is noble is well worth striving to obtain in its fullness. Women throughout history have elevated the lives of men to a high plane, and by so doing they themselves have obtained perfection and happiness. The nurse who aids so many during her life has this same power of inspiration and uplift, even though she may not be conscious of this influence. She should, then, live up to the ideals of Florence Nightingale's pledge, and her silent cheerfulness and intense loyalty to duty will work untold good not only as an angel of mercy to the sick, but as an inspiration to those about her.

The life of a nurse is not a life of ease. Truly, many times during her career success smiles down upon her and it is easy to smile on the world. However, times are sure to come when clouds of hard work and discouragement will hover about her; then it is that she must smile up through the dark moments of dissatisfaction. She should try to be cheerful in all her doings, and keep in mind the purpose of her training and the ideal personality that she has set before herself. This ideal necessitates working conscientiously to be the best nurse possible and striving to be a living monument of integrity, purity, courage and loyalty.

SUMMARY

1. Human nature is complex and all men were not made from the same mold. Each individual differs in his wants, desires, mental ability, temperament and traits. No two people are alike in every particular.

2. Personality is that combination of qualities, mental and physical, that distinguishes one person from another.

3. Although personality and character are synonymous terms, character is used sometimes to designate inner moral qualities of personality.

4. There is no scientific classification of personality types because human personality traits are so varied that it is impossible to give an adequate and acceptable list that would apply to all people.

5. Temperament is a persistent disposition of excitability in the individual.

6. The four kinds of temperaments are sanguine, choleric, nervous and phlegmatic.

7. Every individual possesses qualities of each temperament, but one kind seems to predominate in his life.

8. An introvert is a person who tends to avoid crowds and whose

interests are directed toward himself. He is more interested in ideas than in action.

9. An extrovert finds his interest in objects and things and is a man of action.

10. An ambivert is an individual who is interested both in activities and in ideas. Most people belong to this group.

11. Ernst Kretschmer divided people into three groups: the asthenic, who are tall, thin, long-armed individuals; the athletic, the tall, broad-shouldered muscular group; and the pyknic, who are short, plump and fat individuals.

12. The objection to Kretschmer's theory is that ordinarily people do not show personality traits according to his predisposed physical types.

13. Personality develops slowly and depends upon hereditary qualities, environmental influences and the will.

14. Personality is influenced so early in life that it is impossible to say where hereditary capacities merge with environmental influences.

15. Hereditary predispositions include native ability, traits and tendencies, emotional characteristics, physique and physiologic reactions.

16. Personality develops through experience and is influenced by the example of others, by education and by social influence.

17. Leadership is the ability to influence a large number of people, and is acquired by study, imitation and experience.

18. The qualities of a leader are: self-confidence, sincerity, initiative, loyalty, dependability and cooperation.

19. One can develop leadership and a pleasing personality in the same way one learns a habit. Three suggestions are recommended for developing one's personality: (1) have an ideal as a model for your actions, (2) know yourself, (3) have a plan of life.

20. The ideal must be human in every degree, practical and imitable.

21. An ideal nurse must possess four qualities, namely, tact, will power, amiability and a pleasing appearance.

22. By self-analysis a nurse should learn to know herself as others see her.

23. A plan of life should take into account the desirable traits that are to be developed, and the weaknesses of personality that are to be restrained.

QUESTIONS FOR REVIEW

Essay Type

1. Define the following: personality, temperament, introvert, pyknic, leadership.
2. Contrast the actions of two patients you have attended, one of whom tends to be guided by his intelligence, the other by his emotions. Which one is an introvert? Which is an extrovert? Or are both patients ambiverts? Give reasons for your opinion.
3. What external influences have been the cause of your desire to become a nurse? How has this desire affected your personality?
4. What are the four classic temperaments? Give an example from your experience of each type. List the traits that are characteristic of each type.
5. What temperament prevails in your own life? Why?
6. What distribution of temperaments would make the ideal nurse?
7. Describe a "schizoid type"; a "cycloid type." Why are they so called?
8. Why is it so difficult to differentiate hereditary qualities from environmental influences?
9. Discuss the effect of hereditary traits on personality.
10. What substitute reactions must a nurse make in order to get along with others?
11. What do you mean by charm?
12. How did the example of others influence your life?
13. Why does the civilized world place so much emphasis on education in relation to personality formation?
14. How often should nurses have a formal dance? Why?
15. What is the value of your Christmas plays on character formation?
16. Name the traits of a leader.
17. Why must an ideal be human and practical?
18. What four qualities must an ideal nurse have?
19. What influence has a pleasing appearance on personality?
20. Make a list of traits or qualities most helpful for bedside nursing.
21. Make a list of mental attitudes that must be repressed in bedside nursing.
22. What are the usual complaints of a sentimental patient? What tact have you used when dealing with such a person?

23. Describe the mental reaction you experienced when you took care of your first patient. Do you feel any of the same emotional response in your service at the present time?
24. Why does the doctor sometimes become impatient with a nurse? Is this caused by the actions of the nurse or the personality traits of the doctor?
25. Describe in detail the qualities your own ideal nurse should possess.
26. Which is the more useful quality—tact or amiability?
27. What elements detract from the ideal appearance of the nurse?
28. What plan have you for regulating your study time?
29. Why is a plan of life necessary in order to save time?
30. Why is it so necessary to "know thyself"?
31. What qualities are enumerated in the Florence Nightingale pledge?
32. What influence have good books on a nurse's personality?
33. What senior do you like most? Why?
34. What instinctive tendencies and desires must a nurse control?
35. Describe your ideal patient.
36. What improvement in the rules for nurses would you suggest that would prove more efficient in developing the personality of a nurse?
37. Why are nurses often socially shy?
38. Give five reasons for the statement that persistency and stability are essential qualities of a leader.
39. What qualities are often manifested during a class meeting? Is it possible to judge the personality of each member by her actions during a heated discussion in such a meeting?
40. Can you point to any real conflict in your life that has influenced your personality?
41. What effect has home environment on your personality?
42. List five hospital situations in which discreet tact must be used.

Matching and Completion Type

Fill in the correct words:

1. The popular classification of a type of person who acts quickly without thinking. ....

2. Persistent disposition of excitability in the individual. ....

3. That combination of qualities, mental and physical, that distinguish an individual uniquely from all others. ....

4. Type of temperament that is lighthearted and vivacious.

. . . .

5. Jung's type of personality who finds his predominant interest in objects

and things, and is a man of action. . . . .

6. Kretschmer's type of personality classification of one who is short,

plump and fat. . . . .

7. The ability of an individual to influence a large number of people.

. . . .

8. The three general factors of an ideal are:

a . . . .

b . . . .

c . . . .

9. That quality of an ideal nurse which implies candor, openness, honesty

and purity. . . . .

10. The type of temperament that is slow and deliberate. . . . .

11. The chief characteristic and determining element of the ideal nurse.

. . . .

12. The four qualities of an ideal nurse are:

a . . . .   c . . . .

b . . . .   d . . . .

13. The type of personality that is interested both in activities and in

ideas. . . . .

14. The type of temperament that is impulsive and energetic.

. . . .

15. Personality development results from the following three factors:

a . . . .

b . . . .

c . . . .

Topics for Class Discussion

1. Traits and other factors that are included in "personality."
2. The manner in which physical handicaps may affect mental efficiency and achievement.
3. The types of temperaments observed in the students of psychology.
4. Influence of the will in personality development in relation to: (*a*) native ability, (*b*) emotional adjustment, (*c*) physical make-up, (*d*) ideal nurse.
5. Hereditary and environmental influences in personality development.
6. The influence of the home environment in personality training.
7. The necessity for a nurse to have a definite plan of life.
8. The influence of nursing the child by the mother on the developing personality of the child.
9. The qualities of a leader.
10. The qualities of a tactful nurse.

Sources and References

Allers, Rudolf, *The Psychology of Character* (New York: Sheed and Ward, 1943).

Allport, Gordon W., Personality (New York: Holt, 1937).

Bonner, Hubert, *Social Psychology* (New York: American Book Company, 1953), Chapter V.

Guilford, J. P., *Personality* (New York: McGraw-Hill, 1959).

Harmon, Francis L., *Understanding Personality* (Milwaukee: Bruce, 1948).

Sheldon, William H., and Stevens, Stanley S., *The Varieties of Temperament* (New York: Harper, 1942).

Stagner, Ross, *Psychology of Personality* (New York: McGraw-Hill, 1948).

Strecker, Edward A., and Appel, Kenneth E., *Discovering Ourselves,* 3rd ed. (New York: Macmillan, 1958).

VanderVeldt, James H., and Odenwald, Robert P., *Psychiatry and Catholicism,* 2nd ed. (New York: McGraw-Hill, 1957).

Witmer, Helen L., and Kotinsky, Ruth, *Personality in the Making* (New York: Harper, 1952).

12 • MENTAL DISORDERS

GENERAL CONSIDERATIONS

We have seen that personality is that combination of qualities, mental and physical, that distinguishes one individual from another. A person has a normal personality if he coordinates in an acceptable manner his mental and physical qualities to the average environment without marked deviation from the usual standards of conduct. The main criterion that serves to distinguish normal from abnormal people seems to lie in the adjustment to environment, to frustration, and to reality. *Normality is manifested by the appearance of the individual, by his ability to get along with others, by his consistent work, and by his endurance of difficulty and illness without excessive complaints.* Abnormality, on the other hand, designates any behavior deviations from conduct which is socially approved. As there is no theoretical basis of normality and abnormality, it is difficult to say where normality ends and abnormality begins. It is impossible to draw a sharp dividing line between normal and abnormal personalities. The effective normal person is one who is meeting adequately the demands of tension and the usual problems of life. *The behavior society will not tolerate and which is socially inadequate is abnormal behavior.*

NORMAL AND ABNORMAL ADJUSTMENTS

Most people differ in regard to their abilities, reasoning powers, judgment, emotional trends, tendencies and impulses. No two people think the same or desire the same things. Nature has endowed each one with certain traits and tendencies that are gradually changed by repetition into habits, according to the degree of intelligence and will power that the individual may possess. The *normal* person is reasonably well adjusted to reality, and is able to manage his affairs and regulate his conduct to meet, and to deal adequately with, most of the frustrations of his daily life. He is able to adjust himself to the environment and develop his character without serious deviation from conduct that is considered adequate. The normal man takes a sober, balanced, critical view of himself in relation to the world. He is constantly checking and moderating his tendencies of self-assertion with the tendency of respecting the rights of others, and he submits his will to proper authority. In this respect, a normal man differs radically from the *neurotic* individual. Although he has similar feelings, emotions and conflicts, he has learned to cope with his problems and resolve his frustrations more effectively than the neurotic. The neurotic is unable to adapt himself to the changing environment and is unable to make an adequate adjustment to the ordinary demands of living.

The only sane behavior, when dealing with the regular trials and unpleasant situations of life, is to recognize and admit the difficulty, to face the reality as it is, and to obtain the best possible adjustment in the light of reason. Everyone is required to meet conflicts and perplexing problems in life. The normal conduct is to face reality in the open and admit the difficulties as they present themselves, and adjust one's actions according to the facts and circumstances.

The neurotic individual endeavors to repress the conflicts of life into the realm of unreality instead of facing the difficulty in a direct manner.

How Mental Disorders are Manifested

Mental disorders can assume a variety of forms, which affect perception, memory, emotions, attention, thought and personality. *Perception* is affected by illusions and various forms of hallucinations—visual, auditory, tactile, gustatory and olfactory. Partial or entire loss of *memory* often occurs in the disturbed person. Disorders of the *emotions* are manifested by morbid anger, exaltation, excessive depression, and various kinds of fear. *Thoughts* are often confused and rambling; delusions are usual; obsessions, morbid suspicions, flights of ideas and gradual retardation of the power of reason are frequent. In some forms of mental disorders the patient seems to have a new personality and to see the world as twisted and disturbed with his own traits changed to fit his ideas.

Causes of Mental Disorders

The causes of mental disorders are ordinarily grouped into two general classes, namely, *predisposing* and *exciting*. The predisposing causes exist within the individual, rendering him liable to the development of mental disorders under certain circumstances, while the exciting causes are the physical and psychic conditions which produce the actual attack.

Predisposing Causes

(a) *Heredity*. Weakness of personality or a predisposition to strong emotions, which are readily stimulated and controlled with difficulty, are present in the general make-up of the individual. These neurotic tendencies are manifested in early life through highly emotional reactions, impulsive, intensive, selfish and jealous dispositions that magnify difficulties and reality.

(b) Acquired predisposition. Many individuals who have inherited fairly stable nervous systems are predisposed to neurotic and psychotic afflictions by their faulty discipline and education, much of which is received during pre-school training. Later, during the latency and adolescent periods, they fail to develop stamina to work out a satisfactory technique of meeting difficulties. They gradually acquire habits of easy-going and indolent living. Generally they give in to the impulse to obtain immediate satisfaction by adjusting each difficulty in a manner that gives the quickest relief, even though such action may bring lasting sorrow and misery in later life.

(c) General predisposing causes: age, environmental factors, occupation and previous attacks.

Exciting Causes

Both psychic and physical causes that immediately precede the outbreak of the mental disorders are called the exciting causes. The chief *psychic* cause seems to be mental stress—a sudden emotional shock, such as death in the family, excessive fear, or an auto accident. Long-continued worry, anxiety and disappointments often culminate in mental derangement. Repression of conflicts and trials that should be met and fought in the open develops peculiarities that become morbid.

The *physical* causes may be some degeneration of the cerebral cortex, defective construction of the brain, injury to the nervous mechanism by inflammation, hemorrhage or a tumor. Disturbances of the endocrine system, such as the thyroid, adrenal and pituitary glands, are often exciting causes. Too, infectious diseases that form toxic elements that affect the nervous system may bring about mental disorders. Exhaustion from physical strains, such as exposure and hunger, affect the efficiency of the nervous system and hasten mental peculiarities. The two factors, psychic and physical, often intermingle and aggravate one another in producing mental disorders.

TYPES OF MENTAL DISORDERS

The function of the mind may be disordered in any of its activities. When a disorder of one of its functions is slight, the individual is considered *neurotic,* or peculiar. It is the extreme degree of the disorder that we term *psychotic.* However, a peculiar idea that does not measure up to the external facts may be held in a mind that is normal in every other way. An excessive, unreasonable fear may exist in a normal person; or an uncontrollable fixed idea (an obsession) accompanied by anxiety often results in peculiar actions by otherwise normal people. When these same traits become excessive, so that they lead to conduct that seriously handicaps the individual, or threatens him or those around him, it is time to be concerned. We shall study first the *neuroses* and then the cases of marked mental disorders, the *psychoses.*

NEUROSES

Neurosis is *an emotional disturbance due to faulty personality development.* This disturbance results from improper adaptation either to the environment or to the stresses and struggles that are taking place within the individual. The patient is really expressing some type of mental conflict of which he is unaware.

Neurotic individuals are often called "peculiar," cranky, queer, or fanatic and are unable to solve life's problems in a satisfactory manner. This causes tension, worry and anxiety. When confronted with the difficulties and the harsh demands of life, the neurotic is unable to face reality as it is. He solves his problems by unconsciously adopting a neurotic attitude of using defense mechanisms to protect his self-respect or his ego, usually by flight into sickness, or by regression to the infantile stage. His ailments and physical complaints generally have no organic bases sufficient to cause the symptoms. Neurotics are characterized by *(1) emotional maladjustment, (2) constitutional inferiority* and *(3) mental peculiarity.*

The neuroses are difficult to understand and are often misunderstood because of the common misconception that neurotic disorders are imaginary in nature. These disorders, however, are very real to the individual himself. A neurotic patient is just as truly ill as one who has a physical ailment. He has lost that sense of confidence and security necessary to associate freely with others. This causes him to feel as if he were alone with his anxieties. He is not facing his personal problems in a straightforward manner. This attitude produces psychic tension that affects his emotions. An analysis of a patient's life frequently indicates that he is an unhappy, dissatisfied and frustrated individual. He does not accept inevitable frustrations and, for this reason, he is more tense, resentful, and irritable than some of his associates.

The degree and intensity of neurotic behavior will vary from mere eccentricity in conduct to marked deviation from normal. A slight variation from the norm of conduct is called a *peculiarity*. The intermediate variations of neurotic states and behavior, which are positively or negatively exaggerated manifestations of the normal, are classified according to specific reactions.

There is no universally accepted basis for classifying neurotic patients, because the symptoms of one often overlap the symptoms of another. We will study briefly the following types: *(1) anxiety state, (2) hysteria, (3) obsessive-compulsion, (4) phobias.*

Anxiety State

Anxiety state is a mental disorder in which marked anxiety constitutes the chief clinical symptom. This mental distress may range from a vague apprehension of ill-being to an acute anguish and horror. When an individual is confronted with some danger, there is present not only the anticipatory reaction of anxiety, but also an estimation of whether or not one has the strength and the means to overcome the threat. When a person feels confident of his ability to overcome the dangerous situation, his anxiety is reduced to a minimum. On the other hand, if the individual realizes that the threatening object may cause him harm, he feels helpless, and anxiety builds up to great heights. The amount of anxiety is proportionate to his ability to adjust to the danger that threatens his ego. This tolerance to frustration is specific for each individual. Some individuals are able to withstand more dangerous situations than others.

The most acute anxiety arises when the individual feels that his security or his reputation is threatened. In these cases, the ordinary person will use every suitable means to adjust himself reasonably to the danger now threatening him. The neurotic individual, however, will use defense mechanisms to compensate for the anxiety. The person complains of his inability to exert himself, his inadequacy, his excessive fatigue—not muscular, but the fatigue of emotional wear and tear. The patient grumbles about his inability to exert himself even moderately without experiencing great weakness. His outstanding complaint is one of excessive tiredness, with aches and pains of various kinds. The physical symptoms are numerous, but generally center about the vital organs: cardiac and vascular disturbances, heart palpitation, irregularity of breathing, nausea, insomnia, backaches and loss of appetite. He lacks the ability to attend to or to concentrate on any subject for even a moderate period of time. He is continually in a state of worry and has vague fears. He is moody, pessimistic and mildly depressed. Even slight noises or disturbances tend to upset and irritate him.

The root trouble is mental conflict arising from strong opposing desires, such as repressed hostility or sexual urges, that cannot be harmonized; the patient is unwilling to forsake one or the other of the two incompatible desires. Anxiety neuroses may also be caused by the gradual accumulation of stress, such as that which arises from some threat to one's reputation, some insult to pride and self-esteem, economic insecurity, illness or poverty.

The nurse should treat such a patient with kindness and endeavor to re-educate him by: *(1) building up his health; (2) encouraging a health program* of activity, work, play, fresh air, relaxation and rest; *(3) removing any irritating situation that may disturb him; (4) instructing him in meeting frustrations* by speaking of the sense of values of different things, of self-control and of a plan of life. A clear explanation of the fact that he is struggling with opposing desires, followed by sympathetic persuasion to give up the impossible desire, should aid the patient in accepting the facts of life in a reasonable manner. The cure of anxiety states lies in discovering the source of the anxiety and enlisting the cooperation of the patient to remove the source.

Hysteria

Hysteria is a term used to include diverse neurotic reactions *characterized by lack of control over emotions and actions.* *Conversion reaction* is a term used to identify the type of hysteria in which the individual converts anxiety into physical symptoms. Hysteria manifests itself in peculiar seizures, often resembling epileptic fits; or in paralysis, deafness or peculiar loss of sensations. The symptoms are so numerous and so varied that almost any human ailment may have a genuine conversion counterpart. Sensory, motor, visceral, emotional and mental disorders occur. A sudden onset of the symptom following a strong emotional shock is suggestive of hysteria. The hysteric never injures himself during a convulsive attack. The *dissociative reaction* almost always occurs in the presence of others and promptly ceases when the patient is left alone. The physical symptoms, however, are not pretended, but are an unconscious psychologic mode of reacting to escape some unpleasant situation.

The nurse should obtain the confidence of the patient in order to encourage him to correct his ways of acting by changing his attitude toward the realities and values of life. She may do this by using every opportunity to increase his self-confidence and his self-respect, and by diverting his mind from himself to other people, especially to needy, helpless children such as the handicapped and the orphans.

Obsessive-compulsion

An obsession is *an uncontrolled urge to dwell on some absurd thought* and a compulsion is *an uncontrolled urge to do a certain thing.* An obsession is a demanding, unmotivated recurrent idea, which an individual enjoying unimpaired intelligence recognizes as illogical and not in keeping with his own personality. At times persistent ideas that are difficult to exclude from the mind come to all normal people. For example, a nurse is rather certain that she turned off the sterilizer, yet she returns to the service room to make sure; or she may be sure that she must give a hypo at a certain time, but she returns to check the chart time and again. All of us have experienced occasions when some tune runs through the mind continually for days and we have had difficulty eradicating it from the mind. We forget that the way to remedy this persistent reaction is by substituting a different tune.

Some individuals are so conscious of bacteria present on everything about them that they will not touch even a doorknob without using a handkerchief. Others are constantly taking medicine, pills and tonics to kill pain or prevent the possibility of an ache. Many postpone necessary operations in fear of the pain they might endure. Some few patients, especially those born in a foreign country, have a mortal terror of a hospital when they are first admitted. At the root of each obsession of this kind is either an unfortunate experience or an idea that developed into an attitude. The nurse may dispel the obsession if she convinces the patient that the experience was an isolated item or that the fear of the hospital is without validity.

A serious type of obsession common in the hospital is hypochondria. The hypochondriac is apprehensive about his health or some particular disease or ailment. He is very afraid of sickness, yet is persistently preoccupied with physical complaints. It is difficult to determine what is imaginary and what is real in certain cases. It is useless to try to convince the patient of the erroneous character of his complaints. The nurse, then, must develop an indifferent attitude toward his complaints until the doctor diagnoses the psychic causes, if possible.

Every nurse has had experience some time in her life with the *persecutory* type, who is acutely jealous and suspicious toward the intentions, motives and actions of others; with the *inventive* type who has inventions ranging from gadgets of doubtful value to machines or ideas that are wholly impossible; or with the *reformatory* type who presents impractical schemes for correcting social, religious and economic abuses.

Intellectual obsessions are the cause of the very peculiar conduct of *fanatics* and *radicals*. The individual often is unreasonable, dogmatic, opinionated and prejudiced about one or many topics. The religious fanatic is directed by unreasonable, fixed ideas. The fanatics who think that the young girls of today are forward and brazen are illogical in their thinking and inconsistent in their actions. They fail to notice the splendid qualities of candor, openness and the complete lack of hypocrisy in our young people. A head nurse may have an obsession that a certain girl in training should not become a nurse, and may endeavor to prove her idea by watching this girl's every movement. Such obsessions may cause harm and many disagreeable moments. The sane way of acting is to be in the open and eliminate compulsive ideas. *Scrupulosity* is a compulsive condition characterized by obsessive thoughts, particularly concerning moral and spiritual matters. Such a person regards the most indifferent acts as sinful, and he fears that he is always offending God. The scrupulous individual, in contrast to the normal person, sees sin in acts where there is none, or certainly not to the extent that it exists in his anxious mind. It is necessary for him to place himself under someone in authority and follow strict obedience to his comments.

Phobias

A peculiar reaction caused by an obsession associated with fear is known as a phobia. *Phobias are morbid fears of some object or situation.* Common phobias are those evoked by small animals, mice, snakes and spiders. Phobias like these do not usually interfere with normal adjustment. The patient suffers intense and uncontrollable emotions of fear whenever he encounters some particular situation. At times a phobia may have a paralyzing effect on the person. Some people are excessively frightened during a thunderstorm or when they are left alone in a closed room. The person cannot account for the unreasonable reaction, nor can he control the autonomic resonance of the body and the mind when he suddenly encounters the frightening situation. Some people cannot control themselves when they are aloft on some high place. They become dizzy and have a fear of falling. Some patients have this same fear associated with a high elevated hospital bed.

There are as many kinds of phobias as there are objects to fear. Some patients have an unreasonable fear of pain and shudder when they see a nurse with a hypodermic needle; others fear the dentist's chair, the sight of blood, or the thought of cold water, guns, knives and innumerable objects. There is no particular reason to be distressed by these fears. They will be present whenever the occasion turns up. If one must tolerate a situation to which he is allergic, his tension can be reduced by turning his attention to something else. While looking at a movie where the hero is risking his life on the mountainside, close your eyes until the scene is over. In dealing with a patient with claustrophobia, leave the door open; if the fear is intense, endeavor to have a special nurse assigned to the case. If the patient fears a high hospital bed, get the type of bed that can be lowered or elevated according to the need of the patient. If the fear is associated with the hypodermic needle, have the patient close his eyes and think of home or of the girl friend. Whenever a medication is necessary, permit the patient to tremble or to freeze up or faint, but carry out the essential procedure.

Each subject of a phobia has a history of some incident in his early life when one of these objects or some other object closely associated to it caused excessive fear and anxiety. The original incident generally fades into the unconscious, yet the same unreasonable reaction results every time a similar incident is experienced in the present. In each case, however, the phobia clears up rapidly as soon as the patient is led to recall the original incident, and begins to understand the unreasonable reactions that have resulted from it.

Names of Phobias

Some unreasonable fears are called by their Greek names: *claustrophobia* is fear of closed places; *astraphobia* is the fear of lightning and thunder; *nyctophobia* is the fear of darkness; *acrophobia* is the fear of high places. Other kinds of excessive fears are termed according to the objects feared, such as phobia for black cats, for long-bearded men, for prowlers. One may be afraid to meet people, to be alone, to be in a crowd, to give a speech, to recite in class, to write an examination, to go to a dance. The number of situations causing anxiety seems to be almost infinite: fear of poverty, of death, of becoming blind, of being separated from one's family, of failure, of losing one's job.

PSYCHOSES

Psychosis is a serious disorder of the whole personality of the patient. The individual loses touch with reality; yet he may have normal moments. He lives in fantasy wherein every wish is satisfied, and he withdraws from his environment. Such a one does not seem to be the same person he was before the onset of the mental disorder. He is unable to make a living or conform to the rules of society.

The field of *psychiatry* treats the subject of abnormal mental states in detail. Here we shall merely indicate the phases of abnormal mental states (psychoses) in relation to general psychology. Our purpose is to give a brief general explanation of the different forms of mental disorders, and not a complete exhaustive discussion.

Differentiation Between Neurosis and Psychosis

NEUROSIS	PSYCHOSIS
1. Personality is impaired, but it is social and fairly well organized.	1. Complete disorganization of personality.
2. Individual is always in good contact with reality.	2. Individual disregards reality.
3. The patient does not attempt to change environment.	3. The patient attempts changes in environment by reactions of delusions and hallucinations.
4. Symptoms are somewhat mild.	4. Symptoms are more disruptive.
5. The neurotic does not act toward inner experiences.	5. The psychotic becomes disturbed by inner experience and retaliates toward them.
6. Feelings are fairly well in keeping with the situation and circumstances.	6. Feelings are inappropriate to the situation.
7. Patient continues to show an interest in the environment.	7. Patient is disinterested in the environment.

Classification of Psychoses

There are a great variety of psychoses, but they may be classified under three groups: *(1) functional, (2) organic,* and *(3) toxic.*

A *functional psychosis* is one that cannot be associated with an underlying organic pathology. This type of mental disease is attributed to psychic malfunction resulting from personal or economic stresses, strains and pressures occurring in the individual's life from infancy to death. Whether causative factors will be discovered in the blood, endocrines, tissue chemistry, or in any other part of the body is a matter of conjecture; at the present time doctors have been unable to discover the physical causes to account for the symptoms manifested. Functional psychoses are classified into two divisions: *(1) schizophrenias, (2) manic-depressive states.* Schizophrenias are a group of psychiatric illnesses characterized by *disharmony of thinking, feeling and acting.* Manic-depressive states are a group of disorders characterized by *wide mood swings* either in the direction of elation or depression.

An *organic psychosis* results from physical conditions that may directly or indirectly affect the nervous system. Symptoms of this type of disorder may be caused by the degeneration of brain tissue, the lack of development of specific glands or other structures of the body, localized lesions, accidents, infectious diseases, brain hemorrhages, an embolism, cerebral arteriosclerosis, excessive or defective endocrinic reactions, and many other conditions that may disturb the centers of the central nervous system.

A *toxic* psychosis may be closely allied to the organic type. It is caused by harmful substances that affect the nervous mechanism. For example, lead, excessive alcohol, mercury, arsenic, morphine, heroin and other such substances may cause abnormal behavior.

Functional Psychoses

Schizophrenia

Schizophrenia represents a particular type of personality disorder characterized by a splitting of the mind between thought and fantasy.

The disorder shows a marked disturbance in the patient's relation to reality and his ability to make decisions. *The earliest symptoms are found in the emotions.* The patient loses all ambition and interest in his work and play, becomes apathetic, sulks as if his feelings were wounded and broods over trifles. Incongruity of behavior is one of the marked characteristics of such an individual. At times the patient suddenly and without cause utters inappropriate laughter. Hallucinations and illusions are usually present and at times the patient lives in the land of dreams. The schizophrenic seems to be neither wholly awake nor wholly asleep, but to be living in a strange world. As in sleep, he loses contact with reality and with the world about him; yet he may walk about, use his sense organs to guide his actions and respond to the people about him in an imperfect manner. The world to the psychotic patient is not the same as it is to normal people; it is a world of his own imagery.

The incidence of schizophrenia is high; these cases make up one-fifth of the patients admitted to mental hospitals annually, and about one-half of the resident patients in mental institutions. The occurrence of schizophrenia is relatively rare before puberty and after the fiftieth year. Because of the fact that the mental disorder first manifests itself in the majority of cases about the age of puberty, schizophrenia was formerly classified as *dementia praecox.*

Schizophrenia may manifest itself in four different types, namely: (1) simple, (2) hebephrenic, (3) catatonic, and (4) paranoic.

The *simple type* of schizophrenia is characterized by apathy, dullness, and marked reduction of the patient's interest in himself and in his environment. There is no striking peculiar behavior nor are there any delusions or hallucinations. Despite all treatment he remains listless throughout his life. People of this type are rarely hospitalized, but live as servants and menials. Ordinarily, they do not develop beyond the hobo stage.

The *hebephrenic type* shows a predominant tendency to silly behavior and to constant giggling. The smiling and laughter are entirely inconsistent with the ideas expressed and are often interrupted by the patient talking to himself. Hallucinations, delirium and panic, with loss of self-control, are equally prominent.

The *catatonic type* is characterized by fixed and stereotyped movements. The patient may keep his arms, hands and feet motionless in a fixed position for days or weeks at a time if he is permitted to do so. Some patients are marked by generalized inhibition; others by motor excitement, and the vast majority show both stages.

Finally, the *paranoic type* of schizophrenia is characterized by the existence of highly systematized delusions. Some patients identify themselves with great characters of history and live in the realm of fancy. One patient imagines himself to be Napoleon; another pictures himself as a millionaire and distributes bits of paper as money or checks; another may represent himself as the President of our country. The behavior of the paranoic is unpredictable. His reaction to the environment is almost constantly one of anger and hatred, hostility and aggression. In the early stages the patient reacts to his hallucinations, which occur in several fields, but later he may become indifferent toward them.

With modern treatment—electrical (electroshock therapy), chemical (insulin, reserpine, chlorpromazine) and psychologic (psychotherapy)—the chances of improvement have been greatly increased. In a few cases the patient returns to his occupation. Even though a considerable number of schizophrenic patients, especially those who have had this disorder for over a year, do not recover, the outlook is not absolutely hopeless. Some of the older cases recover suddenly.

The *cause* of schizophrenia is not clear. Although some psychiatrists insist that it is caused by a degenerative change in the cerebral cells, the majority of authorities claim that it is due to psychic, not physical causes. The shut-in type of personality and the introvert, especially those who fail to adjust themselves to the prolonged conflicts and difficulties of life, are more liable to this disorder. Severe shocks, fright and emotional disturbances seem to be the psychic causes of the early symptoms.

Manic-Depressive Psychoses

Manic-depressive psychoses are characterized by disturbance of emotional tone, which results in attacks of depression or excitement or both. Each attack generally terminates in recovery, but leaves a tendency toward recurrence. The psychic disturbances are primarily in the emotions. Innumerable gradations of either excitement or depression may be present. Manic-depressive psychosis is a condition in which the patient has exaggerated moods over which he has no control. At one time he may show pronounced elation; at another time, extreme depression. This tendency to pass from one stage to another is not present in every case, however. Some patients are afflicted only with excessive despondency; others show only marked elation.

In the *depressive phase* the patient's psychosomatic processes are slowed down. He has difficulty in speaking and in thinking. He neglects ordinary hygienic habits, experiences difficulty in sleeping and eating, and he loses weight gradually. The patient feels himself to be weak and helpless, and in most cases, guilty of some grave offense, though he cannot describe the nature of his guilt. He imagines various shortcomings and feels that he has committed some unpardonable act. In extreme cases of depression the patient imagines all sorts of punishment, which fills him with morbid fear.

In simple *retardation* that is closely related to the normal, the patient may be treated in the doctor's office; in *acute depression* and in *depressive stupor* the patient should be treated in a mental institution.

In the *manic phase* all life activities are speeded up. The patient is bewildered with superficial thoughts of his environment; he speaks constantly and continuously. In a severe case the patient is characterized by anger and self-assertion, ceaseless activity, rapid, volatile confused thinking and the absence of a sustained flow of thoughts.

There are different sub-stages of the manic phase. In *hypomania* the patient experiences slight elation; in *acute, delirious* and *chronic mania,* the patients must be given special treatment in a mental hospital.

The treatment of severe manic-depressive consists of hospitalization, where specialized therapy will hasten recovery. The nurse should be most kind, yet firm, with the patient and endeavor to act natural in his presence. It is important that she aid in restoring the patient to the feeling of security in himself and endeavor to revive his trust in the future.

Involutional melancholia, a psychosis of the manic-depressive type, refers to an attack of depression that occurs during the "change of life." This psychosis is about three times as frequent in woman as in man. It occurs in woman frequently between the ages of forty and fifty, and in man between the fiftieth and the seventieth years. Most people who experience difficulty during these crucial years are psychoneurotics, rigid or overscrupulous personalities. In severe cases attacks of anxiety and psychosis, with hallucinations and illusions, may develop. In recent years, electroshock treatment has shortened the duration of the psychosis and has doubled the number of recoveries.

Organic and Toxic Psychoses

Amentia

Mentally deficient persons whose *minds have never developed normally* are classified as *feeble-minded,* according to intelligence tests.

Idiots are in the lowest range of mental development. They are persons who reach a maximum mental age of less than three years and have an IQ of less than 20. They are incapable of performing ordinary actions such as washing their faces or hands, and generally can speak only in monosyllables. They depend on others for all necessities, and must be protected and nourished.

Imbeciles range in mental age from three to seven years, having an IQ of 20–40. The high-grade imbecile can dress himself, follow simple instructions and help out in simple mechanical work. The low-grade imbeciles are incapable of doing any useful work, and depend on the supervision of others to perform routine tasks.

Morons have a mental age of seven to ten, progress very slowly in the lower grades, and can do only light work that does not require much mental effort. They have an IQ of 40–60. Some can make beds, scrub, and take care of animals, and are capable of doing the routine work of the world.

Organic Dementia

Organic dementia is caused by localized lesions and tumors. The mechanism of the brain is affected, and the patient cannot use regions of the brain that are injured or disturbed. This commonly results from accidents and from toxic substances that affect the brain and the nervous system.

Senile dementia is due to old age. The tissues gradually degenerate and some abnormal actions develop. There is at times loss of memory or lack of ability to formulate logical thought. The emotions, too, are affected, resulting in melancholy and delusions. The patient often lives in the past and seems to be oblivious of the present.

Other Psychoses

This group of organic and toxic psychoses includes autotoxic derangements due to the imbalance of the glands of internal secretion, such as *cretinism* and *myxedema,* and *toxic* conditions due to alcohol, syphilis and bacterial infection. Each form has definite symptoms and manifests mental conditions that are studied in the field of psychiatry. In each case the nurse must depend on the recommendation of the doctor and exercise prudence, tact and extreme patience.

SUMMARY

1. There is no sharp line of demarcation between normality and abnormality. A man is considered normal if he can adjust himself to the trials and difficulties of life without marked variation from customary habits of action. Various degrees of abnormality range from peculiarity to psychosis.

2. An abnormal person is one who cannot adapt himself to his

environment without marked peculiarities in habits that society considers unsound and unsafe.

3. A normal man faces reality as it is, and endeavors to solve his problems in the light of reason.

4. Mental disorders are manifested by the loss of memory, by delusions, hallucinations, morbid emotions, and confused, distorted thinking.

5. Delusions are false beliefs that are groundless and extreme. There are four types: grandeur, persecution, inferiority and negation.

6. Obsessions are uncontrolled urges to dwell on some absurd thought.

7. Phobias are morbid fears of some object or situation. There are as many kinds of phobias as there are objects to fear.

8. Anxiety is an emotion that arises when one cannot overcome a danger. It is eliminated by seeking its cause.

9. Psychoses fall into three groups: (1) functional, (2) organic, and (3) toxic.

10. Two divisions of functional psychosis are schizophrenia and manic-depressive states.

11. The types of neuroses are: anxiety states, hysteria, obsessive-compulsion, and phobia.

12. Schizophrenia represents a particular type of personality disorder characterized by a disharmony of thinking, feeling and acting.

13. Manic-depressive psychoses are characterized by emotional disturbance resulting in attacks of depression, or excitement, or both.

14. Many other forms of psychoses result from organic lesions, toxic infections, and unbalanced secretion of the endocrine glands.

QUESTIONS FOR REVIEW

Essay Type

1. Define the following terms: normality, peculiarity, obsession, mania, abnormality.
2. Describe in detail the sane method of facing a difficulty.
3. Describe how a neurosis may be the cause of failure in a nurse's career.

4. Name four peculiarities that you may have noticed in convalescing patients.
5. Why do people avoid a fanatic?
6. What are phobias? Describe some common kinds of phobias.
7. Describe in detail the different forms of delusions.
8. What advice would you give a patient who is overly anxious about her health?
9. Differentiate: illusion, hallucination, delusion.
10. What are the predisposing causes of mental disorders?
11. What mental powers may be affected by mental disorders?
12. Define hypochondria, scrupulosity, hysteria, obsessive-compulsion. Give an example of each condition.
13. Describe abnormal fears that a nurse may develop in the nursery ward.
14. Describe schizophrenia in detail.
15. Why is it so difficult to treat a neurotic patient?
16. What part does heredity play in regard to a neurotic constitution?
17. Describe the symptoms of paranoic type of schizophrenia.
18. What part does jealousy play in causing repressed desires?
19. Describe how a nurse may develop an obsession of dislike for the head nurse.
20. List the differences between neurosis and psychosis.

Matching and Completion Type

Fill in the correct words:

1. An abnormality caused by the failure of the mental development and lack of intelligence in the earliest years of the individual's life.

   . . . .

2. Beliefs that are groundless and extreme. . . . .

3. A slight variation from the norm of usual conduct. . . . .

4. The chief exciting causes of mental disorders are:

   a . . . .

   b . . . .

5. Neurotics are characterized by:

   a . . . .

   b . . . .

   c . . . .

6. An emotion which arises when one cannot overcome a danger.

   . . . .

7. A neurotic condition characterized by obsessive thoughts, particularly concerning moral and spiritual matters. . . . .

8. An abnormal mental state that develops during the "change of life."

   . . . .

9. An uncontrollable urge to do a certain thing. . . . .

10. The three general divisions of psychoses, which include a great variety of abnormal behavior, are:

    a . . . .

    b . . . .

    c . . . .

11. Morbid fears of some object or situation. . . . .

12. The type of patient who is over-apprehensive about his health.

    . . . .

13. The name of the phobia of an individual who has an excessive fear of closed places. . . . .

14. The form of psychosis characterized by attacks of depression or excitement or both, and in which the disturbances are primarily in the emotions. . . . .

15. A type of mental disorder that profoundly alters the entire personality of the patient. . . . .

16. A type of schizophrenia in which the patient manifests stereotyped movements and fixed attitudes. . . . .

17. The term used to classify a schizophrenic patient who is characterized by an existence of highly systematized delusions. . . . .

18. A particular type of personality disorder characterized by a splitting of the mind between thought and fantasy. . . . .

Topics for Class Discussion

1. Normal and abnormal adjustments to emotional problems of life.
2. Phobias, subconscious influence, and the nurse.
3. The attitude society should have toward mental disorders.

4. Methods of overcoming anxiety.
5. Discussion of the hypochondriac patients you have observed.
6. Scrupulosity and its treatment.
7. Obsession and fanaticism in relation to Communism.
8. Distinguishing features of neurosis contrasted to those of psychosis.
9. Demonstration by certain members of the class of the symptoms of each type of schizophrenia.
10. The attitude of the nurse toward neurotic patients.

SOURCES AND REFERENCES

Bosselman, Beulah C., *Psychiatry in Theory and Practice* (Springfield, Illinois: Charles C Thomas, 1957).

Cameron, Norman, and Margaret A., *Behavior Pathology* (Boston: Houghton Mifflin, 1951).

Coleman, James C., *Abnormal Psychology and Modern Life,* 2nd ed. (Chicago: Scott, Foresman, 1956).

Ewalt, Jack R., Strecker, Edward A., and Ebaugh, Franklin G., *Practical Clinical Psychiatry,* 8th ed. (New York: McGraw-Hill, 1957).

Ingram, Madelene E., *Principles and Techniques of Psychiatric Nursing,* 5th ed. (Philadelphia: Saunders, 1960).

Mikesell, William H., and Hanson, C., *Psychology of Adjustment* (New York: Van Nostrand, 1952).

Moore, Thomas V., *Nature and Treatment of Mental Disorders,* 2nd ed. (New York: Grune & Stratton, 1951).

Noyes, Arthur P., and Kolb, Lawrence C., *Modern Clinical Psychiatry,* 5th ed. (Philadelphia: Saunders, 1958).

Render, Helena W., *Nurse-Patient Relationships in Psychiatry* (New York: McGraw-Hill, 1947).

Sadler, William S., *Practice of Psychiatry* (St. Louis: Mosby, 1953).

Strecker, Edward A., *Basic Psychiatry* (New York: Random House, 1952).

Ulett, George A., and Goodrich, D. Wells, *A Synopsis of Contemporary Psychiatry* (St. Louis: Mosby, 1956).

VanderVeldt, James H., and Odenwald, Robert P., *Psychiatry and Catholicism,* 2nd ed. (New York: McGraw-Hill, 1957).

13 • FORMATION OF HABIT

INFLUENCE OF HABIT

Habitual acts influence our lives each day. We are inclined to perform certain acts in the same way. Our lives tend to become routine, and each day is similar to the preceding days. This is especially true in the life of a nurse during her time in training. She becomes accustomed to performing the ordinary actions through regularity without strain and without excessive conscious attention, reasoning, or thinking. We shall consider briefly some of the regular actions of the day that we perform from habit.

Handwriting becomes so distinctive that we write letters of the alphabet in the same way, scratching the same curlicue to the final letter, crossing the t's in the same manner, and misspelling the same words time after time. Writing becomes so habitual that any one of our acquaintances can recognize our script. Then, again, we dress in a manner all our own. Your roommate soon realizes the peculiar and specific manner in which you put on one garment after the other and your regular system of "getting ready." Some nurses can dress in a few minutes, while others mope around, yawning and stretching, instead of dressing immediately. Those who take a few extra minutes "shut-eye" after the bell rings in the morning develop a speedier method of dressing, though generally at the expense of neatness, cleanliness and tidiness, which do not get attention until after roll-call and morning prayer.

Table manners, prayer, posture during the time of study and relaxation, neatness in the care of fingernails, shades and amount of lipstick and powder, poise and manner of walking, punctuality and speed of performing floor duty—are all actions in our everyday life that become habitual. It is important, if we are to acquire perfection, that these habitual activities be well ordered, and performed according to the best norm of decorum and right reason. During the three years of training the nurse should establish habits that will lead to success and will carry over throughout her professional life. She must also cut out all habits that will bring embarrassing and disappointing moments in her life, and perhaps disaster in her career.

NATURE OF HABIT

A habit is a facility of action acquired by repetition, and marked by the ease of performance or the decreased power of resistance. All habits are acquired. The nervous system by its very nature is plastic and, once an impulse has been transmitted through the synapse of a nerve tract, there is a tendency for the stimulus to pass over the same course whenever it is repeated. The synapse (Figs. 2 and 5) has been formed and the repeated stimulus is inclined to take the same course through this nervous juncture. The oftener the stimulus passes through the synapse, the more readily and the easier the nervous mechanism transmits the impulse. The reaction gradually becomes automatic and the impulse is transmitted with accuracy and ease. By repetition, then, the facility in performing the act becomes *stable* and *permanent.*

When the young preclinical student first handles the hypodermic needle and the syringe, all her fingers feel like thumbs. Her hand trembles, her movements are awkward, and her method of puncture is blundering and ponderous. She must be instructed in the manner of holding the syringe so that the bevel of the needle will enter the muscle correctly. She eventually learns the correct method of plunging the needle with her trembling hand into the the tense and twitching muscle of her practice probationer without hitting the bone. Every beginning is hard, and in this case the difficulty is shared by the nurse who holds the needle and by her associate "probe" who must be on the "receiving end." After a few trial efforts, and after necessary corrections have been made, the nurse is able to use the needle with grace, precision and dexterity. The correct synapses are set up in the nervous system, and the impulse is relayed to the different nerve centers with ease and perfection. But the correct method must be learned in the beginning, otherwise the wrong set of synapses are formed, and once formed, are changed with difficulty. The correct technique must be employed when one is learning any new motor activity, and then repetition will establish correct bonds in the synapses.

RESULT OF WORTHY HABITS

Habitual acts become easy. They do not require great attention and, therefore, *lessen fatigue and strain.* They become almost automatic and the satisfaction offsets the effort required in their performance. When a young nurse takes up floor duty for the first time, nervous strain and anxiety take their toll as the day speeds away, and she becomes tired on her feet, even though she has done far less work than the junior or senior nurse on the same floor. She often wonders how the other nurses can do their work and yet have time to sit in the chart room with extra time on their hands. However, after she has been on duty for a few months, and has learned to organize her work, she becomes proficient in her service and fatigue is less noticeable.

Ease, proficiency and *simplicity* of activity develop from practice, provided the right technique is employed from the beginning. *Tech-*

nique is a special term used to denote proficiency in method. For example, a nurse who receives her first appointment to the operating room is nervous, ignorant of her duties, yet willing to learn. Everything is strange and novel on the first day. Then after a few days, she learns the method of folding gowns, sterilizing linens, gauze and instruments; she circulates with another nurse to the patients' rooms before and after an operation; and, then, she learns how to "clean up" the operating room. Later, after she has "scrubbed" for a few minor cases and some major operations, she develops ease and efficiency in doing exactly what the doctor expects her to do. Generally, in three months a nurse acquires good technique and is able to meet most emergencies in the operating room.

Habit and Mental Work

Habits influence our mental and emotional reactions. For this reason the nurse must develop the best methods of reasoning, memorizing and thinking while she is in school, so that her mental life may be adequately directed and formed. It is during the formative years of training that she must establish correct habits so that her habitual acts will be correctly directed throughout her career. We have discussed at length the processes of memorizing and studying. The nurse must strive to put into practice the suggestions that have been given in order to improve her mind and make learning easier and more thorough. It is easy to fall into a slipshod manner of intellectual life—to be satisfied merely with the mediocre and half truths instead of striving to obtain full and complete information. The mind will work rapidly and perfectly if it is trained to do so.

Influence of Wholesome Conversation

The emotional habits of a nurse are well known by her associates. One can learn more of her own habitual "pet peeves" and emotional substrata during the conversation at meals and during the unguarded period of recreation than at any other time. A wise nurse will profit by this friendly chiding and will endeavor to correct the habitual emotional trend that causes unwelcome comments. She does not become ruffled and impatient when one of her peculiarities is brought to the foreground. If the "shoe fits" it is time to make corrections in one's habitual ideas instead of countercharging by insinuations and rationalizations. Wholesome conversation, clever bickering and "kidding" among friends will bring out traits that would have remained hidden for years. When the nurse is young she "can take it," and realize that these habits are present and that they should be corrected. Later in life she will not have the familiar wholesome spirit around her, and will not have the same opportunities of discovering her hidden traits. Some nurses carry their feelings on their sleeves and never realize it. Others let these tendencies become evident in their work and still do not give these habits an extra thought. Some nurses pout when they must endure the least inconvenience; some become impatient and disagreeable when a patient is forced, through necessity, to call for service. These same qualities, evidenced in her work, are brought out in the open when the nurse converses with her friends, and the clever, wide-awake nurse profits by such good friends and endeavors to correct these emotional habits. Life is too short and valuable for the nurse to allow disordered habitual emotions to detract from the happiness that should be hers.

We must not form the idea, however, that only peculiar habitual traits are exposed in conversation. Wholesome and beautiful qualities of habits, too, are realized, and these should be nourished and cultivated. Most of the nurses are kindness itself, refined by suffering and pain, endeavoring to treat the patient with sincere sympathy and understanding, smiling under difficulty, and making hospital life interesting and happy.

Result of Unbecoming Habits

Careless habits lead to waste of time and effort. Many ordinary things could be done with maximum speed and accuracy if they were done with good technique. The ordinary duties, such as making beds, preparing linens, working in the diet kitchen, serving trays, and sterilizing gauze, bandages and instruments, can be performed almost automatically if the nurse would take time to acquire the habit of accomplishing this work efficiently. A nurse who has inferior habits makes the simplest acts complicated. A nurse who is inapt at dancing makes the ordinary dance seem hard. The young probe who has not been accustomed to performing the morning care is liable to spill the water over the bed and the patient. The unskilled hand in the operating room causes confusion and makes the ordinary act, which is so easy for one who knows, appear difficult.

Mental and physical strains accompany careless habits. Confusion and mistakes disturb the mental equilibrium of the person who has defective habits in doing ordinary things. Such a nurse is not sure of herself, and fears that this poor technique will cause her embarrassment and result in unfavorable reports from the patient. The office is often informed of inferior work, and when the nurse is called "on the carpet," she has a hard time explaining her actions. Even if she is not called by those in authority, her own conscience condemns her and this itself causes mental distress. Moreover, careless habits require extra movements that cause physical strain and partial exhaustion.

Finally, negligent habits often lead to discouragement. Other girls are advancing in their studies and in their work, while a nurse with poor habits remains at a standstill and does not make the steady improvements that she should. This waste of time, money and effort may bring on discouragement, and cause the nurse to take up another occupation either by request or volition. A nurse must remember that she can do as well as anyone else if she uses the right method from the very beginning and applies it to her actions.

HOW TO FORM PROFICIENT HABITS

Desire to Acquire a Habit

A nurse will never acquire a habit unless she desires to do so. The old analogy that "you can lead a horse to water, but you cannot make him drink" is true here. The hospital can have the best staff of instructors possible, who demonstrate perfect methods of making beds, of caring for the sick, of assisting the doctor in the operating room, in the O.B. room or in the patient's room, and yet if the nurse is not willing to acquire perfection of action, she will never acquire the correct habitual acts necessary for the particular occasions. The nurse *must be willing* and must *have the desire* to attain perfection, otherwise she will make blunders and cause harm in her care and service.

The incentives to acquire the correct habits and skills are abundant in a nurse's life. The hospital staff comes up to the standard set by the Nursing Association. The cases are so varied that they never cease to be interesting. The emotional elements are present to arouse sympathy, care and the desire for proficient work. Rarely do you find that a girl in training is unwilling to learn the correct methods, but the danger lies in the fact that she permits lethargy and carelessness to slip into her routine work, and she fails to practice the principles she once knew.

Analysis

The nurse can save time in acquiring a habit if she will *analyze* the necessary movements, by *concentrating at the very beginning* on the best way to obtain the desired results. She should seek to *understand* what actions should become mechanical and what elements will require attention each time. For example, there are many ways of making a bed, but in each hospital there is only one acceptable way. The nurse must take care in the very beginning that she understands the manner outlined by the instructor; that she observes the movements of the instructor in showing the student how to fold the sheets or the blankets; that she notices what part of the sheet is tucked under first, what side of the bed is fixed first, where the instructor stands in fixing the sheet, and where she places the other end of the sheet; and that she notes so many other particular items. Then, when the nurse tries to put the instruction into practice, she should strive to imitate this particular method, completely at first, and then, point by point. Eventually she strives to perform this ordinary action with speed, watching for mistakes and clumsy movements.

Proficiency in the operating room, in the laboratory and on general duty requires a mastery of technique. The nurse, therefore, must focus attention on the various acts essential to perfect each skill. Since many habits are more difficult to learn than others, the amount of time spent in analyzing each step depends on the nature of each skill.

Correct Guidance

The ordinary way of acquiring knowledge is under the *guidance and advice* of someone who knows how. Throughout our lives we seek the advice of the expert, or of one who is supposed to have adequate knowledge of a specific subject. We go to a lawyer, priest, doctor or nurse whenever we wish to obtain knowledge on the subjects they understand, and we follow the advice that is given. While we are students we listen to the instruction of our teachers, and thereby save time and energy while we steadily advance in knowledge. In regard to skill and technique, the teacher must give the correct methods, point out the mechanical movements, and stress the points that are difficult and the errors that may be made. Then, during the time the student is practicing, the director must correct mistakes and insist on the correct technique. The corrections are made for the student's improvement and not for any other reason, and the nurse must accept correction in this spirit if she hopes to improve. The teacher should show how a certain task is to be performed; the student must practice, first under the guidance of the instructor in order to do the act correctly from the beginning, and then regularly on her own in order to obtain proficiency. One should not be afraid to seek advice. If the student does not understand, she should ask questions. Advancement in any skill is steady and rapid if the student will seek advice and practice regularly.

Self-criticism

No instructor can possibly correct all the mistakes a student will make in the beginning. The student nurse must practice self-criticism. She should be on the alert for those movements that will add speed and perfection. No two people do the same thing in exactly the same way, though they may be using the same general method. The specific movements that are practical to one student may not be adequate to another because of physical characteristics such as size, weight and length of arms. Self-criticism and observation are essential; otherwise mistakes and excessive movements will appear and destroy the results. A nurse who is perfectly satisfied to drift with mediocrity will never reach perfection in any form of skill.

Repetition

A habit becomes a matter of selection, wherein satisfactory responses are repeated and are made easier by frequent repetition. Habits are acquired by repeated acts. Repetition, with understanding of the purpose of the act, is the very essence of habit formation (Fig. 20). Just as a nurse will never learn how to dance, how to play tennis, how to play a musical instrument or how to study unless she repeats time after time each form of activity, neither will she learn the many skills of nursing unless she repeats the acts essential to the skill. We must consider, though, certain points of special note in regard to the manner and the time element of practice periods. These same elements—frequency, recency and vividness—were considered on page 126 in regard to memory. Here they are applied to skills.

Habits must be repeated often; otherwise, the bond of union at the synapse is soon lost. We forget readily the correct method of action and the evenness of smooth muscular reactions unless we practice often. The opportunity for practice should not be neglected, and, when a nurse tends to become rusty in any skill, she should review mentally the proper method of performing the habit. In gen-

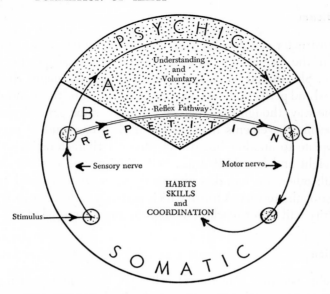

Figure 20.   Habit formation by repetition. Repetition, with understanding of the purpose of the act, is the essence of habit formation. A neural pathway in the early acquisition of habit passes through *A* to *C*. After continued repetition the neural pathway takes a shortcut through *B* to *C*. When given the same stimulus we tend to act in the same way.

eral, the authorities supply ample opportunity for practice in all skills by the usual custom of transferring a nurse to different floors, and at times by placing a nurse "on shift" from one floor to another. The correct time of practice in learning a skill is immediately after the demonstration, when the nervous bonds are fresher than at any other time. This applies to the habit of study as well as to the acquisition of a motor skill.

The periods should be so spaced that some practice will take place every day. In this manner the associations that have been formed are not lost during the interval from practice to practice. The material should be reviewed before it starts to fade in the mind. The periods of practice and the intervals between practice, of course, depend on the skill to be acquired.

In acquiring proficiency one must not neglect the whole method of learning in preference to the partial method. The nurse should endeavor to learn the technique in its entirety at first. Then those points that do not come readily should be emphasized, and more effort and practice should be devoted to them. The bonds should be established with the entire procedure as a unit, rather than with a number of partial actions. Do the whole act first, and criticize mistakes, and then do the whole procedure again.

Speed from the Beginning

The motion and actions of the muscles are not the same in a slow reaction as they are in a speedy reaction. In order to set up the correct muscle reaction when one is acquiring a motor skill, one should aim at speed from the first and thus strengthen the bonds of association. This may cause confusion and mistakes at first, yet practice brings superior results. Once a skill is learned, greater speed results anyway, it is true. Yet when speed is acquired and developed from the beginning the results are superior and the reaction is far smoother.

In learning certain skills, however, such as typing, laboratory dissection, the use of the hypodermic needle, O.R. and O.B. technique, accuracy, rather than speed, is the aim from the first.

Never Let an Exception Take Place

While acquiring a habit and in practicing a technique, never allow an exception. If you change a superior procedure for an inferior one, the bond of union is loosened and it will take some time to return to the original method and manner of acting. Once a new synapse is set up there is a tendency for the reaction to take a two-way course, and hesitancy and lack of control become evident. This applies more specifically to breaking an inferior habit than to the art of acquiring early technique. All people have at some time or other improper habits of action; and when endeavoring to break an old imperfect habit for a better one, we should never make exception by falling into the old habit. The bond of union of the old habit is already strong; and, while forming a better habit, if one yields to the old habit all the former bonds are refreshed at the expense of the new method of action. This refers very evidently to any effort toward substituting a new for a former technique.

Perseverance

In acquiring any perfection, one must continue to practice and persevere until the habit becomes a second nature. The nurse in training is fortunate, for everything in hospital life is new; nevertheless to attain perfection requires effort and continual practice in efficiency. The natural tendency is to take the easiest way. The reasonable course outlined by the will and the mind is proficiency. The young nurse must keep in mind the goal of her years of training so that she may persevere in her course.

HABITS AND THE NURSE

The life of the nurse demands self-discipline, self-control and proficiency. These are the ideals set up by the school of nursing, and a young girl who enters training should endeavor to root out from her character whatever will militate against this standard, and strive to attain the ideal.

Inferior habits are those that are not according to proficiency and right reason in relation to the career of a nurse. Slovenliness and the lack of dependability are indicative of improper habits. Promptness and dependability must be cultivated, and must be practiced by every girl in training.

It is not sufficient to resolve to eradicate careless habits. Good habits must be substituted in their place. For example, a girl who is inclined to neglect sterilizing her hands after taking care of a patient with an infectious disease should not be satisfied with mere reflection on this neglect, but must wash her hands in the proper manner each time she leaves the room, whether she touched any contaminated article or not. She must get into the habit of doing the right thing and not be satisfied with not doing the wrong thing.

In the life of each of us there are many faulty habits that should be rooted out. This can be done with effort, attacking one habit at a time rather than all in general. If we were able to conquer even one imperfect habit a year, we would soon make great strides in "improvement." In regard to the new skills required of us, we must learn the correct methods and endeavor to become proficient by repetition and reasonable exercise.

SUMMARY

1. Habit is acquired ease of action made permanent by repetition. It influences most of our mental and physical activities of the day.

2. The synapses of the nervous system are made permanent by the activity of repeated acts, and tend to react in the same way to similar stimuli.

3. Proficiency, ease and pleasure result from good habits. Physical and mental strain are lessened by the action of good habits.

4. Mental states tend to respond according to previous bonds set up by acquired methods of action.

5. Waste of time and effort results from unworthy habits. Fatigue, mental strain and discouragement accompany careless habits.

6. Proficient habits result from the proper method of attainment, namely: (1) initiative, (2) analysis and concentration, (3) correct guidance, (4) self-criticism, (5) repetition, (6) speed in the very beginning, (7) never letting an exception take place, and (8) perseverance.

7. In hospital work the incentives for acquiring superior habits are plentiful: cases are varied; emotional elements are present to arouse sympathy, care and the desire for proficient work.

8. All skills should be analyzed by observation, reason, and the effects of the habits to be acquired.

9. Guidance and self-criticism are necessary for one to acquire perfect technique.

10. Repetition should follow the laws of frequency, recentness and proper spacing of practice periods.

11. A speedy action of the muscles is different in its activity from slow motion, so speed should be developed in the beginning.

12. A nurse must cultivate proficient habits. They require control and self-discipline.

QUESTIONS FOR REVIEW

Essay Type

1. How do habits influence the life of your roommate?
2. Define habit. What relation has habit to the nervous system?
3. Describe the best technique of making a bed and the points that must be emphasized.
4. What new habits have you formed since coming to the school of nursing?
5. What is the order of procedure in acquiring a new habit in using the hypodermic needle?
6. What mistakes do you ordinarily make while in the Service Room?
7. Enumerate five good habits that you admire in your best friend.
8. What is the necessity of self-criticism in acquiring a habit?
9. What are the results of proficient habits?
10. What elements are characteristics of careless habits?
11. What technique did you find the hardest to learn? Why?
12. Recall from memory the technique of study.
13. What practice periods would you use in acquiring the technique of blood counting?
14. When is the best time to practice an object lesson?
15. What habit did you acquire while under observation of the instructor?
16. Why is it necessary to acquire speed at the beginning of a motor habit?
17. How would you teach another nurse to dance?
18. Describe the different methods of diving learned in Physical Training.
19. What habits are exercised on first-floor duty?
20. In what ways does the hospital afford opportunity for exercising various habits?

Matching and Completion Type

Fill in the correct words:

1. The three results of proficient habits are:

   a ....

   b ....

   c ....

2. Two results of careless habits are:

   a ....

   b ....

3. Facility of action acquired by repetition. ....

4. The term used to indicate proficiency of adapting effective methods in definite situations. ....

5. Correction of mistakes of the students by the instructor is made for one purpose, namely: ....

6. Four incentives supplied by the hospital situation for the acquisition of proficient habits are:

   a .... c ....

   b .... d ....

7. The two reasons why speed is developed from the beginning in learning techniques are:

   a ....

   b ....

8. The eight suggestions given in the text on the subject: "How to form proficient habits" are:

   a .... e ....

   b .... f ....

   c .... g ....

   d .... h ....

TOPICS FOR CLASS DISCUSSION

1. The S-R bond in the formation of habit.
2. Influence of motivation in acquiring special techniques.
3. Analysis in relation to habit formation.
4. Emotional personal habits revealed during recreation and conversation.
5. The incentives offered by the hospital to sustain the interest of the nurse.
6. The whole method of learning a technique in relation to the progressive-parts method.
7. Influence of habit on learning.
8. Each of the eight suggestions: "How to acquire proficient habits."

SOURCES AND REFERENCES

Commins, William D., and Fagin, Barry, *Principles of Educational Psychology*, 2nd ed. (New York: Ronald, 1954), Chap. XIII.

Cunningham, William F., *The Pivotal Problems of Education* (New York: Macmillan, 1940), Chap. III.

Dunlap, Knight, *Habits—Their Making and Unmaking* (New York: Liveright, 1949).

Harmon, Francis L., *Principles of Psychology*, rev. ed. (Milwaukee: Bruce, 1951), Chap. XIV.

Mursell, James L., *How to Make and Break Habits* (Philadelphia: Lippincott, 1953).

GENERAL CONSIDERATIONS

The nurse must be able to think. All our lives we are striving to obtain information and knowledge that will make us successful in our profession, and this knowledge must be correlated so that it can be used when the occasion arises. *The faculty of thought that forms ideas, judgments and reasons is called the intellect.* This faculty must be used continually in any kind of work. When we study we must think; when we are confronted with a new situation we must think; when difficulty and unforeseen happenings present themselves we must think; when on duty or when conversing or discussing, or when administering medicine or giving any form of care, we must think. A great deal of nursing care depends on the capacity of the nurse to think, develop ingenuity, introduce new ideas or to dress up old ones in a new way.

NATURE OF THE THINKING PROCESS

Thought is a *conscious process by which we become aware of the nature of an object.* We have a thought of an object whenever we are aware of anything that answers the query: "What is this thing?" There is a clear dividing line between thought, on the one hand, and sensations and images on the other. We have a thought of a nurse when we know what a nurse is; we sense or imagine a nurse when we are aware of a nurse as she appears to our senses here and now, or as she has appeared in the past. Not only is there a dividing line between thought and sensory processes but also between thought and thought. Accordingly, *every thought is specified by its object.* We have, then, only to indicate the object of whose nature we are aware, and we distinguish that thought from every other thought. We can indicate the object of every thought in a precise way. According to the way we answer the question "What is this thing?" we have a vague or clear, a popular or scientific, a complete or incomplete thought concerning that thing. The object may be sensible or insensible, present, past, future or eternal, merely possible or actual.

If we are endeavoring to find the answer to the question *what* a thing is, we are thinking. We have a mere *idea* of an object when we are aware of what that object is without affirming or denying anything about it. We form a *judgment* concerning that object when we affirm or deny something about what it is. We employ a *reasoning process* concerning that object when we try to find out *what* the object is.[1] In all cases thinking is a process by which we know the nature of any object.

Abstraction

Abstraction is a *process of the mind by which we concentrate upon one quality of an object, thereby separating this feature,* as far as our experience is concerned, *from all other features of that object.*

[1] Gruender, Henry, *Problems of Psychology* (Milwaukee: Bruce, 1937), p. 5.

We make use of this process when we try to classify objects, plan committees for a dance, clean the room, arrange the medicine case, label medicine bottles, fix the hours of duty and vacation, and adjust many other things each day. When we classify objects we try to discover what is common to these objects and separate this quality from all other features by which these objects differ from one another. Thus, when a nurse wishes to arrange her books on her desk, she may do so in many ways according to the one feature she picks out (abstracts) in order to make the arrangement. She may arrange her books as to size or color or subject matter. That one feature is abstracted from numerous other possible qualities, and her attention is focused on that one thing. When one designs a banquet the arrangement depends on the color scheme for the occasion. This one feature is abstracted from any other possible combinations. The list of duties arranged on the floor depends on class periods, hours of practice, the experience of the freshmen, juniors and seniors. The head nurse abstracts, as it were, these different features, and then posts the hours for the week.

We also make use of abstraction when we try to formulate a *definition*. We must note what features are applicable to all those objects which distinguish one group of objects from another, and separate them into a definite class of objects. We select the important from the unimportant so that the definition applies to every object and only to those objects from a possible large group. We do the same thing in forming definitions as the nurse does who arranges her books, or who puts the drugs in proper order in the medicine cabinet. The definition is perfect if it applies to all in a group, and at the same time distinguishes those qualities which other objects do not possess.

We are continually abstracting when we study anatomy. We distinguish five kinds of tissue, and each tissue is distinct in itself because it has certain characteristics that another does not have. We separate structures of the body into ten systems and study each system according to the organs and functions of each. Thus we abstract certain qualities that are common to certain organs and

arrange them in an orderly manner according to definite characteristics.

IDEAS

An idea is the understanding of the meaning of an external object
without representing it as a mental picture. It takes place in the
intellect by the process of abstraction. *We have an idea of a thing
when we are aware of what that object is.* Sensations and all sense
knowledge are the starting points of thinking, and every object,
whether sensory or mental, has certain qualities by which it is related
to other qualities in *shape, size, form, number, similarity, contrast,
cause and effect.* The *intellect* is able to detect and to place in
definite groups such qualities as distinguish one thing from another,
and to obtain the meaning and nature of the object. The conscious
process, then, represents no longer an individual thing but the nature
common to several objects, and such a thought is known as a
universal idea of a thing. We are, however, not yet aware of its
universality. We become aware of its universality when we compare
this idea with objects of a similar nature; for then we find out that
these qualities can be applied to many individuals. This process of
the mind is different from perception. In perception a definite thing
presented to the mind is recognized or understood. In conceiving a
thing—manner of forming ideas—*the intellect deals with the universal idea or class of objects without reference to any particular
object of that class.* The nurse, for example, has the percept of a
given scalpel, uniform, or room. Each particular object is perceived.
A *concept* of scalpel, or room, or uniform, on the other hand, is a
very different mental product that is formed in the intellect. The
word "scalpel" when conceived, is not this scalpel, but any and every
scalpel; the word "uniform" is not this uniform but any and every
uniform; the word "hospital" is any medical place that cares for
the sick and convalescent. *The concept contains the definition and
meaning in general,* while a *percept deals with a particular object.*
The intellect abstracts from any group of objects some particular
special qualities that refer to all the objects that have the same

qualities. An idea of a heart, then, is that of a living structure that forces the blood through the body whether it is a human heart, a frog's heart or a fish's heart. An endocrine gland is perceived as this gland, such as the thyroid, but an idea of endocrine gland is conceived as a ductless gland that secretes a hormone into the blood stream, whether it is a thyroid, or pituitary, or adrenal, or any other gland that has similar structure and function. The idea in all cases deals with the meaning of a thing and can be applied to all objects of the same class.

Some ideas cannot be imaged; for example, "justice," "honesty," "goodness," "modern," "scientific." They are concepts of the intellect, resulting from a comparison of the relationships of many objects from which the meaning is derived.

JUDGMENT

Judgment is an act by which the mind compares two ideas and pronounces their agreement or nonagreement. When the mind perceives that the comparison of two ideas is true, it agrees; when the mind perceives that the comparison is not identical, it disagrees. Judgment is concerned chiefly with thoughts of relationship among sense objects, images and ideas. *It compares time, size, weight, goodness, beauty, equality and similarity of one thing with another.* As judgment is a conscious mental process of making a decision about something, a nurse will respond immediately when she is asked if she was on time for duty. She understands the meaning of the question, and she knows whether or not she was on duty at a certain hour; the intellect by its process of judgment unites these two ideas and passes a decision "yes" or "no." Judgment, then, is an act of the intellect whereby the mind combines or separates two terms by affirmation or denial.

As soon as the intellect apprehends the concept of a new thing, it compares the new idea with a concept already understood from past experiences, and agrees or disagrees. For example, an object that looks like the heart is presented to the senses; the intellect abstracts from that material the meaning of the object and immediately asserts whether the new material is the heart, or is not the heart. The intellect forms a judgment in every case. The process is continually going on in thinking. Every new experience that a nurse encounters is compared with that universal idea formerly acquired, and the intellect pronounces identity or nonidentity of the contents of the two ideas.

REASONING

Reasoning is an act of the intellect by which we try to find out what a thing is. In the process of reasoning *the mind compares two ideas with a third idea and thus derives a new judgment.* For example, a positive Schick test indicates susceptibility to diphtheria; four of the preclinical students reacted positively to the test; therefore, these four students are susceptible to diphtheria. The first concept is expressed as a general principle, the second concept is a particular case, and the third idea is drawn from a comparison of the first two thoughts. *This standard form of reasoning, as used in logical thinking, is known as a syllogism.* The truth of the last judgment follows as a necessary consequence from a consideration of the first two statements. Reasoning is the highest form of thinking, and it is the one great function of the intellect that makes man entirely different from any other animal.

The two chief forms of reasoning are *induction* and *deduction*. Any reasoning process, however, may, and usually does, use both forms.

Induction

In the process of induction a general judgment is drawn from a number of particular judgments. It reasons from effect to cause. General truths, definitions, principles, rules and theories are derived by this process. The diphtheria organism, for example, is found in every case of diphtheria; the bacillus can be isolated and grown in pure cultures; the organism, in pure culture, can be inoculated into a susceptible animal and gives rise to the disease; the bacillus is observed in and recovered from the experimentally diseased animal. Therefore, the diphtheria organism is the cause of diphtheria. The general truth is derived from particular cases. Induction is a method of research which leads men to discover new knowledge.

Deduction

In the process of deduction a general law or principle is applied to a particular case. It reasons from cause to effect. Deduction is the method of diagnosis. The doctor observes the symptoms, separates relevant from irrelevant data, reads the x-ray reports, uses laboratory tests, and from his background of professional knowledge, isolates mentally those laws and principles which are applicable to the particular case in hand.

HOW TO THINK CLEARLY

Attitude of Mind

One might as well talk to a practice dummy as to try to convince a man obsessed with a pet idea. He will not listen to reason or to fact. Many people have eyes that see not, and ears that hear not. The first prerequisite to thinking and reasoning is the willingness to accept a logical conclusion. Preconceived ideas are fatal to good reasoning. If a person already has his mind made up, no matter what is said to the contrary, he cannot think correctly. He is already warped. He will hedge and squirm when in a tight place, still he will not open his mind to the truth or to the facts. If you want to think clearly, you must be willing to put away emotions and a set mind. The mind must be willing to take things as they are, not as they should be according to one's limited experience and biased convictions.

Thinking requires mental activity and the mind must be on the alert to inquire about the problem. The words, *what, why, when, how, where,* must be dominant in the mind of a person who wants to think. This questioning attitude of mind brings forth the problem immediately; he can then seek the relationship, the causality, the difference and the similarity of the problem with former experience. The mind is naturally curious and wants to know the reason for things. This questioning attitude awakens all the latent power of the mind, which will then ask *what* a thing is, *why* it acts in such a way, *how* it acts, *when* it will act and *where* it worked. The alert mind is stimulated to seek the answers to these questions.

CLEAR IDEAS

The chief reason so many students make mistakes in thinking and why they have difficulty with study is that they do not understand the terms used. They do not know the meaning of words, and on this account they do not understand what they are talking about. One must have a clear statement of the problem in order to reason correctly, and this is obtained by endeavoring to understand the tools of language, that is, the meaning of words. This knowledge is obtained by defining the terms in precise and simple language, so that the meaning of the idea is clearly understood. Too much emphasis cannot be placed on this phase of thinking. It is impossible to think clearly and correctly unless one understands the meaning of the language he is endeavoring to use. Difficulties in study, in expression, in any form of thinking, generally are due to the fact that the student is confused about the meaning of the words he is employing. First, know what you are trying to think about; obtain a clear understanding of the problem and then look up the facts that will answer your questions. One must keep in mind the problem to be solved; and to do this one must have clear, definite ideas, brief, complete and concise definitions of the terms used, and specific data to answer the questions, why, when, what, where and how.

SEEK INFORMATION TO ANSWER YOUR QUESTIONS

Clear thinking supposes true information. This information must be sought by an open mind, and each question must be answered by the facts that are relevant. Many people take only the evidence they wish to find, and not the facts as they are. Exaggeration and imagination should not be permitted. Instead, the evidence must be sought with one purpose in mind, namely, the truth. The truth is objective and accurate; if your data is distorted, the conclusion is sure to be wrong.

The proofs offered in reasoning are not always what they seem to be. Someone has said that facts are facts and must be considered as such. Nevertheless, it is necessary to keep one's ears open for contradictions. Often the evidence is only partially true, and does not include all the facts involved. Half truths are convincing unless shown to be partially wrong. A nurse must be careful to distinguish that part of a seeming proof that relates to a specific problem in-volved, and that part of the statement that has nothing to do with her problem.

The two chief causes of distorted evidence are: first, *the emotional element in gathering data,* and second, *illusions in the act of percep-tion.* We are inclined to consider only those facts that agree with our opinion. Because of this tendency, some authors suggest that one must be supercritical toward those facts that are satisfactory to the mind, and endeavor to find testimony that will refute one's desires. Of course, it is possible to go to the other extreme in this regard.

At times evidence is erroneous because of illusions. This can result from expectation, desire, emotions or unfavorable conditions of perception. All these considerations must be evaluated when one seeks information. Clear thinking will detect false premises in the reasoning process.

You can prove anything you set out to prove if you keep repeating half truths. This is the method in some advertising. If you listen to the cigarette advertisers, and if you fail to examine the data given in their "chatter," you will begin to believe that there is only one good brand of cigarettes. If you listen to the advertising of coffee, you soon get the opinion that this special coffee is better coffee and is a more soothing potion for the nerves than any other kind of coffee. The fortune teller and the mediums of seances convince people by telling them what they want to hear, and the listener fails to distinguish the facts. Keep your eyes open for half truths in any form of evidence.

FORM SPECIFIC CONCLUSIONS

The conclusion of thinking is the judgment formed in the mind after comparing the evidence presented with facts already known. It must be specific. If it is too general, then the evidence was not clear, and the conclusion is generally wrong. Avoid broad generalizations in the conclusion. The unprejudiced mind will agree or disagree if the reasoning process has been based on the truth, and will give a specific, definite, concise conclusion. What we have stated in regard to attitude of mind is of special importance in relation to the results of the thinking process. A biased, emotional mind reaches a conclusion before it starts to think.

DON'T JUMP TO CONCLUSIONS

Many people form a judgment before they consider all the facts in the problem, and indulge in false reasoning. The results are often distorted because a person will form a conclusion before he has considered the data. This habit makes clear thinking impossible. Look up *all* the data required, and avoid broad generalizations from only a few facts.

VERIFY YOUR CONCLUSIONS

Experiment rationally to see whether or not your convictions reached in reasoning are valid. This can be done readily in regard to scientific or actual objects. Verify your conclusion in as many cases as you can in order to find whether your reasoning was true or false. Do not be afraid to make mistakes. If you make a mistake, it is evident that you are doing something. Only static people who never do anything in life make no mistakes. If your reasoning proves true when tested, conviction and independence are the reward.

THINKING AND THE NURSE

The art of thinking must be developed by the nurse. This is done by the method we have just studied, namely, *by keeping an open mind, by obtaining clear ideas, by seeking all data of the problem* in order to answer the questions of what, why, where and when; *by keeping the mind alert for contradictions,* and finally *by testing out specific conclusions.* This method should be practiced in reading, in writing essays, in studying lessons, in discussions, in debates and, above all, in ordinary conversation. Do not be satisfied with a mere statement, but ask for the reasons whenever you do not understand a thing. Do not be satisfied to absorb, but endeavor to find out all about any topic of interest.

Keep this questioning attitude foremost in your study and you will make great progress in thinking. Thinking will keep you alert and will make you successful in your profession.

SUMMARY

1. The nurse must acquire the art of thinking clearly, logically and perfectly. This is attained by applying the correct method of thinking, by concentration and observation.

2. The faculty of thought that forms ideas, judgments and reasons is called the intellect. This faculty correlates ideas, compares one with another and distinguishes one from another.

3. We have an idea of a thing when we know what a thing is without affirming or denying anything about it; we have a judgment concerning an object when we affirm or deny something about what that object is; we have a reasoning process concerning that object when we try to find out what that object is.

4. Abstraction is a process of the mind by which we concentrate upon one quality of an object.

5. Induction is a process of the mind by which a general judgment is drawn from a number of particular judgments. It is reason from effect to cause.

6. Deduction is a process of the mind by which a general law is applied to a particular case. It is reason from cause to effect.

7. A clear understanding of the problem is the starting point of thinking. This is obtained by learning the meaning of words and by clarifying ideas.

8. The evidence to be compared in reasoning must be based on the truth, and must be sufficient to answer the questions, why, what, when, how and where.

9. Half truths cause erroneous opinions. The nurse must be on her guard to distinguish between what is true and what is false.

10. Facts must be verified and the conclusion must be tested in order to make certain the truth of any judgment.

11. An open mind is essential to clear thinking. Emotions, illusions and biased opinions destroy clear thinking. The mind must be willing to accept any conclusion derived from the truth.

12. Form specific conclusions and avoid generalizations from insufficient evidence.

QUESTIONS FOR REVIEW

Essay Type

1. Define intellect, judgment, reasoning, concept, idea.
2. What is the difference between the imagination and the intellect?
3. What is the starting point of clear thinking?
4. Why is reasoning so important for the nurse?
5. What is thought? How is it specified?
6. Differentiate: idea, judgment, reasoning.
7. Define abstraction. Cite three examples.
8. Distinguish between induction and deduction.
9. Formulate five definitions of different terms used in anatomy.
10. Why is an idea said to be a spiritual process of the mind?
11. What qualities of relationship exist between one object and another?
12. What is a universal idea?
13. What ideas cannot be imaged?
14. Distinguish between a concept and a percept. Give an example.
15. Distinguish between a perception of and an idea of a chair.
16. What is the difference between an idea and a judgment?
17. What is a syllogism? Give three examples.
18. Summarize the method of clear thinking.
19. What role do half truths play in false opinions?

20. Why must one verify an opinion?
21. What should a person do with contradictions?
22. What is the normal thing to do when one discovers he has made a mistake in reasoning?
23. What happens when you argue with a biased person?
24. What bearing have emotions on reasoning? Give an example.
25. Why do we accept false opinions?
26. What effect have strong desires on reasoning?
27. Where do you find it easiest to think? Why?
28. Analyze the processes of the mind when you try to solve a riddle.
29. Why is the questioning attitude important for the nurse?
30. Why are many nurses inclined to accept written false statements as true?
31. Why must one be supercritical in judging statements that agree with one's opinion?
32. What hospital work requires you to think most?

Matching and Completion Type

Fill in the correct words:

1. A process of the mind by which we endeavor to find out what a thing is. . . . .

2. An act of the intellect in which it compares two ideas and pronounces their agreement or nonagreement. . . . .

3. The form of reasoning during which a general law is applied to a particular case. . . . .

4. The faculty of thought that forms ideas, judgments and reasons. . . . . .

. . . .

5. Two chief forms of reasoning are:

a . . . .

b . . . .

6. The seven qualities considered by the intellect as distinguishing one thing from another are:

a . . . . e . . . .

b . . . . f . . . .

c . . . . g . . . .

d . . . .

7. Two chief causes of distorted evidence are:

a . . . .

b . . . .

8. The process of the mind by which we concentrate upon one quality

of an object. . . . .

9. The five specific words that must be dominant in the mind of a person who wants to think are:

a . . . . d . . . .

b . . . . e . . . .

c . . . .

10. The five general ways suggested to develop the art of thinking are:

a . . . . d . . . .

b . . . . e . . . .

c . . . .

TOPICS FOR CLASS DISCUSSION

1. Every thought is specified by its object.
2. The "meaning of words" applied to clear thinking.
3. The influence of the intellect when the mind compares the qualities of relationships in the process of learning.
4. The questioning attitude awakens all the latent powers during the process of learning.
5. After you have written complete answers to each of the following questions, list for each answer: (1) particular ideas, (2) universal ideas, (3) judgments.
    a. What were your particular reasons for choosing this school instead of some other one?
    b. What do you think about when you hear the term "technique"?
    c. What things about your room do you like particularly?
    d. What are some of the big problems you will likely face when you are supervisor of the medical floor after your graduation?
    e. What are your favorite television programs?
6. Solve the following problem. Each fact is relevant. The solution generally requires at least fifteen minutes of intense reasoning. Give complete reasons for your answer.

Problem:

Three nurses on the medical floor are: Suzanne Dougherty, Ann Cauley and Kathleen Cossman. They are junior, senior, and graduate nurses, but not necessarily in the order named. On the same floor are three patients of the same last names: Mrs. Dougherty, Mrs. Cauley, and Mrs. Cossman.

1. Mrs. Cauley lives in New York.
2. The graduate nurse lives halfway between New York and Washington, D.C.
3. Mrs. Cossman earns exactly $4,000.
4. Suzanne Dougherty beat the junior nurse at tennis.
5. The graduate nurse's nearest neighbor, one of these patients, earns twice as much as this graduate, who earns $3,000 a year.
6. The patient whose name is the same as the graduate nurse lives in Washington.

Questions: What is the name of the junior? of the senior? of the graduate?

Sources and References

Bittle, Celestine N., *The Whole Man* (Milwaukee: Bruce, 1945), Chap. IX.

Brennan, Robert E., *General Psychology,* rev. ed. (New York: Macmillan, 1952), Chaps. XXII, XXIII, XXIV.

Gruender, Henry, *Experimental Psychology* (Milwaukee: Bruce, 1932), Chaps. XIV, XVI.

Gruender, Henry, *Problems of Psychology* (Milwaukee: Bruce, 1937), Chaps. I, II.

Johnson, Donald M., *The Psychology of Thought and Judgment* (New York: Harper, 1955), Chap. I.

Moore, Thomas V., *Cognitive Psychology* (Philadelphia: Lippincott, 1939), Chaps. III, IV.

Morgan, John B., *How to Keep a Sound Mind* (New York: Macmillan, 1946), pp. 277, 303.

15 • ATTENTION AND THE LAWS
OF LEARNING

MEANING OF ATTENTION

Attention plays an important role in daily life since the process of thinking depends upon it in a large measure. In fact, the power of attention is an indispensable condition for success. Since the mind is inclined to wander from one object to another, clear thought and accurate observation are impossible without attention.

At any given moment the mind is aware of a number of things but is more clearly conscious of one, or of a group of related objects. Some objects are present in consciousness but are not noticed; others are noticed but are not examined and soon fade from the mind; still others are noticed and considered carefully, and upon these a person concentrates his consciousness to the disregard of other stimuli. *This focusing of the mind on one definite object is termed attention.*

Suppose, for example, a nurse is scrubbing during a major operation. She is aware of the attending nurses, of the direction of the light, of the breathing of the patient, and of the numerous instruments on the table before her; but her entire consciousness is focused on the demand of the surgeon she is assisting. She has her mind applied to one object among the many presented simultaneously. Each time the surgeon speaks or gives a sign with his hand, the nurse responds immediately with the correct instrument. All her faculties are keyed to act at once toward the one object, the doctor.

NATURE OF ATTENTION

Attention is essentially the mental response of concentration upon a specific object. This mental process is accompanied by bodily resonance. The manner in which a nurse responds to her name is familiar to everyone. She becomes alert, turns her head in the direction of the one addressing her, listens with mental readiness, gradually changes her facial expression, breathes more slowly, and her whole body becomes set for the favorable reception of added stimulation. The bodily attitudes are called *external attention,* to distinguish them from attention proper, *internal attention.* The physical responses become the sign by which to judge whether or not one is attentive. Generally, they are vividly manifested by facial expressions, such as the fixed muscle reactions of a girl who is "called to the office" or the forlorn, droopy expressions of a group of nurses when they report for morning roll-call. Attention or lack of attention is "written" on the face.

TYPES OF ATTENTION

Attention is twofold: *spontaneous* and *voluntary*.

Attention is *spontaneous* when the mind is attracted to the stimulus without any effort on the part of the individual to select this particular stimulus. The stimulus is strong enough to force itself into the center of consciousness, regardless of all other conditions that are present at the moment. All human beings have this type of attention. Such stimuli as loudness, suddenness, bigness, newness, brightness, interests, and desires will produce this mental state. This is why everyone in the school is aroused by the sound of a firecracker, or the crash of a "smashup." In a short time the scene of the accident is surrounded by a milling, curious crowd. A new style of dress catches the eye of the passer-by. A black eye or a rosebud nose is observed even by a stranger and causes questioning among friends. This spontaneous attention flows along smoothly and without conscious effort.

Attention is *voluntary*, on the other hand, when the state of consciousness is a deliberate focusing of the mind toward a particular stimulus that does not inherently attract the person. *It requires some effort of the will.* The individual is aware of an effort to select this particular stimulus from among others more attractive. This type of attention depends on facts other than those present in the stimulus—such as value, ultimate goal and past experiences. Consequently, voluntary attention comes from training and development of the personality. It depends on habits, native energy, desires and bodily health. This type of attention makes possible the acquisition of important and valuable objects of life and the rejection of the trivial and insignificant. Habits of voluntary attention are important to a nurse. Her hours of study, mental and physical training and self-improvement are dependent on this type of attention. Hence, the power of voluntary attention is one of the most important of all human attainments.

CHARACTERISTICS OF ATTENTION

The important characteristics of attention are those of *shifting, scope, span* and *intensity*.

Shifting

Uninterrupted attention to a single stimulus object cannot be maintained for a great length of time. Attention is a selective process of the mind, but it is a highly shifting affair. When one first attends to

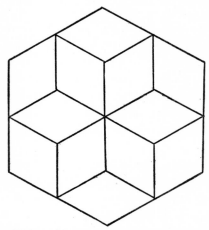

Figure 21.   Shifting blocks. (Muse: *Textbook of Psychology.*)

an object, he gives it a superficial inspection, noticing very few general details. If there is nothing attractive about the object, attention may change from one object to another, and then to another, and so on and on. When attention is centered on a particular object, natural fluctuations are not stopped but limited. Attention shifts from one object to another. Observe Figure 21 and notice how your attention fluctuates from one perception to another. It is impossible to hold any view for any length of time. The image changes every few seconds, though there are individuals who can attend to the percept longer than others. This is pronounced when objects are presented through the sense of sight and touch. Place a dot of ink on a sheet of paper and observe how readily it will disappear from vision and then reappear. If you gaze at a pencil, or a pair of scissors for a short time, the object tends to fade from consciousness and then become clear. When one listens to the ticking of a watch held a short distance from the ear, he becomes aware of periodic waning in intensity and clearness. Attenton, then, is not constant, but has the tendency to fluctuate.

Scope

It is possible to attend to only one unitary response at a time. Although it may seem that one is attending to many different things, the individual is at any instant attending to only one thing. It is possible to be aware of many other surrounding items; nevertheless, attention passes from one object to another in such rapid succession that we can place our full and vivid focus on only one object at a time. A series of acts may occur, however, in regard to a particular object, and such combination results in sustained attention.

Span

How many objects can be observed at a glance? The average person can perceive four or five different objects exposed for the duration of one fifth of a second. This is known as the *span of attention,* that is, *the number of items one can observe in a glance.* By practice one can acquire the ability to observe more than five objects, especially if they appear in words or sentences.

The manner in which the mind shifts from one situation to another explains why a nurse can do more than one thing at a time, though attending to only one object at a definite instant. For instance, a nurse can, at one and the same time, prepare a tray, walk and listen to another nurse talk, as attention shifts from one situation to another. She is, however, placing her full attention on only one thing at a time.

Intensity

Intensity of attention is the degree of concentration placed on the object. The intensity of voluntary attention is determined by the *inherent qualities* of the object, by the *extrinsic motives,* which may influence the will, and by the *subjective value* of the object in relation to the future. Though the study of Anatomy, for example, may be difficult, the nurse is attracted to this subject chiefly by its value in relation to her profession. She forces her mind to concentrate on this subject, though there may be many other objects seeking to engage her attention.

Any stimulus will attract attention if it arouses vivid sensations, if it is moving or rhythmical, if it is pleasant or unpleasant. Such stimuli possess qualities of vividness, contrast, unusualness and repetition. The mind is naturally attracted to such qualities and the individual will concentrate on them from among other stimuli.

EFFECTS OF ATTENTION

Attention *increases mental acumen, aids the memory* and, as described under Nature of Attention, *stimulates physical responses. Subconscious sensations,* which may be present at the same time that we are consciously attending to some object, *may also influence our behavior and actions.*

Attention Increases Mental Acumen

Attention intensifies each of the mental states. Sensations that attract attention are increased in strength. They are impressed clearly and distinctly on the mind. Even a weak stimulus is increased to such a degree that it predominates among other stimuli that are inherently stronger. If a nurse during recreation, for example, expects a phone call, she hears the bell above the rhythm of dance music and the chatter of the nurses. Attention affects the *emotions* so that a slight verbal stimulus, which would not be noticed at other times, arouses a marked reaction. This emotional resonance is observed in the conduct of a nurse who may have come in late the previous evening, or in the reaction of one who made a blunder in the Service Room, when a friend merely hints about the incident.

Attention clarifies *perception.* Perception develops through the accumulation of sensory experiences in regard to many objects that are related to past experiences. Attention affects perceptual knowledge since the external object must be observed exactly; otherwise, the meaning of the object is not clearly known. Some objects by their nature attract spontaneous attention. Other objects, however, are valuable for the individual and must be perceived by voluntary attention; this requires active and forced concentration. In such cases voluntary attention is essential for clear perception.

Attention intensifies and coordinates *thoughts*. Conceptual knowledge depends on clear ideas, which are the result of concentration. The hour of study is soon over when the nurse is interested in her classwork. Her thoughts flow in an orderly manner through her mind. Thoughts, too, are associated during the time of attention by contrast, similarity and relationship in time and space with other ideas in the mind.

Attention Aids the Memory

A good memory depends on clear and distinct impressions of the object. This is obtained by concentrating all the powers of the mind on the object, by observing each detail, by associating the object with the environment, and by contrasting the object with other stimuli already known to the mind. Attention sinks the object deep into consciousness. The memory keeps the impression there, and recalls the object when it is needed. Attention, then, impresses the object clearly and distinctly in the mind and by so doing aids the memory.

Subconscious Influences

The *subconscious concerns those sensations of objects which are present at the time we are attending to something else,* and *which receive very slight notice in consciousness.* We realize that they are present but we pass them on to the background of attention. Our minds are interested in something else, yet we are dimly aware of the existence of these weaker sensations. For example, when we are studying pharmacology we are aware of other sensations such as the presence of our roommate, the distant hum of an airplane, the ticking of the clock, the change in the amount of light, the circular motion of an annoying fly. All these sensations, though shrouded from consciousness, still make an impression on us because we can recall them afterward. Such sensations, which are dimly perceived in consciousness, are present in the subconscious.

Subconscious sensations influence our actions in a number of ways, such as gesturing while we are speaking, tapping on the desk while we are studying, keeping time to imaginary music while we are under the shower, scribbling in our psychology books while we are listening to the lecture, absent-mindedly putting on our nurse's uniform when we intend to wear a white pleated dress. Normally, we focus our minds on certain objects, yet we are dimly aware of other objects in the background of attention.

ATTENTION NECESSARY FOR THE NURSE

The power of concentration can be acquired by all. Spontaneous attention, which results from intense sensory stimuli and interest, is easily acquired in every career, but the nursing profession requires voluntary attention. This is obtained by forcing the mind to return to the problem to be studied, by doing perfectly the duties demanded on the floor and in taking care of the sick, by limiting distracting objects that scatter attention in different directions, by keeping a clear mind through healthful exercise and fresh air, and by studying or working during the times one should study or work. Consequently, attention necessary for the nurse is acquired by doing the work perfectly at the time the work should be done.

LAWS OF LEARNING

In our consideration of memory we applied certain principles that aid the memory in retaining and reproducing past experience. These same principles are applicable to the intellect and are considered here as laws of learning.

Law of Exercise or Use

A reaction becomes more prompt, more certain and easier by repetition. We learn by doing. Learning is not a passive process by which knowledge is absorbed, but an active process that requires attention, observation, and all the activity of the powers of mind. But knowledge once acquired soon fades and is forgotten unless it is used. Repetition tends to make the reaction more certain and more prompt, provided the person tries to understand and organize in his own mind the content of what he is studying. Nothing is difficult if you know it, but the process of acquiring knowledge requires work and energy. By repetition, ideas are linked together and are retained in the memory. The acquisition of knowledge depends on the *frequency,* the *recency,* the *intensity,* the *duration* and the *vividness* of the repetition. Many authors devise special laws in regard to each of these characteristics of the Law of Exercise.

Law of Effect

This law states that *we tend to repeat that reaction that is accompanied by, or is immediately followed by, a pleasant state of affairs.* The opposite is also true—that we tend to inhibit those reactions that give an annoying state of mind. Pleasure or happiness is the motivating force of life, and those reactions that tend to increase pleasure are favored over those reactions that fail to give pleasure. We learn by experience to repeat certain actions that will broaden our knowledge and at the same time increase our pleasure. Attention from others, rewards, publicity and responsiveness create interest and motivate acquisition of knowledge. A word of praise from the supervisor, for example, increases a sudent's interest in a particular technique to continue this work with confidence and enthusiasm.

Law of Trial and Error

By the Law of Trial and Error we mean that *an individual learns by trying one type of activity after another, and that he will eventually choose the method of procedure that is satisfactory.* This law concerns original and new situations. When a person is placed in a new and puzzling circumstance, he is likely to try at random one thing after another until he is able to solve his problem. In the initial trial he will invariably make mistakes and will continue to do so until he understands the nature of the procedure. An individual, however, learns by mistakes and rarely is anyone successful immediately. The essence of progress in any sensorimotor type of learning, such as skills and techniques, is: (1) failure to accomplish a task the first time an attempt is made; (2) correction of mistakes; (3) repetition of the actions until one can carry out the procedures skillfully. A mistake is merely a challenge to do better the next time, and it is an incentive to repeat the course of action intelligently.

Law of Readiness

The Law of Readiness states: *One tends to learn quickly and accurately when the individual is prepared to react.* "Readiness" in this sense denotes a mental state that urges him to respond. If a nurse, for example, is waiting in the chart room for a certain light to come on, she will act at once when the stimulus of the light appears. Her mental powers are set to respond to the stimulus. Numerous factors prepare the mind to react according to the Law of Readiness, namely, intention, ultimate goal, appreciation of the value of acting, and alertness of the sense organs.

Law of Similarity

We tend to react to similar ideas that we have experienced in previous reactions. The word "nurse," for instance, causes one to think of some individual girl, of uniform, cap, bib, hospital, patient, bed, doctor, or any number of ideas similar to it, similar in sound, meaning and form of emotional appeal. Since there is no limit to the number of qualities to which a given idea may be similar in some respects, there is no end to the number of ideas a given stimulus will arouse in consciousness. If there is no exact perception to which previous reactions have been made, *one tends to respond to some element analogous to those the mind has experienced in the past.* This tendency is called by many authors the Law of Analogy. For example, if some unusual or unfamiliar food is served at the table, the girls give it a name analogous to some known dish. One idea gives rise to another to which there is a linkage of similarity, and in thinking, the mind flows from one idea to another by this association.

Law of Contrast

The mind *tends to recall opposite ideas that are associated in our mind:* Heat suggests cold; black, white; virtue, vice; wealth, poverty; health, sickness; bright, dim; empty, full.

Law of Relationship in Time and Space

The mind in the presence of an object or event, whether actual or imaginary, *tends to link ideas formerly connected in time and space* with the objects and events that are now present. An idea that is associated with time and space brings forth in the mind other ideas and events that took place at that time and at that place. The process of thinking links time and locality to ideas, and thought moves along in an ordinary logical manner during the period of concentration and study.

SUMMARY

1. Attention is the act of focusing the mind on one definite thing. This is accompanied by mental and physical activity.

2. Attention keeps the mind from wandering indiscriminately in the process of thinking.

3. Attention is twofold: spontaneous and voluntary.

4. Internal attention takes place in the mind, which becomes alert and ready to respond immediately.

5. The characteristics of attention are shifting, scope, span and intensity.

6. Voluntary attention is necessary for the nurse.

7. Attention is acquired by limiting distracting thoughts and by doing the work perfectly at the time the work should be done.

8. Subconscious concerns those sensations of objects that are present at the time we are attending to something else, and are placed in the background of attention.

9. Laws of Learning summarize the manner in which the mind functions and retains the knowledge acquired.

10. The following laws are considered: Exercise, Effect, Trial and Error, Readiness, Similarity, Contrast, and Relationship in Time and Space.

QUESTIONS FOR REVIEW

Essay Type

1. What is attention? Subconscious? External attention? Internal attention?
2. Describe the external attitude of attention during your lecture on anatomy.
3. What distractions are common during the evening hours of study?
4. What are the four characteristics of attention? Explain each.
5. Can you study efficiently while the radio is playing? Give reasons.
6. Explain why you can do many things at one time and yet can attend to only one thing at a time.
7. How many items can you observe in a flash?
8. What objects attract spontaneous attention?
9. What are the effects of attention?
10. How does attention increase mental acumen?
11. In what ways does your roommate distract you when you are studying?
12. Describe the Laws of Exercise in relation to the study of scientific words.
13. Describe the Law of Effect in the action of any two patients.
14. What is the Law of Readiness? Give an example.
15. What is the Law of Similarity? Contrast?
16. Name two procedures for which you have acquired proficiency through trial and error. What mistakes were made in the initial trial? How were these corrected?
17. How can you improve your study by applying the laws of learning?
18. What are the laws of learning?
19. What is concentration?
20. Comment: "An activity is learned more easily, to the extent that it is found interesting."

Matching and Completion Type

Fill in the correct words:

1. The four characteristics of attention are:

a .... c ....

b .... d ....

2. The act of focusing the mind on one definite thing. ....

3. The law of learning that states that an individual learns by trying one type of activity after another, and will eventually choose the method of procedure that is satisfactory. ....

4. One tends to learn quickly and accurately when one is prepared to act. ....

5. A characteristic of attention that states the fact that it is possible to attend to only one unitary response. ....

6. The law of learning that states that we tend to repeat that reaction that is accompanied by a pleasant state of affairs. ....

....

7. The type of attention that requires deliberate focusing of the mind when the stimulus does not inherently attract the person. ....

....

8. The law of learning that expresses the thought that any reaction becomes more prompt, more certain and easier by repetition. ......

....

9. The type of attention that results from strong stimuli such as loudness, brightness and bigness. ....

10. The type of reaction of the mind when we are attending to something else and the sensations receive very slight notice in consciousness.

....

11. A characteristic of attention that expresses the fact that attention is continually changing and one cannot attend to a stimulus for a great length of time. ....

12. The three factors that determine the intensity of voluntary attention are:

a ....

b ....

c ....

13. The three laws of learning that are the same as the three primary laws of association are:

a ....

b ....

c ....

14. The characteristic of attention that depends on the amount of concentration placed on the object. ....

Topics for Class Discussion

1. The effect of attention on mental acumen.
2. External attention distinguished from internal attention.
3. Attention is not constant but tends to fluctuate.
4. A mistake is merely a challenge to do better the next time.
5. The power of attention is an indispensable condition for success.
6. Voluntary attention comes from definite training and development of the personality of the individual.
7. The motives that prepare the mind to react according to the law of readiness.
8. The manner in which subconscious sensations may influence your actions.

Sources and References

Hilgard, Ernest R., *Theories of Learning*, 2nd ed. (New York: Appleton-Century-Crofts, 1956), Chaps. II, VII.

Krech, David, and Crutchfield, Richard S., *Elements of Psychology* (New York: Alfred A. Knopf, 1958), Chaps. V, XVI.

McGeoch, John A., and Irion, Arthur L., *The Psychology of Human Learning* (New York: Longmans, Green, 1952), Chaps. VII, VIII.

Woodworth, Robert S., and Schlosberg, Harold, *Experimental Psychology*, rev. ed. (New York: Holt, 1954), Chap. IV.

16 • INTELLIGENCE TESTS AND EDUCATIONAL MEASUREMENTS

GENERAL CONSIDERATIONS

The expression that "all men are created equal" applies to the fact that each has a human nature endowed with special rights. However, it is evident that people differ both physically and mentally. Some reason better than others; some are more alert; some have a better memory, greater power of the imagination, greater control of their emotions, greater attention, and better judgment than others. We, ourselves, realize that we have certain perfections in our mental ability that others do not possess, and that we are weaker in certain aptitudes than others.

Why do people differ so radically in traits and abilities? Because of heredity and environment. Heredity has to do with the germ plasm and includes all the native traits and tendencies that we receive from nature, and the potential qualities that we receive from our parents. How much we *can* learn depends largely on the *hereditary* mechanism with which we begin our lives. How much we *will* learn depends largely upon *environment,* that is, on training, self-improvement, association and external surroundings. Both hereditary and environmental conditions are important in attaining superiority in any one mental state.

At first thought it seems to be impossible to estimate the degree a person differs in any one ability or in many qualities of mind compared to some standard. What is the average standard of ability for a certain age? How can it be estimated? How can the estimate be used to advantage? These are some of the topics we shall discuss in our consideration of intelligence tests and educational measurements.

NATURE OF INTELLIGENCE

Various meanings have been given to this word "intelligence." The ability to understand, the ability to think, the ability to reason, the ability to apply knowledge, the ability to apply one's self, are all synonyms of the word. The definition that expresses these concepts concisely is: *Intelligence is the ability of the individual to learn quickly and use knowledge correctly.* Anyone who would have such ability must be a good observer, must be able to reason, to judge correctly the relations among things, to remember, to obtain knowledge quickly, and must maintain the proper mental adjustment.

Many people can judge the intelligence of a person in any given case. This judgment, though, is susceptible to error on account of emotions, biased opinions and insufficient evidence. Often the people in the same community do not recognize superior talent, a truism that is expressed in the words "a prophet is without honor in his own country." Very likely this lack of appreciation results from familiarity and constant association that make skill and acumen appear ordinary.

Popular ratings of intelligence among nurses are summarized in expressions such as, "She is keen." "She is mentally rigid." "She can't even read a thermometer correctly." "She is very clever in the operating room." "She is as dumb as they make them." All of these phrases express opinions of intelligence ratings, though stated rather crudely.

The general opinion of the members of a class concerning certain students approximates the rating of intelligence in most cases. Each student has the opportunity of observing whether or not certain ones are alert, practical and capable of assimilating special knowledge. Even here, erroneous opinions may prevail on account of clever personalities and other pleasing traits that supersede superior intelligence.

We must have a standard of comparison in order to judge intelligence. The mental tests that are given in all educational fields at the present time seem to fulfil adequately this requirement. These tests are applied to a great number of cases, have been standardized, and express rather correctly the ability of the individual in regard to reasoning, memory, observation and alertness. They are far superior to subjective opinion and general notions; they are objective and form a scientific basis for judgment of intelligence.

Growth of Intelligence

All knowledge comes through the senses. At birth we are endowed with abilities to receive knowledge through the senses, but the mind itself is without any preconceived ideas. This lack of knowledge at the time of birth is described by the psychologist as "tabula rasa." As we acquire knowledge the clean tablet of the mind begins to be filled. Intelligence increases gradually from birth to maturity, just as the structures of the body develop gradually. From birth until we are five years old we grow most rapidly in general intelligence. During the next five years the growth is steady, and easily measurable. From the age of ten to fifteen improvement is less easily demonstrated. Many psychologists suggest that the adult level of intelligence is reached at the age of sixteen to eighteen years. This means that the maturity of the native mechanism for acquiring knowledge has reached its perfection. Of course, it does not mean that the average boy knows as much as the average adult. Knowl-

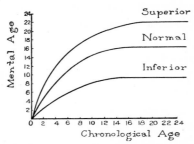

Figure 22.   Hypothetical growth curve for superior, normal and inferior intelligence. (Adapted from Henry E. Garrett, *Great Experiments in Psychology*, D. Appleton-Century Co., 1951, p. 226.

edge should go on accumulating and experience should continue to enrich life until old age. The average age of general mental ability has been placed by experimental evidence at sixteen to eighteen.

All individuals do not develop mentally at the same rate or reach their maximum learning capacity at the same age. An inferior intelligence develops more slowly and reaches its maturity at an earlier age than the normal or superior. This is expressed graphically in Figure 22.

DISTRIBUTION OF INTELLIGENCE

There is a great difference of intelligence in a large group of people. The greater number can grasp ideas readily, while others have a difficult time learning; at the same time other students are superior, while a few fail no matter what the subject matter happens to be.

The theoretical curve of probability, long known by mathematicians, states that when innumerable independent forces work together to produce a given result, the results vary according to a definite curve known as the curve of chance, or the theoretical curve. If you toss up two pennies simultaneously on the table and repeat this experiment hundreds of times the chance is that you will have both heads of the pennies come up 25 per cent of the time, both tails 25 per cent and the head-tail combination 50 per cent of the time. Now, in regard to the curve of distribution of intelligence, although it would not be so sharply divided because of multiple factors, we should expect very similar combinations that would correspond with this hypothetical curve. The theoretical curve of intelligence is based on the assumption that if we were to measure a large unselected group of the population in any city, we would find that the measurement of intelligence would vary from one extreme to another. Most people of the group would have average intelligence and these would be within the central tendency. As one departs from the medium line toward either end, the number would be smaller and smaller. A few would be inferior, the large number average, and a few superior. Approximately 66 per cent of the people have intelligence with a standard deviation from the median, and the others, about equally divided, have either an inferior or superior intelligence (Fig. 23).

INTELLIGENCE TESTS

An intelligence test is an objective method of measuring the ability

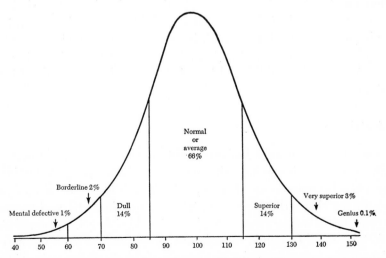

Figure 23. Distribution of intelligence (IQ's) in the general population according to 1937 Revision of the Stanford-Binet scale.

of the individual to meet a relatively new situation. Its purpose is to test the ability to acquire knowledge rather than to discover what knowledge has already been acquired.

Intelligence tests attempt to measure innate capacity to learn, particularly the ability to acquire knowledge of different subjects taught in school. As innate intelligence is not something tangible or self-evident, as is a book or a chart, it can be measured only indirectly; its presence must be inferred from the observed activity of the individual, his reactions to certain carefully chosen and controlled situations. A similar method is used in studying electricity, the existence and strength of which is inferred from the observations of its reactions and its effect on something we can see. Likewise, we indirectly estimate the intelligence of an individual by comparing his score in objective examinations with the average scores of a large group of individuals who have taken the same tests.

Alfred Binet, a distinguished French psychologist, is the founder of a modern testing movement. He conceived the idea that intelligence is not a single power but a complex of abilities. He believed that intelligence is largely native, although he recognized the fact that previous experience influences the result of most psychologic tests. Binet sought information that a child need not have acquired at home or at school, but which he would have to be able to understand to meet ordinary situations. In 1906, after experimenting for fifteen years, he published his series of tests known as the Binet-Simon tests.

Mental Age

Binet gave a standard of comparative scores made on these tests. The standard chosen was the average performance of individuals of each chronologic age. For example, if a child can obtain a score on the test that is the average of eight-year-old children, but is unable to pass tests that are more difficult, he is said to have the mental age of eight years. If a child of eight is able to obtain a score no higher than the average score for six-year-old children, then he is said to have the mental age of six years, and is classified as having inferior intelligence. If an eight-year-old child can obtain the score average of ten-year-old children, then his mental age is ten and he is considered as of a superior intelligence. *Mental age, then, is a numerical expression of the amount of intellectual development that has taken place at a given time.* It does not predict anything for the future, and without the chronologic age it does not reveal whether the individual is bright, stupid or average. The chronologic age must be known and taken into consideration to give an index of intelligence. This is found in the "IQ" or intelligence quotient.

Intelligence Quotient (IQ)

The intelligence quotient is the ratio of the mental age to the chronologic age. This can be expressed in a formula:

$$\frac{\text{What one has} \quad (MA)}{\text{What one ought to have} \quad (CA)}$$

The IQ, then, is obtained by dividing the mental age (MA) by the chronologic age (CA) and expressing the result on the basis of one hundred. For instance, if a child has the mental age of ten and the chronologic age of ten, then $10 \div 10 = 1$, or IQ 100; if child has a mental age of eight, but a chronologic age of ten, then $8 \div 10 = .8$, or IQ 80; if a child has a mental age of twelve, and chronologic age of ten, then $12 \div 10 = 1.2$, or IQ 120.

The advantage of the intelligence quotient is that it gives a basis for judging not only the present but the future. The IQ remains relatively the same. If a girl has an IQ of 100 it would mean that she has grown, is now growing, and is likely to continue to grow in mental ability at the average rate. It expresses, then, a person's *relative mentality* or brightness, not only now but in the future. Actually, however, the IQ does not remain absolutely constant throughout life. Some students develop a real change in growth rates from time to time, perhaps because of variation in physical and emotional conditions, or of variation from one test to another.

CLASSES AND TYPES OF INTELLIGENCE TESTS

The two main classes of intelligence tests are *verbal* and *non-verbal*. The verbal tests are for all those who read and speak the language, while the nonverbal tests are useful in testing of deaf and foreign people. Under each of these two classes there are *two types*, namely, *individual* and *group* tests. The individual tests are devised to test one individual at a time—a procedure that necessarily takes a great deal of time for the one giving the test. The group test is popular as it can be given to a number of individuals at the same time.

Stanford-Binet Tests

The Binet-Simon tests, revised in 1916 and later in 1937 by Lewis M. Terman, and now called Stanford-Binet tests, are the best-known individual tests. The revisions contain problems that test immediate memory, common sense, ability to follow directions, ability to give meanings, reasoning, knowledge of abstraction and so on. These are standardized into age scales from the third through the eighteenth year. These age scales were standardized by thousands of questions until 75 per cent of a group of each chronologic age could answer correctly.

Wechsler-Bellevue Intelligence Scale

The Wechsler-Bellevue Intelligence Scale is another popular test; it is practical, informative, and easy to administer. It was needed to test the intelligence of older people. One difficulty with the Stanford-Binet is that it does not distinguish well among superior adults. The standardization group of the 1937 Stanford-Binet included no individual over eighteen years of age. The application to older persons was considered justifiable since older persons must compete with younger persons in life. The Wechsler-Bellevue Intelligence Scale, published in 1939, was devised to test the intelligence of two groups: adolescents (ages ten to sixteen) and adults (ages sixteen to sixty). The test uses a point scale in contrast to the age scale of Binet. Each item is credited a certain number of points, the points earned being added to determine the total or full-scale IQ. Thus, there are three kinds of IQ's listed: verbal IQ, performance IQ, and the full-scale IQ. But these IQ's should not be confused with the IQ of the Stanford-Binet test. They are not directly comparable. The Stanford-Binet IQ is a true ratio of the mental age compared to the chronologic age, while the Wechsler-Bellevue IQ's are in reality standard scores.

Standard Scores

The Stanford-Binet IQ is a numerical expression of the *rate* of intellectual development of the individual; it is more appropriate in childhood, when mental growth is most rapid, than in the period of adolescence when increments in mental age from year to year become so small that they are not readily measurable. It is preferable, then, to use the standard scores and the percentile ratings for adults or adolescents when they reach a chronologic or mental age of fifteen or more. *The standard scores are units of measurement for each mental test, and indicate a relative position in a group in terms of distance of one's score from that of the average score of the group.* For example, in a test which contained 115 questions most of the students would answer 70 correctly, which would be about 50 per cent of the raw score (the number of questions); the standard score would be (0) zero (Table 2). Those students who would answer 80 of the questions would be scored plus one; 90 correct answers, plus two standard; and those students who would answer 101 or more correctly would be scored plus 3. On the other hand, those students who would answer less than 70 questions would be rated minus 1, 2, 3, accordingly. The National League for Nursing mean standard score has been set as 500 instead of (0) in order to do away with negative numbers and decimals (Table 2).

TABLE 2. COMPARISON OF RAW SCORES, STANDARD SCORES, NATIONAL
LEAGUE FOR NURSING STANDARD SCORES, AND PERCENTILES

(Am. J. Nursing 51:409 [June] 1951)

Raw Score	Standard Score	NLN Standard Score	Percentile Score
101	+3.0	800	99.8
91	+2.0	700	98.2
80	+1.0	600	84.0
70*	0.0	500	50.0
60	−1.0	400	16.0 ·
49	−2.0	300	1.8
39	−3.0	200	0.1

* Average score.

Percentile Rating

When we wish to compare one group of students with another group of the same type—one group of nurses with another group of nurses, or one group of high school students with another—the percentile and standard score methods are commonly used. Percentile shows the proportion of a group that fall below a given score, or the proportion of a group that are above an average score. Thus, if a student is in the 70 percentile, it means that she has made a score as high as 70 per cent of the students though 30 per cent ranked higher. The percentile rank of 50 is average. To say that she is in the 40 percentile, then, means that she ranked as high as 40 per cent of the students who took the tests, while 60 per cent of the students ranked higher.

Army Alpha Test

Used during the period of the first World War, the Army Alpha test was devised to test adults who speak the English language. It is a paper and pencil test divided into eight parts. It includes questions on the following items: auditory attention, arithmetic problems, practical judgment, words to show same or opposite meaning, sentences disarranged in a random fashion, completion type of serial numbers, verbal analogies and miscellaneous information.

Army Beta Test

This is a nonverbal kind of test that was designed for the illiterate. This is also a paper and pencil test divided into eight units. Each unit consists of a series of pictures or drawings that may be understood by a person without the aid of language. The directions are given by means of pantomime.

Army General Classification Tests

The Army General Classification Tests, which now exist in several forms, were used to classify more than 10,000,000 members of the armed services. Since the Army later adopted a revised edition of the AGCT, the original tests have been released for civilian usage. They contain three types of test items: *vocabulary problems,* which measure verbal comprehension; *arithmetic word problems,* which measure quantitative thinking; and the *block-counting problems,* which measure spatial thinking. The experience of the Army during the two world wars has demonstrated the value of group tests of intelligence beyond any doubt.

Satisfactory group tests are now available for all grades from kindergarten through college. A great variety of standardized tests have appeared in recent years. Some of the most prominent of these are: intelligence tests, pre-nursing and guidance tests, aptitude tests, achievement tests and personality tests.

APPLICATION OF INTELLIGENCE TESTS

Generalizing from data obtained in comprehensive testing, psychologists have widely accepted the classification of individuals according to the 1937 Stanford-Binet tests as given in Table 3.

TABLE 3. DESCRIPTIVE CLASSIFICATION OF 1937 STANFORD-BINET IQ's
(ADAPTED)*

Range of IQ	Descriptive Term	Percentage
Above 150	Near genius	0.1
130–149	Very superior	3.0
115–129	Superior	14.0
85–114	Normal (Average)	66.0
70–84	Dull	14.0
60–69	Borderline	2.0
40–59	Morons ⎤	1.0
20–39	Imbeciles ⎬ Mental Defective	—
0–19	Idiots ⎦	—

* Bernreuter, R. G., and Carr, E. J., *The Interpretation of IQ's on the L-M Stanford-Binet* (J. Educ. Psychol., 1938), 29:314.

According to the above grouping, many writers consider IQ's of 85 to 115 normal, those below as subnormal, and those above as supernormal. Then, too, it is considered that IQ's below 60 indicate mental defectiveness which implies not only low intelligence, but usually social inadequacy. Most clinicians recognize this classification of mental defectives as rough and arbitrary, and attempt to apply other criteria such as self-sufficiency, adjustment to reality and success in school.

Tests are also used for the following purposes: to classify and select students, officers and special personnel for various positions of work; to measure pupils' achievement; to discover individuals' capacities; to improve habits and abilities with relation to reflective thinking; to increase wider and richer interest in studies; to motivate study; to improve study, skill and work habits; to increase facilities to adjust socially; to develop creative work; to augment stores of vital information; to test the efficiency of educational units; to measure teachers' effectiveness; to distinguish between bright and dull persons; to diagnose pupils' weaknesses and the causes of maladjustments of workers who fail in their work; to obtain information on causes of delinquency; to develop a functional philosophy of life.

Evaluation of Intelligence Tests

The psychologic tests are the best objective standard we have at present for judging the intelligence of an individual. They give an indication of a person's capabilities and the possibility of his acquiring new knowledge. One must keep in mind that a high intelligence quotient does not mean that a certain person has acquired great knowledge, but that he has the ability to obtain knowledge if he will use his native powers. He is relatively bright and can attain efficiency in his classes provided he works and uses these powers. Scholastic ability demands docility, regular habits, prolonged interest, and continuity of effort, as well as intelligence.

No one emphasizes more than the advocates of the intelligence test that, even were the test perfected to the highest degree, this criterion would remain only one of several means of judging human nature. The mental tests are used chiefly as a basis of classification of students in order to group them, if possible, so that the assignments given to the bright student may be more difficult and quantitatively larger than those given to the average student. The superior intelligence advances more rapidly, and by classifying the students in groups we give them the opportunity to use their abilities. The use of psychologic and educational measuring instruments has been primarily responsible for the development of programs of diagnostic and remedial instruction, especially in reading and arithmetic. Knowledge derived from the testing data revealed the necessity to develop special methods of remedial instruction.

The results of intelligence tests must be considered in relation to other traits, such as emotional tendencies, economic status, personality and training. An individual's ability and resources at any given time may vary in either direction from what might be expected of him on the bases of his age and grade placement. Thus, it is necessary to consider each person as an individual, rather than merely as an unknown name in a group.

Everyone considers kindness, unselfishness and purity as traits of surpassing value, compared with superior intelligence without these traits. Since the chief factors in the causation of delinquency are, as a general rule, emotional rather than intellectual, training in virtue and self-control outweighs cleverness and superior intelligence.

We must remember, then, that the intelligence tests are only one criterion of judging individual abilities, and that in estimating complex human nature we must consider intelligence in relation to other variables.

PERSONALITY TESTS

Tests have been devised to give us insight into the whole personality of the individual. The two that will be described, the *Rorschach Test* and the *Thematic Apperception Test,* are known as projective tests.

Rorschach Test

The most widely used test to determine personality traits is the Rorschach Inkblot Test. The examiner presents to the subject a series of ten cards, one at a time, each containing bisymmetric inkblots, saying only, "What could this be?" or "What do you see?" The subject is allowed to turn the card and look at the blot from different positions. Different people, of course, see different things. Responses are scored in terms of the total number of items seen, whether the items involve the whole inkblot or only part of it. The kinds of things perceived, such as animals, people and plants are included in the score, as well as the qualities of each object, such as color, form and movement.

The test is based on the theory that what the person sees in an inkblot will be determined by his intellectual capacity, his motives, ambitions, fears, attitudes, feelings and characteristic modes of adjustment. Through his interpretations and creations he projects the inner aspect of his personality, without suspecting that he is doing so.

The scoring of Rorschach data is becoming fairly well standardized, but the interpretation of the scores is far from standard. The interpretation is necessarily subjective; that is, it calls for experience, ingenuity, insight, and common sense. The over-all validity of the test is not high, and seldom, if ever, does the test achieve the predictive value of the standard intelligence test. On the other hand, it would be incorrect to state that this test of personality is without value. Rorschach testers have reported considerable success in differentiating normal and psychotic individuals, and in distinguishing between different kinds of psychotics.

Thematic Apperception Test

Another popular personality test is the Thematic Apperception Test, which is usually abbreviated T.A.T. It consists of twenty cards with pictures resembling actual scenes or objects, but the situations are ambiguous and indefinite. This gives the subject freedom to interpret what he sees. The subject is asked to tell a story about the picture—what is happening, what led up to the situation, and what the outcome will be. In other words, he makes up a story about each of the pictures. Each person sees what he needs to see in each view. The story is likely to be influenced strongly by the person's inner state, by his likes, his dislikes, his needs, motives, ambitions, fears and attitudes. Thus, each response is assumed to have its cause in the personality make-up of the individual.

The objections applied to the Rorschach test apply to the Thematic Apperception Test. The interpretation of the test lacks validity, as the scoring is highly subjective and has not been reduced to factual terms that any and all observers will accept.

TESTING IN NURSING EDUCATION

During the past twenty years the National League for Nursing has made steady progress in standardizing and coordinating classroom instruction by employing a variety of tests directed by the Committee on Evaluation Services.

Realizing that the individual student of nursing should be protected against disappointment and waste of time if she has not the ability or educational capacity to do the work demanded by the school of nursing, the League has been employing a Pre-nursing and Guidance Test Service.

Its purpose is to promote a selection of better-qualified students, and thereby have assurance that such students are likely to complete the courses required for graduation. Then, too, well-constructed tests have been useful in maintaining and advancing professional standards for promotion, graduation and licensing of those nurses best qualified for specific work.

The National League for Nursing has been supplying four types of programs through its evaluation service: *(1) Pre-nursing Tests, (2) Achievement Tests, (3) Graduate Nursing Tests, (4) State Board Test Pool Examinations* for use in professional nursing schools. Similar tests are now available for use in approved practical nursing schools.

Pre-nursing Tests

Pre-nursing Tests are of two kinds: *(1) Pre-nursing and Classification Examination (PACE)* for practical nursing schools, and *(2) Pre-nursing and Guidance Tests (PNG)* for professional nursing schools. These tests have been given to secure the best possible personnel for nursing education, to ensure a better selection of student nurses in the briefest time, with the minimum waste of educational resources, and also to provide the best basis for individual guidance necessary to successful adjustment to nursing.

To accomplish these objectives, the Committee on Evaluation Services has prepared and published a battery of tests that procure evidence of the applicant's ability of performance and the student's success in the nursing program.

For the *practical nursing program* the Pre-nursing and Classification Examination (PACE) includes tests in vocabulary, general information and judgment. A comparative score based on the total performance of the applicant provides an over-all estimate of her likelihood to succeed in the educational program. The result of this examination must be interpreted along with other available information from the high school record, interview, physical examination and the like.

For *basic professional nursing school* the Pre-nursing and Guidance Tests (PNG) are made of five separate groups: general scholastic aptitude, reading, mathematics, science, and history and social studies. The purpose of these tests is to procure evidence of the applicant's educational and cultural background, scientific knowledge and understanding, and interest, as well as her skill in fundamental processes, i.e., speed and level of reading, comprehension, English usage and expression. These tests are scored and the results are tabulated by the Committee to guarantee reliable and uniform correlation with thousands of other applicants who take the same tests. The individual profile charts and the personal data blanks are forwarded to the school of the applicant's choice to be used, first to aid in selection, and then in guidance, both prior to admission and thereafter. Later, the Committee provides personality tests, the results of which the school may use in connection with orientation or other aspects of the school's program. The National League for Nursing has no part in determining "acceptable" scores on any of the tests. The institutions that use the tests and know the requirements of the local situation set their own policies for accepting applicants and evaluating students.

This battery of tests has proven to be very effective in identifying those applicants who *can* complete nursing programs and become licensed nurses. Of the 3,000 graduates who had taken the PNG tests between January 1945 and July 1945, 2,669 met the licensure standards in their respective States.[1] All of the graduates who were in the highest percentiles, 94-100, were able to pass the state board examinations, while approximately only one half of those in the

[1] Am. J. Nursing, *51*:202 (March) 1951.

lowest percentile, 0-6, could meet the licensure standards. Success in the state board examination of the graduates of another percentile rating is listed in Table 4.

TABLE 4. PERCENTILE OF PRE-NURSING COMPOSITE SCORE OF STUDENTS WHO TOOK THE TESTS IN 1945 AND LATER GRADUATED, COMPARED TO THE PERCENTAGE OF EACH PERCENTILE OF GRADUATE STUDENTS WHO PASSED THE LICENSURE STANDARDS

(Adapted from Am. J. Nursing 51:202 [March] 1951)

Percentile of PNG Composite Score* (1945)	Percentage of Students Graduated Who Met Licensure Standard
94–100	100
70–93	97
31–69	90
7–30	74
0–6	52

* Based on scores of 7,061 applicants.

Although tests and educational measurements are used by the schools of nursing for better selection, better understanding and better guidance, the committee on admission of any nursing school must take into consideration other important factors, such as an applicant's emotional stability, maturity, interest, personality, motivation, physical examination, her high school record, personal interview and written references.

Achievement Tests

Achievement Examinations prepared for the standard courses taught both in the professional nursing schools (NLN Achievement Tests) and in the state-approved schools of practical nursing (PNA Achievement Tests) are being used throughout the States. The use of these tests tends to improve basic instruction by increasing the interest both of the student and of the faculty, as the students' percentile ratings indicate the standing of their school compared with that of other schools throughout the country. This interest develops greater proficiency in classroom instruction, better acquisition of the latest methods of hospital procedures, and helps to root out certain weaknesses indicated by the achievement tests. The school uses the achievement tests to find out if the students are acquiring the skills and knowledge they will be expected to have. However, their greatest value is in evaluating a *program* rather than evaluating the *students* enrolled in that program.[2]

At the present time the majority of the basic professional programs administer one or more of the following twelve NLN Achievement Tests during an academic year:

Anatomy and Physiology	Medical and Surgical Nursing
Chemistry	Obstetric Nursing
Microbiology	Pediatric Nursing
Nutrition and Diet Therapy	Communicable Disease Nursing
Pharmacology and Therapeutics	Psychiatric Nursing
Fundamentals of Nursing	Social Science

The tests also give a norm to follow whereby a transfer student or an applicant with some previous training could be safely granted advance standing in a school of nursing. Too, the student's progress in the school can be adjusted to her ability by these achievement tests, rather than by arbitrary time standards.

Graduate Nursing Tests

The Evaluation Service of the National League for Nursing offers a selection of graduate nurse's programs to help college and university faculties to select and place students in graduate work. The Committee makes available three plans: *Plan A* lists three types of examinations, namely, general scholastic aptitude test, reading comprehension test, and clinical test; *Plan B* includes a choice of general scholastic aptitude or reading comprehension test, and clinical test; *Plan C* consists of the clinical test only. The time and the arranged central places of the examinations are announced by the League. The individual colleges and universities, however, decide which plan an applicant takes and the uses of the standard scores to decide whether

[2] Am. J. Nursing, 56:60 (January) 1956.

the applicant is likely to profit from and succeed in the program to which she seeks admission.[3]

State Board Test Pool Examinations

The State Board Test Pool consists of a battery of reliable, valid and practical achievement tests to be used for state board examinations by cooperating committees. All fifty states, the District of Columbia, and the four Canadian provinces now use the State Board Test Pool Examinations. The pool, when first used in 1944, consisted of thirteen tests; this number was reduced in 1949 to six, and in 1953 was further reduced to the following five: medical nursing, surgical nursing, obstetric nursing, pediatric nursing and psychiatric nursing.[4] Each test includes questions designed to evaluate: (1) the nurse as a member of a profession; (2) facts and principles of the biologic and physical sciences; (3) physical health and development, physical needs, nutritional principles and diet therapy; (4) emotional and mental health and development, and other social science facts and principles; (5) human relations and psychologic aspects of care; (6) cause, transfer, control and incidence of disease and abnormal conditions; (7) what to do and how to do it in nursing, exclusive of psychologic aspects; (8) pharmacology.[5] The results of each test are reported to the state board of examiners in terms of the National League for Nursing standard score, which is 500 as the average (Table 2, p. 300). Each board, in turn, sets its own standard necessary for state licensure.

The ideal would be for all the states to have the same standard for interstate registration and for licensure. A recommended score of 350 has been accepted by many state boards of examiners as a minimum standard of performance in each test. While the adoption of such a score may not be feasible immediately, as some districts cannot meet this requirement, it could be used to facilitate interstate licensure. Until the time uniform standards are acceptable, the

[3] Am. J. Nursing, 56:60 (January) 1956.
[4] Am. J. Nursing, 52:614 (May) 1952.
[5] Nursing Outlook, 7:298 (May) 1959.

State Board Test Pool Examinations offer a way to expedite licensures by endorsement of some nurses. Many states are using the suggestion the American Nursing Association Committee submitted in April 1954 "that any candidate for interstate licensure who received a score of 500 or above be granted a licensure upon verification of the original license, and such other things as the statutes require without further investigation of the nursing program or secondary education.[6] Very probably in the near future many other state boards will accept certain standards of competence of graduate nurses so that a license granted to practice nursing in one state will be recognized by all states cooperating in the minimum standard of skills and abilities.

SUMMARY

1. It is evident that people differ in their mental qualities. Some have superior, others have inferior, and the greater number have average intelligence.

2. This difference in mentality is due to heredity and environment.

3. Intelligence is the ability of the individual to learn quickly and use knowledge correctly.

4. Popular rating of intelligence is prone to be erroneous on account of emotions, biased opinions and insufficient evidence.

5. An intelligence test is an objective method of measuring the ability of the individual to adapt to a relatively new situation.

6. Intelligence develops from birth until maturity. On the average, maturity of the native mechanism for acquiring knowledge is reached at the age of sixteen to eighteen years.

7. Mental age is a numerical expression of the amount of intellectual development that has taken place by a given time.

8. Intelligence quotient is the ratio of the mental age to the chronologic age, expressed in the formula:

$$IQ = \frac{\text{Mental age}}{\text{Chronologic age}}$$

[6] Am. J. Nursing, 55:1094 (September) 1955.

9. The advantage of the intelligence quotient is that it gives the basis for judging the brightness and alertness of the individual now and in the future.

10. There are two main classes of intelligence tests, verbal and nonverbal; and two types, individual and group.

11. The Stanford-Binet 1937 revision and the Wechsler-Bellevue Intelligence Scale tests are popular individual tests.

12. The Stanford-Binet IQ is a numerical expression of the rate of intellectual development of the individual; the Wechsler-Bellevue IQ's are comparable to standard scores.

13. Standard scores are units of measurement of each mental test, and indicate a relative position in a group in terms of distance of one's score from that of the average score of the group.

14. Percentile rating indicates the proportion of a group which falls below a given score, or the proportion of a group who are above an average score.

15. Intelligence must be evaluated with other variables, such as emotions, training and personality.

16. The National League for Nursing supplies four types of evaluation services: (1) Pre-nursing Tests, (2) Achievement Tests, (3) Graduate Nursing Tests, and (4) State Board Pool Examinations.

QUESTIONS FOR REVIEW

Essay Type

1. Define the following: mental age, intelligence test, intelligence quotient, standard score, percentile rating.
2. Why is it difficult to judge the ability of a friend?
3. What abilities are measured by an intelligence test?
4. What influence have heredity and environment on native ability?
5. Describe the development of intelligence in relation to the age of a child.
6. Does mature intelligence mean that a student has much knowledge?
7. Could a person of superior intelligence be grossly ignorant in a subject?
8. What was Binet's concept of intelligence?
9. Show by example the meaning of mental age.

10. How can the intelligence quotient be obtained from the knowledge of the mental age?
11. Could you guess the approximate IQ of ten nurses in your class?
12. Why does the teacher often like the brilliant student?
13. Is good judgment always found with superior intelligence?
14. Differentiate IQ of the Stanford-Binet test from IQ of the Wechsler-Bellevue test.
15. Why does the National League for Nursing use 500 as its standard score instead of the usual (0) zero?
16. How would you obtain the percentile rating if an intelligence test were given in this class of students of psychology?
17. Name three uses of the results of intelligence tests.
18. What factors other than the IQ must be considered in estimating human behavior?
19. What would be the percentile score of a nurse who ranked 600 NLN standard score in an achievement test?
20. Summarize the Testing Program in Nursing Education.

Matching and Completion Type

Fill in the correct words:

1. The two fundamental reasons people differ so radically in traits and abilities are:

   a ....

   b ....

2. The ability of an individual to learn quickly and use knowledge correctly. ....

3. An objective method of measuring the ability of the individual to meet a relatively new situation. ....

4. The ratio of the mental age to the chronologic age. ....

5. The type of test that attempts to measure capacity to learn. ....

   ....

6. The name of the French psychologist who conceived the idea that intelligence is not a single power but a complex of abilities. ....

   ....

7. The five abilities included under the term "intelligence" are:

a . . . .   d . . . .

b . . . .   e . . . .

c . . . .

8. A numerical expression of the amount of intellectual development that

has taken place at a given time. . . . .

9. The two main classes of mental tests are:

a . . . .

b . . . .

10. According to the classification of 1937 Stanford-Binet tests, the range

of IQ's of an average individual is listed as: . . . .

11. The (0) zero standard score would be listed by the National League
for Nursing in a larger numerical number, namely:

. . . .

12. At least three advantages of using achievement examinations in nursing
training are:

a . . . .

b . . . .

c . . . .

13. Since 1953 the State Board Test Pool consists of the following five
tests, namely:

a . . . .   d . . . .

b . . . .   e . . . .

c . . . .

14. The recommended score accepted by many state boards of examiners
as a minimum standard of performance in each state board test is:

. . . .

15. The four types of evaluation services supplied by the National League
for Nursing are:

a . . . .

b . . . .

c ....

d ....

16. Two personality tests are:

a ....

b ....

Topics for Class Discussion

1. The qualities of mind included under the term "intelligence."
2. Testing in nursing education.
3. Advantage of intelligence quotient (IQ) compared to mental age standard.
4. Many brilliant students with high intelligence quotients turn out to be failures.
5. Evaluation of mental tests and other requirements for entrance to the schools of nursing.
6. Is it true according to the theoretical curve that "7 per cent of the students in our psychology class should fail to receive a passing mark at the end of the semester"?
7. State Board Test Pool Examinations.
8. Rorschach and Thematic Apperception Tests.

Sources and References

Anastasi, Anne, *Psychological Testing* (New York: Macmillan, 1954).

Cronbach, Lee J., *Essentials of Psychological Testing* (New York: Harper, 1949), Chaps. VI, VII.

Fox, Charles, *Educational Psychology* (London: Routledge & Kegan Paul, 1951), Chaps. II, XIII.

Freeman, Frank S., *Theory and Practice of Psychological Testing* (New York: Holt, 1950), Chaps. V, VI.

Garrett, Henry E., *General Psychology* (New York: American Book Co., 1955), Chap. VII.

Nunnally, I. C., Jr., *Tests and Measurements* (New York: McGraw-Hill, 1959).

Ruch, Floyd L., *Psychology and Life,* 4th ed. (Chicago: Scott, Foresman, 1953), Chap. VI.

Super, Donald E., *Appraising Vocational Fitness* (New York: Harper, 1949), Chap. VII.

Terman, Lewis M., and Merrill, Maud A., *Measuring Intelligence* (Boston: Houghton Mifflin, 1937).

INDEX

317

demand of yourself definite
quotas and qualities of work